Beetles

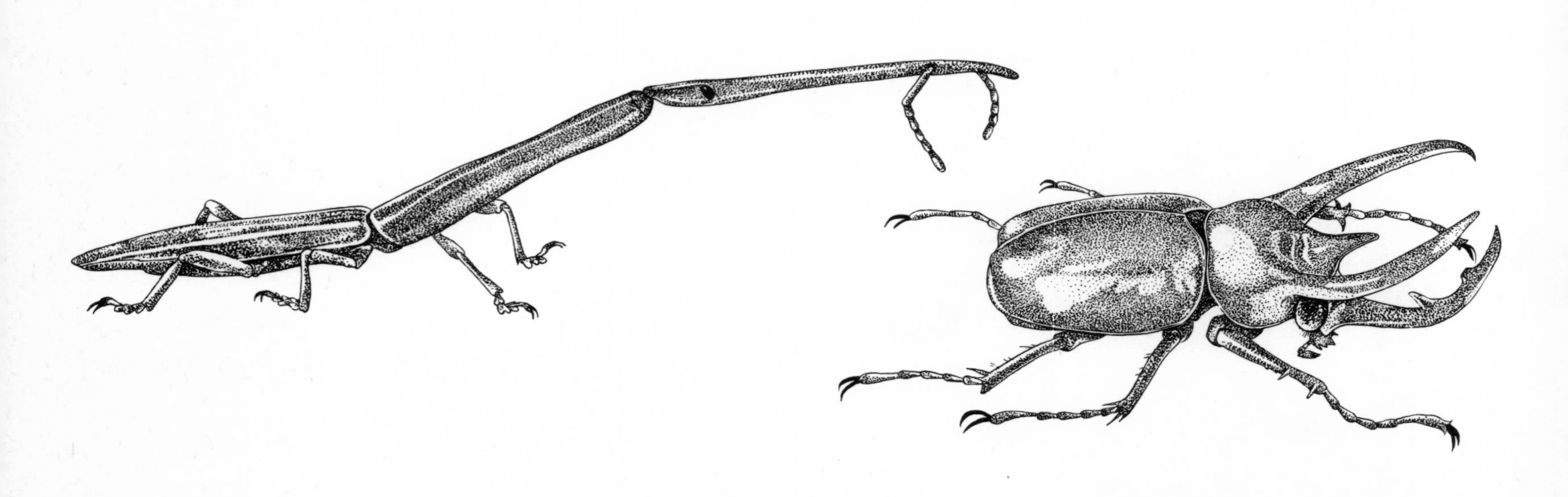

Bernhard Klausnitzer

Beetles

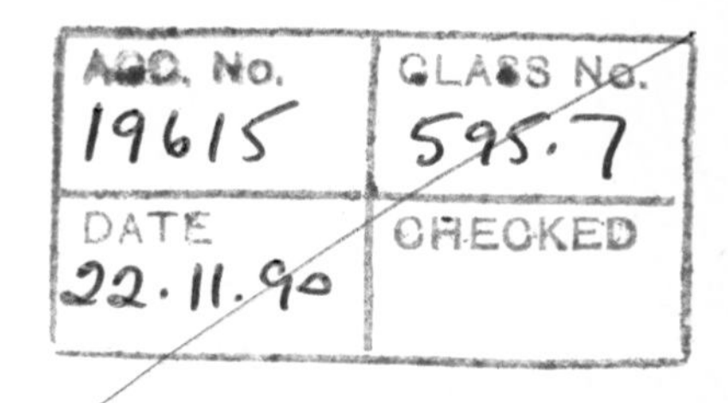

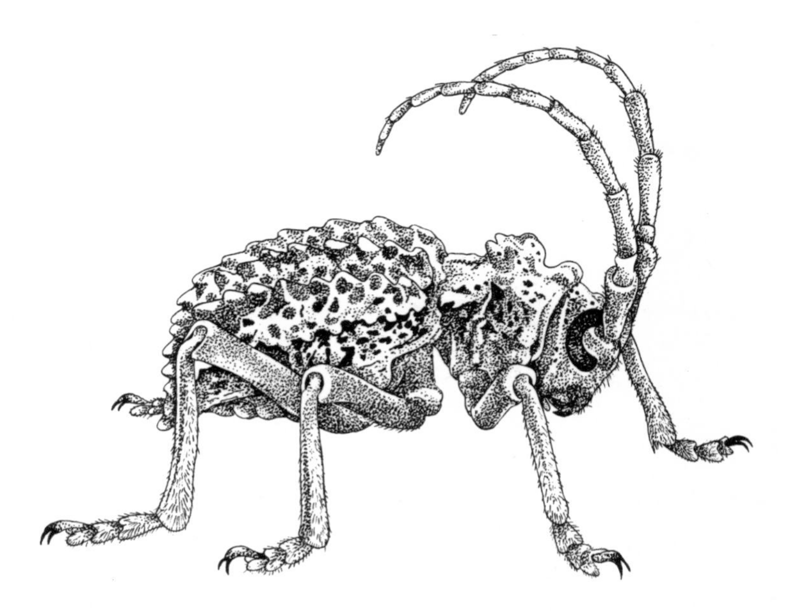

Exeter Books
NEW YORK

Translated from the German by Sylvia Furness
Revised by Sharon L. Shute

First published in USA 1983
by Exeter Books
Distributed by Bookthrift
Exeter is a trademark of Simon & Schuster
Bookthrift is a registered trademark
of Simon & Schuster
New York, New York
Drawings and design:
Traudl Schneehagen
Photographs: Manfred Förster

ISBN 0-89673-141-3
Printed in the German Democratic Republic

Contents

Foreword

Many readers may well ask: Why ever should there be yet another book on beetles? There are, after all, so many already and new ones keep appearing! But let us hope that in the future too, new books on this subject will continue to be written and printed, and it is quite certain that they will always find interested readers. For there is an endless fascination in recounting the great variety within this group of animals, in selecting features peculiar to them, in depicting for the nature-lover the fascinating beauty of beetles, their usefulness to man as well as the damage they cause—a truly inexhaustible subject! From the earliest times, beetles have attracted the notice of man in a wide variety of ways, and so the most diverse relationship between man and beetle have developed. I should like to attempt an account of these, starting out from a consideration of the anatomy, biology and distribution of beetles living today. I should like to think of this book to be a modest attempt both for a natural history and a cultural history of beetles—a venture that has not, as far as I know, been undertaken so far, whereby emphasis is laid on special more than on general aspects. As lecturer for Ecology and Systematic Zoology at the Karl Marx University Leipzig, I enlisted the co-operation of distinguished experts to ensure that the book should be as interesting as possible. As consultants, Dr. L. Dieckmann, Eberswalde, and Prof. Dr. H. Luppa, Leipzig, have contributed greatly to the scientific accuracy of the text by their good advice and many kind suggestions. My special thanks are also due to Herrn M. Förster, Leipzig, for his excellent organization of the photographic material in the book, and to Frau T. Schneehagen for her expert graphic work and design. Specialists from many institutes and museums in various countries have cooperated most kindly in providing literature, offprints, and other material, and perhaps most of all, in a lively exchange of ideas: R. B. Angus, M. Baehr, L. Baert, P. Basilewsky, C. Berthèlemy, C. Besuchet, R. Bielawski, S. Bily, A. Bons, M. Brancucci, V. M. Brovdij, B. Burakowski, R. A. Crowson, J. G. M. Cuppen, S. Cymorek, M. L. Danylevskii, N. Degallier, J. H. De Gunst, C. V. Demelt, G. Demoulin, M. G. De Viedma, A. Egger, S. Endrödi, A. M. J. Evers, M. Fiori, H. Franz, J. M. Franz, H. Freude, G. Friese, H. Fürsch, M. Geisthardt, M. S. Gilarov, J. Giudicelli, R. D. Gordon, H. Habeck, H. Habermann, N. Hayashi, C. H. F. von Hayek, I. Hodek, C. L. Hogue, A. Hoňek, A. Horion, M. D. Hubbard, K. Hurka, M. Ienistea, J. M. Illies, F. Janczyk, O. Jarisch, J. Jelinek, C. Johnson, E. Kangas, Z. Kaszab, R. Kinzelbach, O. Kraus, E. Kreissl, J. Krikken, N. S. Kryžanovsky, K. Kumanski, Sv. G. Larsson, J. F. Lawrence, G. A. Lohse, J. J. Lusis, W. M. Mamaev, J. E. Marshall, M. Matsuka, J. T. Medler, S. E. Miller, P. Minelli, A. W. Miser, M. Miyatake, C. Montes, J. Muggleton, T. Nakane, N. B. Nikitsky, P. Nohel, T. Nyholm, I. Okada, G. Osella, V. Ostafitžuk, J. C. Otero, Z. Pecha, B. Petersen, A. Pfeffer, R. Plontke, A. G. Ponomarenko, A. Popov, V. A. Potockaja, K. Rasmussen, Ph. Richoux, P. Riha, H. Sasaji, I. Ch. Šarova, K. E. Schedl, W. Schedl, G. Scherer, E. Schneider, A. N. Želochovzev, J. C. Scott, H. Silfverberg, N. G. Skopin, A. Smetana, G. Soika, C. Spangler, J. R. Starzyk, J. Stehlik, W. Steinhausen, R. zur Strassen, B. R. Striganova, W. Szymczakowski, E. Taylor, Z. Tesar, H. U. Thiele, G. Tiberghien, W. Topp, E. Tortonese, N. Uygun; E. Vives, W. Vogt, H. D. Volkart, A. Warchalowski, R. C. Welch, R. Wiebes, K. A. J. Wise, W. Wittmer, K. Witzgall, D. K. Young, J. Zahradnik, H. Zwölfer.

I should particularly like to thank Dr. F. Hieke of the Zoologisches Museum, Berlin, and Dr. R. Hertel, Staatliches Museum für Tierkunde, Dresden, both of whom have placed at my disposal a great deal of material from among the wealth of their museums' possessions, for reproduction as illustrations. But thanks are also due to the Ägyptisches Museum of the Karl Marx University Leipzig, the Museum für Völkerkunde, Grassimuseum Leipzig, Institut für Pflanzenschutzforschung der Akademie der Landwirtschaftswissenschaften Kleinmachnow, Bereich Eberswalde, the Geiseltalmuseum of the Martin Luther University Halle and the VEB Carl Zeiss Jena. And not least, I should like to thank the publishing house of Edition Leipzig for their manifold support and assistance.

Bernhard Klausnitzer

Introduction

"Nowhere does the art of Nature manifest itself more brilliantly than in the insects. In the case of the larger animals, the plasticity of the material rendered their shaping much less difficult. But in those small, almost insignificant creatures, what functional expediency, what indescribable perfection was here provided! Where did Nature find room to lodge so many senses on the body of a gnat—and there are other insects even more minute? Where are its organs of sight, smell and taste situated? And what is the source of the creature's voice, so clear for its size? With what delicate hand are its wings joined to its body, its shanks extended and its body curved. How did Nature lend the gnat its burning thirst for human blood? With what art did she sharpen the barb so that it could penetrate the skin. Indeed, more than that, she has formed it for a double purpose, so that not only is it sharp enough to pierce but at the same time tubiform to serve as an instrument of suction. Yet for all that, this organ is so delicate that it can scarcely be seen. In the same way, Nature has given the woodworm teeth so that it can bore through wood, and at the same time provided it with a source of food in the wood itself. Undeniably, we admire the elephant's back upon which he is able to transport whole towers, the neck with which the bull tosses his enemy into the air, the tiger's rapacity and the lion's mane. But in truth, nowhere does Nature show herself so great as in the smallest of her creatures. Therefore I implore the reader, albeit he has little regard for many of the objects, nevertheless not to disdain the description of them, since in observing Nature, nothing ought to be considered unimportant."

These lines were written by no less an author than the great Roman writer Gaius Plinius Secundus (Pliny the Elder) (A. D. 23–79). Still today, the infinite variety of insects, and of beetles in particular, continues to draw the interest of observers.

The present book attempts to indicate some aspects of the relationships that have developed between man and beetle in the course of history, and in addition to present a selection of those unique features that the world of beetles can offer. For it is precisely these special particularities that have always attracted man's notice. They were the reason for the veneration of the pill-rolling beetles in Ancient Egypt, and for the numerous references in works of literature to fireflies and glow-worms. The poisonous properties of certain species of beetles have been exploited for good and bad ends. Many beetles came to be feared by man, because they destroyed both food stocks and growing crops. Other beetles were regarded as carriers of good fortune and revered accordingly. But seen as a whole, it appears that man failed to develop any close relationship with beetles that could be compared, for example, to that with butterflies, bees, or indeed, mammals and birds. Although beetles far outnumber in species every other order of animal, and exist in numbers that run into thousands of millions, man has yet remained curiously remote from them. This can be seen first in writings that have come down to us from the Ancient Greeks, and has persisted right up to the present day. And yet there have always been some specialists who have been irresistibly fascinated by the variety of form among beetles and have devoted their whole life to the study of beetles. They have brought together a vast wealth of knowledge that enables us to recognize as finite the apparently infinite variety that exists among beetles. Their writings teach us to see the universal and the particular in beetles. It is only through this recognition of the universal that we are able to appreciate the particular, the unique, the exceptional features, the "record achievements." If, in the following chapters, we are able to bring the reader a little closer to this fascinating group of animals, the beetles, then the purpose of this volume will have been fulfilled.

The Scarab—"Sacred" Symbol of Ancient Egypt

Ever since the days of the advanced civilization of Ancient Egypt, the scarab has held a special significance for many peoples, especially for those of the Mediterranean area. In earlier times in particular, scarabs were very common insects and attracted man's attention on account of their size, their rapid movements and the curious habit they have of rolling up balls of dung. In Ancient Egypt, they were considered a symbol of the Sun God Ra. It has been assumed that the ball of dung rolled along by the scarab beetle became a symbol for the sun. And the act of burying the ball of dung in the sand and its subsequent retrieval was symbolically linked with the rising and setting of the sun. At certain periods, the scarab was represented bearing the disc of the sun in its claws. Another reason for equating the scarab with the Sun God was the belief that all dung beetles were male and that they could produce their young by their own procreative action. According to the beliefs of the ancient Egyptians, the Sun God did not have his origin in the union of two beings of different sexes, but was born without impregnation out of primary matter. There exist other theories to explain the scarab cult in Egypt, but they lack convincing evidence or fail to correspond with known facts. It has been suggested, for example, that the ancient Egyptians already knew about the metamorphosis that the dung beetle undergoes. This transformation of the beetle's outward form is seen as the intellectual motivation for the religious practice of mummification. The suggestion is that the dead were mummified in the hope that after a thousand years of "pupal sleep" they would experience a third transformation and resurrection. The underground death chambers and the pyramids are equated with the ball of dung containing the egg. Although this interpretation has been disputed, the scarab was certainly regarded by the Egyptians as a type of immortality. The emergence of the new beetle from out of the sand could well have led to this view.

It is known that reproductions of the scarab have been discovered in Egypt from as early as the 3rd millennium B.C. An embalmed scarab has been found belonging to the later period of the New Empire (about 700–33 B.C.). In the sacred written documents, the hieroglyphs, a representation of the scarabaeus stands for creative power and it is interpreted as a symbol of the God of Creation, Cheper. The scarab also became associated with other gods as the symbol of creation. Later it came to signify the soul which was to unite with the God of Creation. The scarab also represents the abstract concept "cheper" which originally means "to become, to come into being; that which has become or came into being; the being, the form" and from which the concepts "Being" and "Becoming" have developed. The god Cheper is one of the many outward forms assumed by the god Ra. He is usually represented with a scarab above his head, and in certain cases he has a scarab in place of a human head (Figs. 1, 2).

Even in classical times, scholars were pondering the origins of the scarab cult. For example, the Greek philosopher Plutarch (A.D. 46–120) wrote: "The beetles were revered because it was believed that in them, obscure images of the power of the gods could be perceived; in the sex of beetles there are no females, only males, which deposit their seed in a ball formed out of dung; they roll this along, pushing it from behind, just as the sun gives the appearance of driving the sky in the opposite direction as it moves from setting to rising." Clement of Alexandria (died ca. 216), a writer of the late period of Roman Antiquity adds to these ideas when he writes: "They represent the sun by means of the image of the beetle because it forms a portion of cattle dung into a spherical shape and then rolls it along backwards. They also assert that it lives for six months under the ground, and the second half of the year above ground, and that it procreates by depositing its seed into the ball of dung; there are said to be no females among them." The physician Caspar Schwenckfeld still was of this opinion. In his work *Theriotropheum Silesiae* he writes: "There are only males, and they bring their progeny into the world without females." Claudius Aelianus (160–240), another writer of the Late Roman era, suggests another reason for the scarab cult: "This beetle is a creature possessing no members of the female sex. It allows its seed to fall into balls of dung which it rolls along. It does this for 28 days, until the ball is warmed through, and the next day it brings forth its young. Those Egyptians of a warlike disposition bear a scarab engraved upon their rings, by which the lawmaker indicates that all who fight for their country must without exception show manliness, just as the beetle has nothing female in its nature." The Greek philosopher Plato (427–347 B.C.) was of the opinion that the scarab was venerated because, like the creator who has shaped the world, it too makes use of the most perfect mathematical form for its creation shaped out of dung.

1 The Creator of the World and Sun God Cheper, with scarab head

The earliest scarab representations carried no engraving on the underside. Perhaps even at that early time the beetle was already considered sacred. Amulet reliquaries in the form of a scarab were also found in very early periods. Huge representations of the beetle in black stone were set up in the temples. Later on, scarabs were also used as seals, made of amethyst, carnelian, rock crystal or other material, and set in metal finger rings. Many of them bear the names of kings, or historical inscriptions. Their significance might be compared with the commemorative coins minted today. Other scarabs carried information or depicted sacred animals. In the treasure shrine of the Ancient Egyptian King Tutankhamen (about 1330 B.C.) a representation of a winged scarab, flanked by the goddesses Isis and Nephthys was found. It was widespread practice to wear a scarab round the neck as an amulet to bring good fortune (Fig. 4). The inscriptions on the reverse side are in keeping with their use for this purpose: "Good Health," "Life," "Good Wishes," "My Heart is True" are found frequently. From the original significance as a symbol of religious veneration, the wearing of a scarab had obviously become a fashionable and widespread custom. Perhaps it could be compared with the custom today of wearing a sprig of white heather or shamrock for luck. The manufacture of scarab amulets must have been a very lucrative business. Thousands of them have been preserved to this day, having come to light in a wide variety of countries; many, for example, were found in Sardinia. With the spread of the cult of Osiris and its associated concept of the Judgement of the Dead, breast amulets or heart scarabs began to be made (Fig. 6) which were large in size and bore a religious text on the reverse, for example, chapters from the Book of the Dead (very often Ch. 30). These scarabs were placed upon the breast of the dead or upon the mummified heart. Sometimes they bear falcon wings at the sides. At the time of the 26th to 30th Dynasty, a series of six or more such scarabs was placed upon the mummy. Heart scarabs (as well as others) were usually made of greenstone. Associated with the heart scarabs was the idea that at the Day of Judgement the heart should not bear witness against its own master. The 30th chapter of the Egyptian "Book of the Dead" (Fig. 5) says:

> "Oh, my heart, thou innermost part of my being!
> Do not turn against me as witness before the tribunal.
> For thou art the god who dwells within my body,
> My creator who has charge of all my limbs."

It is interesting that in the course of the long history of Egyptian civilization, different types of scarabs can be distinguished, each of which had as its model a different genus of dung beetle (Fig. 7). Although it is a view that is no longer considered a convincing one today, earlier Egyptologists claimed that the scarabaeid types are in chronological sequence, so that they can be used as index fossils to the various cultural-historical epochs. Many of the scarabs bear names and these frequently permit an even more exact dating of archaeological finds. It is from inscriptions and illustrations on large scarabs that we learn about important hunting expeditions or about the marriage of Pharaoh Amenhotep III to Teje in about 1400 B.C. The only precise information we possess about the period of the Hyksos or "shepherd kings" is that obtained from representations of beetles, since almost all other cultural and historical evidence was completely destroyed.

2 The god Cheper with scarab as head, on tomb of Nofretiri

Veneration of the scarab also passed into other religions. The late classical doctrine of gnosticism which was much influenced by Christianity, made use of representations of scarabaeids on amulets. It was usual to depict three scarabs in a row, which was to be interpreted as a symbol of the Trinity. In front of them, three falcons were drawn symbolizing the souls of the just. Behind them were three crocodiles or snails representing the souls of the wicked. In the Israelite religion kĕrūb (cherub), the Guardian of Paradise, mentioned in the Old Testament, is sometimes derived from the pockmarked scarabaeus (*Scarabaeus variolosus* and *Scarabaeus cicatricosus*). The body of these two species is covered with indented spots. These spots were obviously thought to be eyes. The Israelite Prophet Ezekiel wrote of the cherubim: "Their entire body, neck, hands and wings were full of eyes."

But it was not only religious veneration that was bestowed upon the scarab. Various miraculous powers of healing have also been ascribed to it, which may in part have had their roots in the religious veneration. In the Egyptian Papyrus Ebers dating from the year 1500 B.C. we can read a formula of exorcism that begins in this way: "Split the (living) scarabaeus down the centre with a bronze knife, take the left half of it and tie it to the left arm."

As the symbol of the Sun God, the scarab was believed to be a remedy for the four-day fever. Many of the amulets that were worn were undoubtedly considered as protection against bewitchment. A prescription contained in a papyrus of different origin, provides information about the use of the beetle in popular medicine. "Take a large scarab beetle, cut off its head and wings, sieve it, put it into oil and apply it. After that, boil its head and wings, put them into snake-oil, sieve the liquid and let the patient drink it."

And of course, Arabian civilization is also familiar with the scarab. In the writings of the scholar Kamal al-Din ad Damiri (1349 or 1341–1391), we can read the following: "It bites animals in the genitalia in order to drive them off . . . They generally have their origin in cow dung, which, as already mentioned, they collect and pile up. Curiously enough, the beetle dies on perceiving the scent of roses and other pleasing smells, but when it is replaced on the dung, it immediately returns to life.

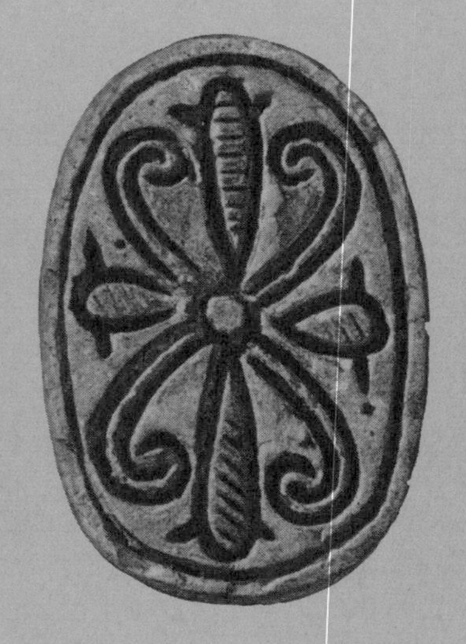
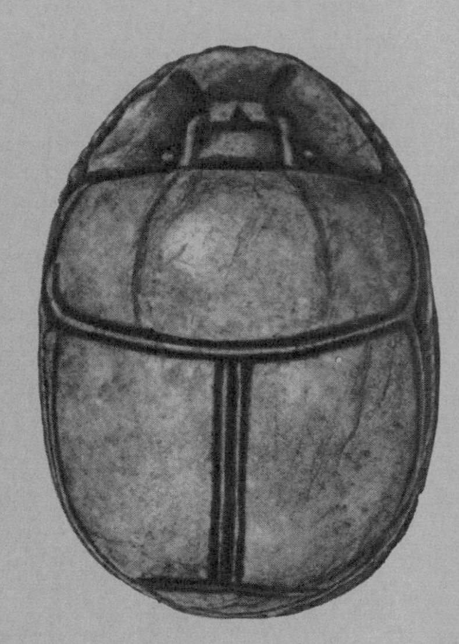

3 Scarabs, ceramic, 2nd century B.C.
a) Reverse and obverse, length 1.8 cm
b) Reverse, length 1.9 cm
c) Obverse, length 2.2 cm

It has two wings which are visible in flight, six legs and a large bulge on its back. It walks backwards but yet does not fail to find its nest. It is also called alhabertal. When it wants to fly, it shakes itself, whereupon the wings emerge, and it flies off. Its consumption is forbidden. Characteristics: uncooked and unsalted, dried and imbibed without any additive, it is efficacious against scorpion sting. The appearance of a beetle in a dream signifies a rash and deadly enemy or travellers carrying stolen goods."

The Arabian scholar al-Qazwini who died in 1283 writes in his *Curiosities of Creation and Created Beings:* "The Dung Beetle (chunfasy') is the small, black creature which is generated out of stinking dung. If a camel swallows a dung beetle while feeding, it dies, and the beetle is found among its excrement. If one throws a dung beetle on to a gazelle, the latter will surely die. There is one species called Gu'al. It forms balls out of dung, and carries them to its home. If this creature is placed in the centre of a rose, it remains lying there so quietly that it seems to be dead. If it is then placed amid dung, it moves and returns to its previous condition." This curious aspect of scarab behaviour when exposed to the scent of a rose, which clearly has no rational basis, dates back to Aelianus, who stated in his writings that the scent of a rose so revolts the scarab that it will even die if it is enveloped in such a flower.

It is scarcely surprising in view of the great significance the beetle had for so many people, that it was frequently mentioned or used as a simile in literature of all kinds, including some in which a fair share of scorn was directed against the scarab cult. Plutarch arranged for an embalmed scarab to be served up to an excessively austere philosopher who could not endure music of any kind at a banquet. The significance can be understood when one considers that for the Ancient Greeks, the scarab was held to be an enemy of scholarship and art and the rose a symbol of culture. This anecdote concerning Plutarch is the subject of an engraving, which bears the following lines:

"As to you, scarab, the rose means death,
It is pleasure to the bee:
Thus virtue is favourable to the good
And hostile to the wicked."

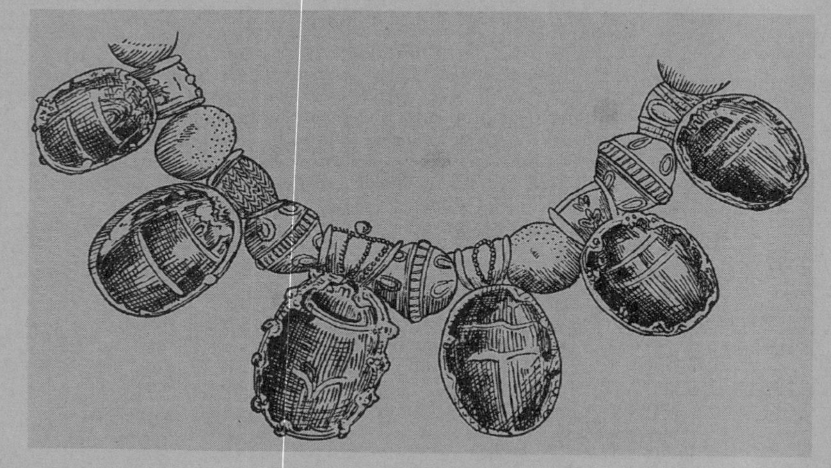

4 Ancient Egyptian necklet-amulet made of scarabs (Louvre).

6 Heart scarabs with human head, found at Aniba; 2nd century B. C.
a) Green stone, length 7 cm
b) Black stone, length 10.5 cm

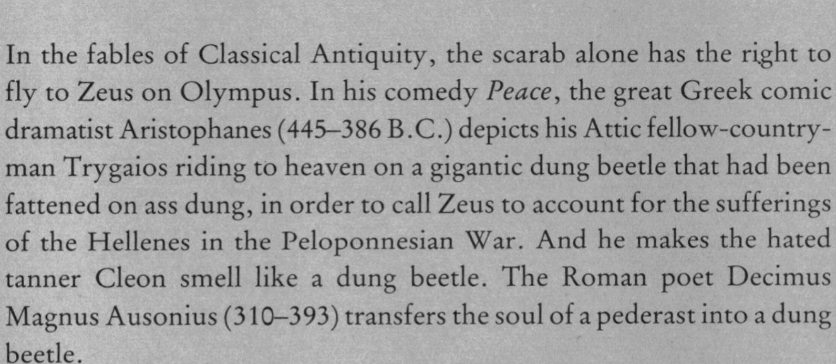

In the fables of Classical Antiquity, the scarab alone has the right to fly to Zeus on Olympus. In his comedy *Peace*, the great Greek comic dramatist Aristophanes (445–386 B.C.) depicts his Attic fellow-countryman Trygaios riding to heaven on a gigantic dung beetle that had been fattened on ass dung, in order to call Zeus to account for the sufferings of the Hellenes in the Peloponnesian War. And he makes the hated tanner Cleon smell like a dung beetle. The Roman poet Decimus Magnus Ausonius (310–393) transfers the soul of a pederast into a dung beetle.

The pre-Homeric poet Pamphos ridiculed the scarab cult in verses such as this: "Greatest and most glorious among the gods, thou who wallowest in dung, O Zeus, in the dung of the sheep, of the horse, of the mule."

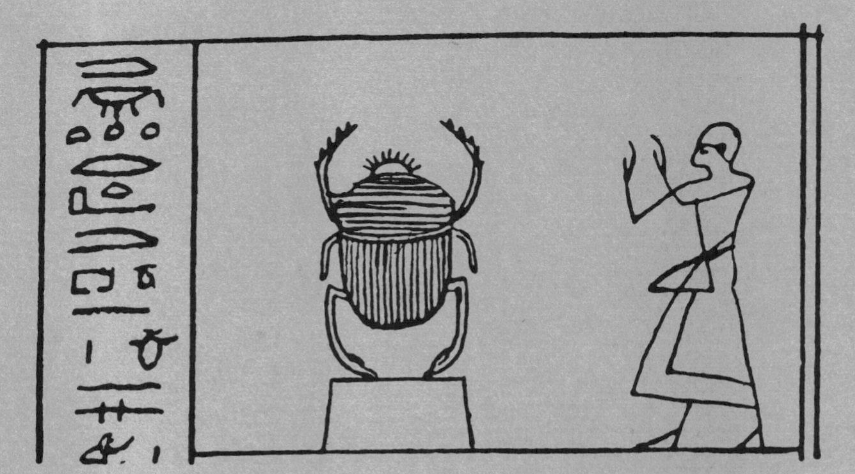

5 The dead man pays homage to Cheper (Vignette from the Book of the Dead).

In Christian animal symbolism in medieval times, the scarab was considered as a symbol of the sinner. In the Physiologus, the vitally important zoological chapbook which dominated the whole of the Middle Ages, and which is known to have been in use since the fifteenth century (possibly even since Classical Antiquity), we can read the following about the scarabaeus. "In the days of Nisan, the Month of Flowers, the dung beetles are formed out of dung or excretion, they come forth out of it and live in that dung and stench. And they themselves form the dung into the shape of round eggs, from the dung of camels and horses, they roll these along backward on the ground and so warm them, until they form and create their progeny in the centre of them, which then break out of the balls and creep forth. And the latter remain with them and spend their life amid the same stench. From this we see and clearly understand that the dung beetles are the heretics, defiled with the stench of heresy. But the balls of dung which are formed out of dung and which they roll back and forth on the ground are evil thoughts and heresies, which have been created out of wickedness and foulness."

7 The natural models for scarabs of Ancient Egypt.
Right: the beetle stylized
left: the natural form within the oval of a seal.

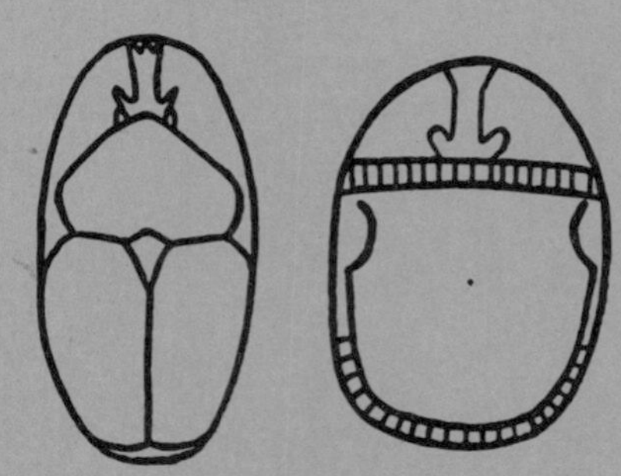

Hypselogenia

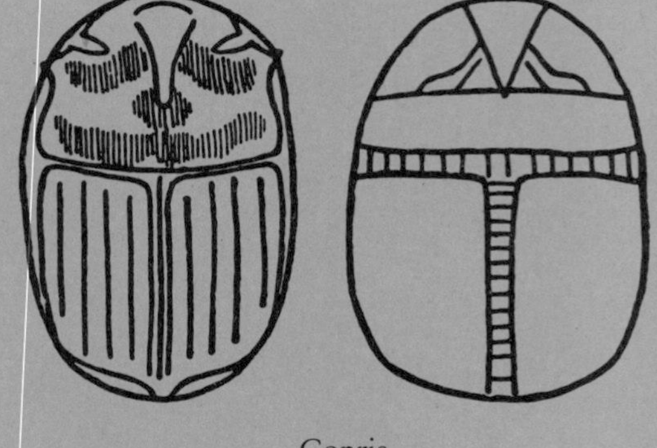

Copris

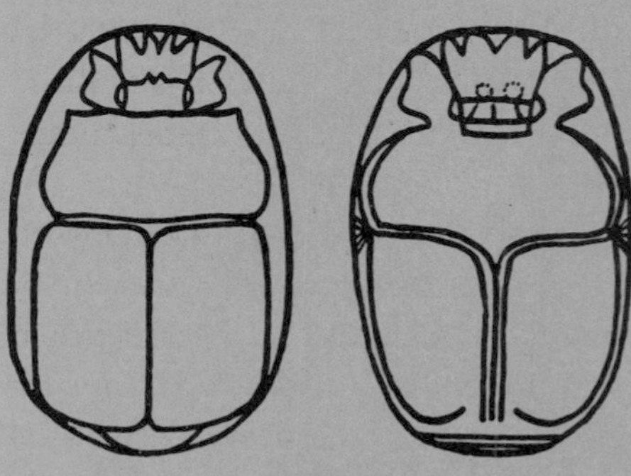

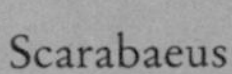

Scarabaeus

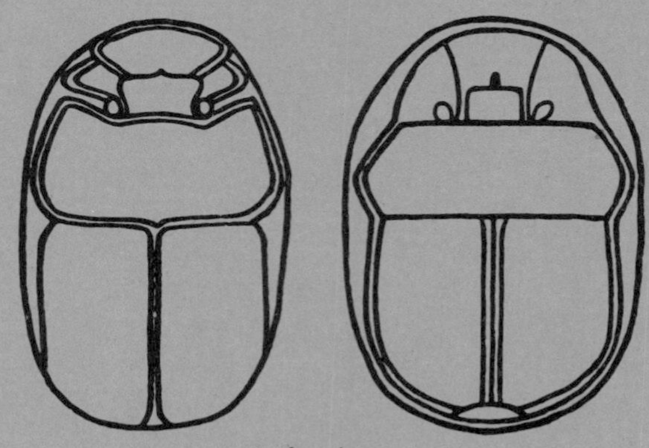

Catharsius

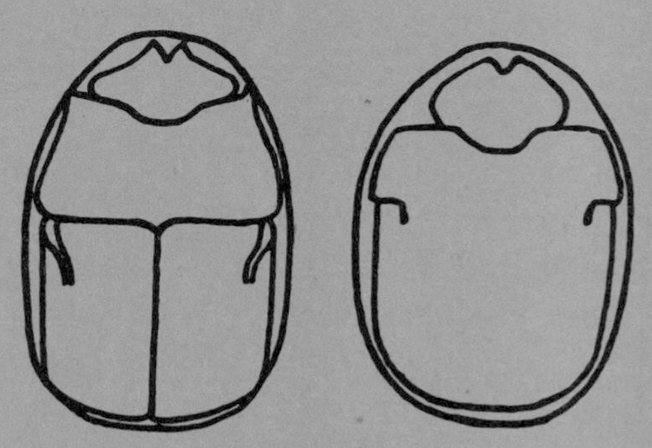

Gymnopleurus

To close our observations on the scarab, let us include one of the fables of the great Greek fabulist Aesop, who lived in about 550 B.C.

"Once when the eagle had plundered the nest of a beetle, the beetle in retaliation, stole the eagle's eggs and persisted in rolling them out of the nest, until the eagle went before Zeus and complained. The god told him to place the eggs in his lap. Now, as Zeus sat with the eagle's eggs in his lap, the beetle flew round about the god. Then the latter forgot himself and stood up, in order to drive the troublesome creature away from his head, and so he broke the eggs." The lesson of the fable has been preserved to this day in the saying "Blacker and wiser than a scarab."

Beetles, an inspiration to poets and painters

The origin of the German word "Käfer" (beetle) and weevil

The German word "Käfer" (beetle) can be traced back in its early forms as far as the 9th century and is a word of Germanic stock. In the 9th century, beetles were called "cheuur" (chevar), in the 10th century "chefuar," in the 11th we find the words "cheuove," "cheuer," "Keuir." The 12th century has "cheuer" or "Keuer" and by the 13th century, among other orthographies, we already find "Kever." The Old High German "chevar" and the Middle High German "Kaver" were, however, generally used to denote grasshoppers. The words are derived from the verbs "kauen, nagen" (to chew, gnaw) and "Kiefer" (jaw).

The English word beetle comes from the Old English "bitula" and derives from bitan, to bite.

That the original meaning of "Kever" was the larvae of grasshoppers can be seen from very many early sources. Over a long period of time there was a gradual change in meaning, and from "chevar", "Kever" signifying grasshoppers, "Kever" came to mean "Käfer" (beetle) with the meaning which it has today.

So what name was used in the earlier centuries to denote beetles, if that is, they were noticed at all? On this point too, early sources provide interesting information. A word of Germanic origin "webila" was used for beetles. The word denotes a movement back and forth, flickering, swarming, teeming—no doubt the rapid, crawling movement of the beetle was seen as a typical feature. This word can also be traced far back in time. In the 9th century it was written "uubil" or "uuipil," in the 11th century it was already "wibil" and this form "wibel" appeared in the 12th century, together with other spellings. It can be shown that the word "wibel" was used to denote virtually all beetles then known—Stag beetles (Lucanidae), Lamellicorns (Scarabaeidae), Fireflies (Lampyridae), Longicorns (Cerambycidae), Blister Beetles (Meloidae), Weevils (Curculionidae) and Pulse Beetles (Bruchidae). There were even sub-classifications of the word "wibel," such as "scearnwifel" (dung beetle), tordwifel (dung beetle) and "golduuipil" (firefly).

But the centuries of the "wibel" were numbered. Gradually the word "kever" penetrated to those territories in which "wibel" alone had previously been dominant. Incidentally, one cause of this development has been seen in the sudden establishment of the use of "kever" to denote the Cockchafer as well. Suddenly, at the very time when these two words were vying for dominance, this prototype of a beetle was no longer a "wibel," and this probably marked the beginning of the end for this word. For a long time both words continued to be used concurrently, "wibel" for the Coleoptera, "kever" in the more comprehensive sense of "chewing, gnawing insects." If it was necessary to draw distinctions within the category "kever," particular names existed for insects such as grasshoppers, caterpillars and of course "wibel." Finally "wibel" succumbed and "kever" underwent a semantic change which took effect rapidly. In the 15th century, Leaf Beetles ("Laubkäfer"), Green Beetle ("Grünkäfer"), Horse Beetle ("Rosskäfer"), May Beetle ("Maikäfer") were already familiar as independent compounds.

Now the question remains: does any trace still exist of the old word "wibel"? In the 18th century, "wibel" disappeared from the written language (although it still exists in English as "weevil"). It was retained in certain German dialects for some time, where it may still be in use today. In a few cases, the word lives on in compounds or as a dialect term for particular species (for example, for the grain beetle and the pea beetle).

Beetles in poetry and prose

The beauty and strangeness of beetles have prompted many poets and writers to use beetles as motifs in works of poetry and prose. Let us look at a few examples.

Most of the poetry seems to be dedicated to fireflies and glow-worms (Lampyridae) (see p. 16). Another beetle frequently celebrated in verse and prose is the May Beetle or Cockchafer of the family Scarabaeidae. One might mention the *Maikäferkomödie* (May Beetle Comedy) by the Swiss writer Josef Viktor Widmann (1842–1911). In the works of Wilhelm Busch, Cockchafers again play an important part. The Russian composer Modest P. Mussorgski (1839–1881) wrote music for a poem about beetles, in which the subject was probably once again the May Beetle. Paul Keller (1873–1932) has described "Maikäfer und Engerling" (The May Beetle and its larva). A very well-known story is *Der erste Maikäfer* (The First May Beetle) by Wilhelm Raabe (1831–1910). And we might also mention the poem "Maikäfermalen" (Painting May Beetles) by Joachim Ringelnatz (1883–1934).

Other examples of the beetle motif can be found in literature. For example, in his story *Der Goldene* (The Golden One), Bruno Frank (1887–1945) describes a Ground Beetle that brings light into the life of a prisoner. A very well-known poem is "Marienwürmchen" (Ladybird Beetles) in *Des Knaben Wunderhorn*. In the poem "Abseits" (Apart) by Theodor Storm (1817–1888) there is the following line: "Ground beetles hasten through the shrubs in their golden coats of mail."

In his poem "Das Ährenfeld" (The Field in Ear), Hofmann von Fallersleben (1798–1874) writes:
"The beetle came with his wife, and here sipped a measure of cool dew." Peter Paul Plenzer wrote a poem entitled "Korbblütlerwelt" (The World of the Compositae) in which beetles also appear:

"With all the bright creatures lives
That which is kindly to our eye:
A Painted Lady soars toward the light,
A Ground Beetle makes off among the daisies.
To the parsley fern, scarcely recognizable,
Greenfly present their masks—
What drama, scarcely to be named:
Ladybirds cherish the thought of such fare!
O Divine Spirit, who may perceive Thy thought, creation, poetry,
Ordering the events in this pageant of the animal and plant world?"

And finally, some proverbial gypsy sayings on the subject of beetles:
"The dung beetle is a beauty in the eyes of its mother."
"A dung beetle loved a wood louse greatly
and wandered round the village with her,
And that amazed him even more."
"He is like a dung beetle, with whom one neither eats nor plays."
An old country saw says "A glut of May Beetles means hard times for the reaper."

Fireflies as symbols of beauty

In ancient China, fireflies (Lampyridae) were a symbol of beauty. In Chinese art, as well as in that of Japan, fireflies are frequently the subject of woodcuts or are used as motifs in colourful pictures drawn on silk.

There is a delicately executed woodcut by Hosoda Eishi (1756–1829) entitled "Catching Glow-worms at Night." It depicts three beautiful women on a river, surrounded by swarming glow-worms. One of the girls is trying to catch the beetles with a fan, while a second holds in readiness a cage containing fireflies that have already been caught. Another beautiful woodcut by Kunisada (1786–1864) should be mentioned. It too shows glow-worms being caught with fans. In Japanese art, the capture of fireflies sometimes takes on an erotic quality, as, for example, in a picture by Torii Kiyomitsu (1735–1785). He depicts a girl after her bath, dressed in an open, transparent bathing wrap, who is trying to catch glow-worms with a fan. The glow-worms are shown as blushing.

There is a whole series of Japanese poems dedicated to fireflies. Izumi Shikibu (974–1034) writes:

"When, forgotten by a man, I visited the Temple of Kifune
and saw fireflies flying round the font of holy water,
shines into my melancholy:
May my yearning soul,
freed from my body,
fly out mysteriously
with the beetles of the marsh."

Toyoma Rogetsu (1666–1751) composed a death poem:

"How swiftly it springs into light,
how swiftly it is quenched,
light of the firefly . . ."

Yosa Buson (1716–1783) wrote a poem entitled "The Glow-worm":

"Under the mosquito net
Allow a glow-worm to fly:
It will make you happy."

Another beautiful poem is "The lost child and the firefly" by Yoshida Ryusui:

"The lost child
weeps and weeps, and yet
still reaches out to catch the firefly."

Mokichi Saito (1882–1953) wrote:

"In the first glimmer of morning
You climb up high on a blade of grass,
Little firefly.
And my short life too
Shall not pass away in vain."

We also find a poem to a firefly in Chinese poetry, in this one written by Li-Tai-Pe (701–762):

"Firefly
If the rain beats upon your light, it cannot extinguish it.
If the wind blows upon your brightness, it only shines the more clearly.
And if you were to fly up into the distant heavens,
Close to the moon, you would be one of the stars."

The firefly is also venerated in Islamic art, for example, in a poem by Muhammed Igbal (1873–1938). Speaking of itself, the glow-worm says:

"If nights are darker than the eyes of gazelles,
I take fire and light up my own path."

Friedrich Gottlieb Klopstock (1724–1803) wrote a poem "Zwei Johanniswürmchen" (Two Fireflies), and Wilhelm Busch also mentions the firefly in his *Naturgeschichtliches Alphabet* (Natural History Alphabet).

Anatomy, "Record Performances" and Behaviour of Beetles

Diversity of external form and characteristic features

What is a beetle?

One of the earliest definitions of the beetle can be found in the writings of the great Greek philosopher Aristotle (384–322 B.C.): "The bloodless winged creatures are either those with wing cases (elytra) = coleoptera; these namely carry their wings under a cover, as for example the dung beetle and the blister beetle . . ."

This definition, which already contains one vital distinguishing feature is somewhat expanded in the writings of Pliny. "To protect their wings, some insects have a horny covering, as have beetles, for example, whose wings are fine and fragile. On the other hand, they have no sting. One large beetle has very long horns, divided at the extremity, that close in a bite. This beetle is called Lucanus. Another kind uses its feet to roll together quite large balls of dung, within which it protects its young from the cold of the winter. Many beetles produce a humming noise in flight. Fireflies and glow-worms shine in the night like fire.

Their light is emitted from luminous organs in the side and hind segments of the abdomen when they spread their wings. When they fold their wings again, the light disappears beneath them. Fireflies are not seen before the fodder crops have ripened, and they disappear again after the harvest."

Scarcely anything was added to this sum of knowledge during the Middle Ages, as we can see from the book *Theriotropheum Silesiae* (The Silesian Zoological Garden) written by the physician Caspar Schwenckfeld (1563–1609). Schwenckfeld presents a whole series of different species and groups of beetles, and also gives the following definition of the entire order:

"Scarabaeus, beetles, Chafers; this is a family of insects with fragile wings covered by hard, protective wing cases. It would appear that Pliny uses the name Scarabaeus to include all sheath-winged insects. There are many species, large and small, with and without horns, black, grey or tending towards yellow, red, blue and so on.

They feed on dry wood, grain and the dung of domestic animals." If we take a look at J. Hübner's *Natur-, Kunst- und Handlungslexicon* (1731) (Lexicon of Nature, Art and Behaviour), we find under the heading Scarabaeus the following entry: "Scarabaeus, a beetle; since these are to some extent employed in the preparation of medicines, we would do well to mention some of the various kinds. They include Scarabaeus, or *Cantharus cornutus*, stag beetle, Pilularius, horse beetle, *Canthareilus unctuosus*, cat beetle, *Cantharus rutilus major*, May beetle, dito minor, marsh beetle, *Bufonis viridis*, toad beetle, Pistrinarius, meal beetle, Cadaverum, carrion beetle. The horns of the stag beetle and an infusion of the beetle in oil are used by the apothecary."

An encyclopaedia dated 1974 gives the following definition: "Beetles, Coleoptera: insects 0.25–160 mm in length. At rest, horny fore wings or elytra (wing covers) protect the membranous hind wings; the legs are developed for running, burrowing, climbing, swimming or jumping. Beetles have mouthparts adapted for biting and are largely phytophagous; a number are aquatic. Development: egg, three or more larval stages, a dormant pupal stage."

As we can see, there exists a certain continuity in the definitions of beetles as a group within the animal kingdom from as far back as Aristotle, and even the ancients had appreciated one essential criterion, the modification of the fore wings into highly chitinized wing cases (elytra). But what other features are typical of beetles, by what characteristics can we recognize them and distinguish them from other insects? The various forms of leg development do not provide characteristic features exclusive to beetles. Similar conditions are found in almost all groups of insects. Grasshoppers, Dragon-flies, Sawflies, Cockroaches and other insects also have mouthparts adapted for biting. Nor are indications of habit a great deal of help here, for there are many other insects that are also plant-eaters or that live in water. And the majority of all existing insects undergo complete metamorphosis. If we want to find a valid definition of the beetle, we must look rather more closely. For our definition we would like to consider three important characteristics, the first of which was mentioned by Aristotle.

1. The fore wings are modified into more or less strongly chitinous elytra, upon which vestigial signs of venation occur only rarely. In species not capable of flight they form a swelling at the shoulders (humeral callus) which serves to protect the joint of the hind wings. The hardness of the elytra accounts for the softness of the upper side of the abdominal segments (the tergites) that are covered by them. Not all beetles have the abdominal segments covered by the elytra. For example the Staphylinidae have at least four segments exposed. The softness of the tergites refers only to the covered segments.

2. The hind wings, if present, are usually folded beneath the elytra. Their wing venation is highly derivative and influences the manner of folding. The hind wings are the sole functional organs of flight.

3. In all adult insects, the thorax consists of three segments which in adult beetles are fused together. The ventral sclerite of the first and that of the second thoracic segment are united. The dorsal sclerite of the first thoracic segment forms a large plate visible from above, known as the pronotum. The dorsal sclerite of the second thoracic segment forms the scutellum which is usually triangular and lies at the base between the elytra. The sclerite of the third thoracic segment is fused to the abdomen, and the dorsal plate belonging to it is scarcely ever visible externally. In the case of beetles, the division of the body into three regions, typical of all insects, has consequently become a matter of detail. The following three regions can be distinguished: head—prosternum and mesosternum—metasternum and abdomen (ventral aspect) or head—pronotum—mesonotum and elytra (dorsal aspect).

The largest beetles in the world

The potential maximum size of insects is limited by a whole series of factors. Nevertheless there exist among them species of considerable size. One of the largest insects in the world is at the same time the largest of the beetles. It is *Titanus giganteus*, a Longicorn Beetle (Ceram-

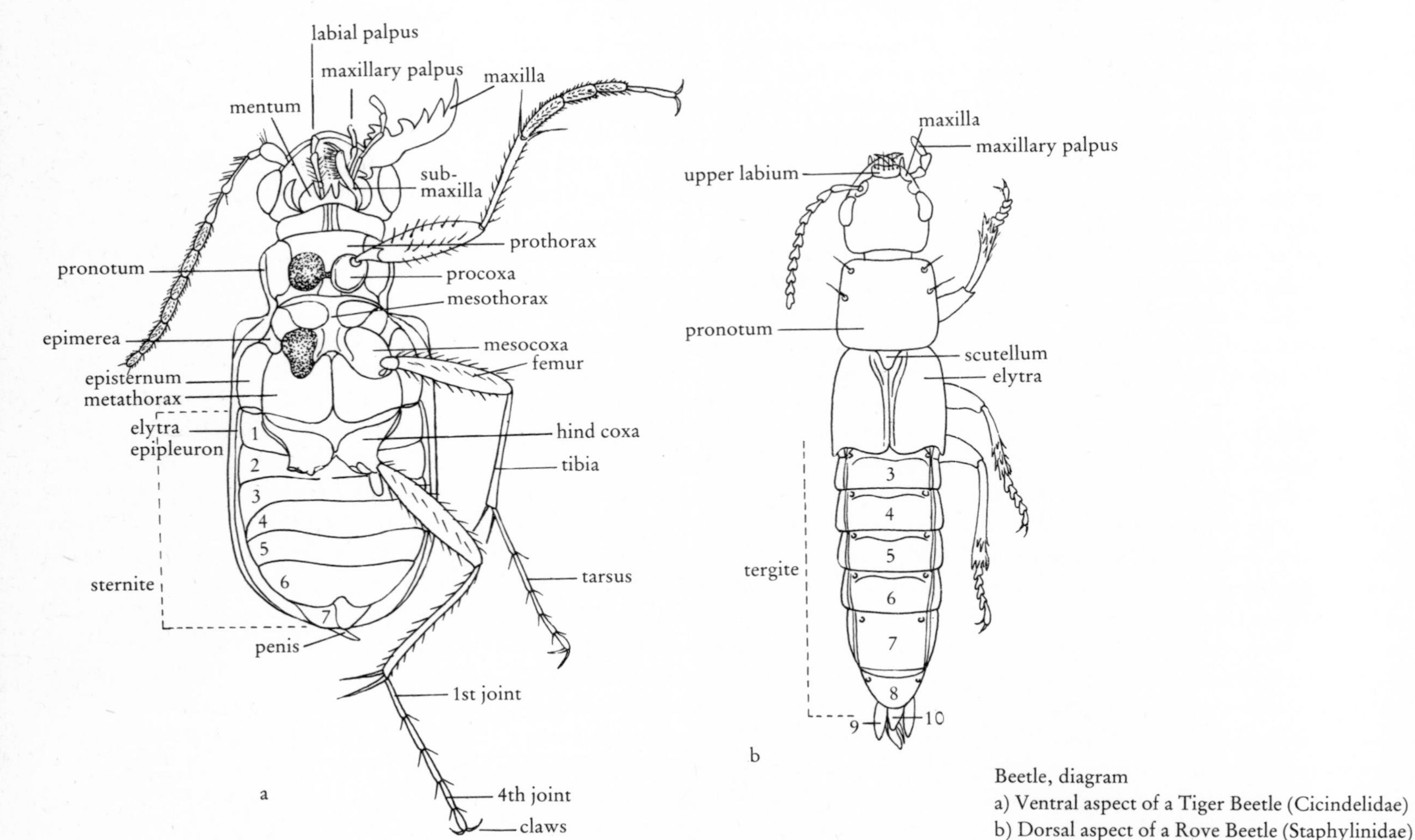

Beetle, diagram
a) Ventral aspect of a Tiger Beetle (Cicindelidae)
b) Dorsal aspect of a Rove Beetle (Staphylinidae)

bycidae) (Fig. 8). These creatures can attain a body-size of 15 to 16 cm (according to some authors, as much as 20 cm). We know scarcely anything about the habits of this Giant Longicorn Beetle. It is probable that the larvae develop in rotting wood. The beetles are extremely rare and are occasionally found in a particular river system of the Amazon region. Another Longicorn Beetle *(Xixuthrus heros)* from the Fiji Islands is up to 16 cm and the leg span and antennae are larger than in *Titanus*.

In addition to this indisputably the largest of all beetles, there are many very large species in various other families. One might mention as an example the Violin Beetles *(Mormolyce)* of the family Carabidae, a genus found on the Sunda Islands of Malaya, the representatives of which reach a length of up to 10 cm (Fig. 9). Among the Click Beetles (Elateridae) there is the genus *Tetralobus*, the representatives of which occur in Africa and grow to 7 cm in length. For a Click Beetle, this is truly gigantic. The Metallic Beetles (Buprestidae) also include some giants. They are to be found among the *Euchroma* species of South America, of which *Euchroma gigantea* can grow to a length of 8 cm. Passalid Beetles (Passalidae) are found only in the tropics. Most of the species are large, the genus *Proculus* holding the leading position with a body-length of 9 cm.

Within the large family of Scarabaeid Beetles (Chafers, Scarabs, Lamellicorn Beetles) (Scarabaeidae), there is a sub-family Dynastinae (Figs. 11, 27). Included are the well-known Hercules Beetles from tropical South America. Probably the largest species is *Dynastes hercules*, which, including the frontal cephalic horn arising from the head, measures some 15 cm in length. The beetle which attains the greatest dimensions in terms of volume also belongs to this family. It is the Actaeon Beetle *(Megasoma actaeon)*, which also lives in South America. The male can reach 9 cm in length, 5 cm in breadth and 4 cm in height. But other representatives of the Scarabaeids also grow to a considerable size (Fig. 10). Among the Dung Beetles, Scarabs (Scarabaeidae) is the genus *Heliocopris*, some species of which are up to 6 cm long (Fig. 17). The Goliath Beetles (*Goliathus* spec.; Scarabaeidae) of Central Africa that belong to the subfamily of Cetoniinae are widely known (Figs. 15, 16). Their largest species (for example, *Goliathus druryi*) grow to more than 10 cm in length. The family of Brentid Beetles (Brenthidae) includes species of considerable length. Some of them can be up to 7 cm long, but at the same time they retain a proportionately attenuated form (Fig. 23). The Snout Beetles or Weevils (Curculionidae) have also produced large species, such as the Palm Weevils (*Rhynchophorus* spec.).

The giants among the Central European fauna are of more modest proportions. Here the longest species is the European Stag Beetle *(Lucanus cervus)*, in which the male can, in some cases, attain a length of up to 10 cm, including the highly developed mandibles. Great variation in size among individuals is a particularly striking feature of this species, but also one which can be observed among all other large species (Fig. 24). The smallest of the male Stag Beetles are only 3 cm long. Other large species among the fauna of Central Europe are the Capricorn Beetle *(Cerambyx cerdo)* (Cerambycidae) and the Syrian Conifer Longhorn Beetle *(Ergates faber)* (Cerambycidae), both of which can be 5 cm long. The Rhinoceros Beetle *(Oryctes nasicornis)* (Scarabaeidae), which reaches 4 cm in length, also makes an impression of massiveness. The Ground Beetles (Carabidae) have produced a very large representative in the Giant Ground Beetle *(Procerus gigas)* which can be as much as 6 cm long. Among aquatic beetles, the leading position is held by the 5 cm long Water Scavenger Beetle *(Hydrous piceus)* (Hydrophilidae). The largest of the Predacious Diving Beetles is the dytiscid *(Dytiscus latissimus)* (Dytiscidae) which can be 4.5 cm long and 2.5 cm broad. Even tropical water beetles rarely exceed these dimensions.

The weight of the largest beetles can be quite considerable. The lead is held by *Megasoma actaeon* (Scarabaeidae) with 30 g and the Hercules Beetle *(Dynastes hercules)* (Scarabaeidae) with 15 to 37.5 g. It would require twenty specimens of the smallest of the mammals (the Etruscan shrew) to equal the weight of one large Hercules Beetle. The Goliath Beetles (*Goliathus* spec.; Scarabaeidae) can also be very heavy.

Numerous attempts have been made to measure the strength of beetles. It has been shown, for example, that a Passalid Beetle (Passalidae) is capable of drawing a loaded toy car weighing 175 g. The beetle itself weighs 1.9 g. A Rhinoceros Beetle (Scarabaeidae) can lift 850 times its own weight. A Dor Beetle *Geotrupes stercorosus* (Scarabaeidae), was able to move from one point to another a load weighing 80 g, that is, 400 times its own weight, and it was just able to lift 100 g. A beetle of the same species weighing 0.5 g carried along a 400 g load.

The smallest beetles in the world

The smallest beetle in the world is at the same time one of the smallest insects known. It is one of the Feather-winged Beetles (Ptiliidae) of which the North American *Nanosella fungi* measures 0.25 mm in length and weighs 0.4 mg. The same family contains the smallest known European beetles of the genera *Oligella* and *Micridium* which are 0.5 to 0.6 mm long. As a comparison, it might be mentioned that one-celled slipper animalcules *(Paramecium caudatum)* grow to 0.12 to 0.33 mm in length. Minute beetles occur in other families as well, for example, among the Clambidae (0.5 to 0.7 mm) and the Sphaeriidae (0.5 to 0.7 mm in length).

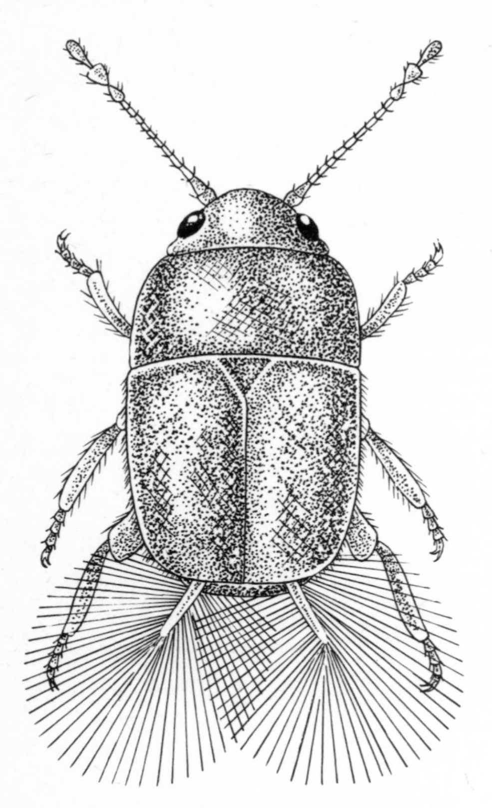

Acrotrichis sericans Heer, 0.7 mm, the wings extend beyond the elytra (Fringed Ant Beetles, Ptiliidae).

Beetles with curious adornments

In very many families of beetles there are species which have some kind of cuticular outgrowths, spines, horns or other processes occurring usually only in the males, which render the creatures rather conspicuous. The biological significance of these "ornamentations" is in most cases unclear. In the case of certain Dung Beetles (Scarabaeidae), they are probably connected with brood care.

The most conspicuous are the numerous horn formations carried by some Lamellicorn Beetles (Scarabaeidae). We can observe such phenomena among our own indigenous fauna in the Rhinoceros Beetle (Scarabaeidae, Dynastinae), Horned Dung Beetle and Three-horned Dor Beetle (Scarabaeidae).

And of course the tropics provide many more variations: the large frontal horn of the Atlas Beetle *(Chalcosoma atlas)* (Scarabaeidae) (Figs. 25, 26), the Hercules Beetle *(Dynastes hercules)* (Scarabaeidae), (particularly the species *Eupatorus gracilicornis*), numerous Dung Beetles with large horny processes in the genera *Phanaeus*, *Heliocopris* and *Onthophagus* (Scarabaeidae), (Figs. 17–22). Tropical Rhinoceros Beetles are frequently not satisfied with only a single horn, as we see from the example of *Strategus simson* or *Trichogomphus robustus*. Star performers in horn-growing are members of the genus *Golofa* (Scarabaeidae), (Fig. 28). The Rose Chafers (Cetoniinae; Scarabaeidae) also present us with a wide variety of toothed or bifurcated horns (Fig. 41).

In many other families of beetles there are species with strange ornamentations. We might mention the genus *Notoxus*, also indigenous, which belongs to the Anthicidae family. Arising from the pronotum, these beetles have a powerful, forward-pointing horn with which they are able to attack the large Blister Beetles (Meloidae). Representatives of the genus *Notoxus* are attracted to the cantharidin of the Blister Beetles (Meloidae) (and particularly of the Oil Beetles, genus *Meloe*) (Meloidae). But it is not certain whether these chance attacks on *Mèloe* can provide the real explanation of the curious horn formation.

Here we must not fail to mention the subfamily Hispinae belonging to the family of Leaf Beetles (Chrysomelidae). The entire upper surface of the body of these beetles, as for example *Hispella*, *Hispa* and others, is covered with long stout upright spines, lending them a most bizarre appearance.

The most colourful beetles in the world

Coloration in beetles is either due to the presence of melanins (brown, black) and carotenoids (red, orange or yellow) or is an optical effect produced by special cuticular structures; it reflects a genetic pattern. Whereas colourings that depend upon the presence of carotenoids usually fade after the beetle has died, the iridescent, structural colours depending upon purely physical effects, are often timeless. The majority of beetles are not conspicuously coloured. But the beetles that have always made the greatest impression on man are precisely those species which have a brilliant colour pattern.

We find some very brightly coloured individuals among the Tiger Beetles (Cicindelidae). Some fine examples are *Cicindela chinensis* from Eastern Asia that has elytra of iridescent metallic green, blue or copper red, or the North African *Cicindela regalis* with a pattern of vivid blue stripes on a yellow ground. A very beautiful Ground Beetle (Carabidae) also occurring in Europe is the *Callistus lunatus*, with steel-blue head, brick-red pronotum and bluish-black elytra with orange-red bands. Even within the generally sombrely coloured family of Rove Beetles (Staphylinidae), a few species are richly coloured, such as the exceptionally large *Emus hirtus*. The head, pronotum and the end of the abdomen are covered in a dense pelt of golden-yellow hairs, the underside has a brilliant metallic shimmer. And without exception, the Soft-winged Flower Beetles (Melyridae) and the Checkered Beetles (Cleridae) have beautiful coloration (Fig. 31). There are species with the most wonderful patterns of colour. Within the family of Flat Bark Beetles (Cucujidae), particularly in the genus *Cucujus*, there are some representatives with brilliant red colouring. Pleasing Fungus Beetles (Erotylidae) are often very colourful, usually with a combination of blues and reds. The Metallic Beetles, Jewel Beetles or Metallic Wood-borers (Buprestidae) are particularly splendid with a brilliant range of wonderfully iridescent colours (Figs. 34, 36–39). Red, green and blue tones combine with beautiful metallic lustres. Probably the most resplendent coloration throughout the whole beetle world is achieved in this family. Structural colours are often combined with pigmentary colours. A microscopically thin colourless lamina lies over the pigmented ground. The physical phenomenon of optical interference between reflexions coming from the superimposed laminae produces the iridescent colours that are then varied by the changing angle of incidence of the light. Many of the tropical representatives of the Lagriid Bark Beetles (Lagriidae, a sub-family of the Tenebrionidae) are distinguished by delicate pastel tones of green, grey, blue and purple. The family of Lamellicorn Beetles (Scarabaeidae) includes many brilliantly coloured species. Some representatives of the sub-family Rutelinae are entirely gold or silver coloured (Fig. 35). They genuinely have the appearance of creatures wrought of metal. The species in question belong to the genus *Plusiotis* and occur in Central and South America. Within the sub-family of Rose Chafers (Cetoniinae), the beauty of colouring is considerable, even in the case of the Goliath Beetles (Scarabaeidae), which often have a delicate patterning of velvety fawn colouring on a white ground (Figs. 15, 16). In other species of Rose Chafers (Scarabaeidae, Cetoniinae), which in addition are often beautifully marked, the metallic iridescence is comparable to the opalescent play of colour in precious stones (Figs. 40–43, 145). And the Longhorn Beetles (Cerambycidae) have every reason to be proud of their coloration (Figs. 44–47). Special mention might be made also of the Alpine Sawyer *(Rosalia alpina)* whose sky-blue elytra are marked with diagonal bands of velvety black. The Leaf Beetles (Chrysomelidae) provide many brightly coloured and particularly metallic-coloured species (Fig. 52). Even the Colorado Potato Beetle *(Leptinotarsa decemlineata)* is a good example of fine colouring. Because of the sparkling emerald green lustre of the upper surface of certain of the Tortoise Beetles (Cassidinae), such as the Brazilian *Desmonota variolosa,* they are sometimes used in jewellery, mounted like precious stones (Fig. 50). The Snout Beetles or Weevils (Curculionidae), the family of beetles with the largest number of species, has produced some gleaming metallic colours and includes among its ranks many brilliantly coloured species in red, green, blue and yellow (Figs. 53–58). Completely white beetles are decidedly rare. Usually this coloration is achieved by a covering of white scales. There is only one group in which there are species that have elytra composed of pure white chitin; these are, curiously enough, representatives of certain species of the family of Darkling Beetles (Tenebrionidae).

Coloration seems to be related to geographical distribution. Thus South America, the Orientalis and Australia are extraordinarily rich in gleaming metallic colours. In tropical Africa, on the other hand, white, red, yellow and brown pigmentary colours predominate. This is associated with the fact that the fauna of tropical Africa has largely the character of a steppe fauna. Metallic colours occur particularly in a tropical rain forest.

Variation in coloration and marking

Within many species of beetle there is an extraordinary degree of variation in colouring, as we can see from the example of the tropical Rose Chafer *Neptunides polychromus* (Scarabaeidae) from East Africa (Fig. 43). Occasionally the spectrum is so broad that differing colour forms have been relegated to different species. Although this variability occurs in very many different families of beetles, it is particularly striking in the case of Ladybirds (Coccinellidae). Let us consider a single example. The Ten-spotted Ladybird *Adalia decempunctata*, a species widespread throughout Europe, shows a remarkably wide range of variation. More than 80 clearly distinct colour forms have been described and named. Let us look at three extremes: there are individuals with black elytra with a reddish shoulder band; in others, the elytra are black and carry in each case five large yellow spots; and finally there are individuals with yellow elytra, each elytron bearing two to eight black spots. The Tortoise Beetle *Charidotella sexpunctata* (Chrysomelidae, Cassidinae) from Brazil shows a striking colour change; in twenty minutes it can turn from shining gold by way of greenish tones to dull yellowish-brown.

Are they really beetles?

Among the Leaf Beetles (Chrysomelidae) there exists the sub-family Chlamydinae, to which the genus *Fulcidax* belongs. Anyone looking at these creatures fleetingly might well take them for fragments of ore or pieces of crumbling soil. But this is probably the most singular form to be found among beetles. Of course, many other groups diverge considerably from the widely accepted, familiar "normal form," and yet it is always possible to recognize quite readily that they are indeed beetles, even when,

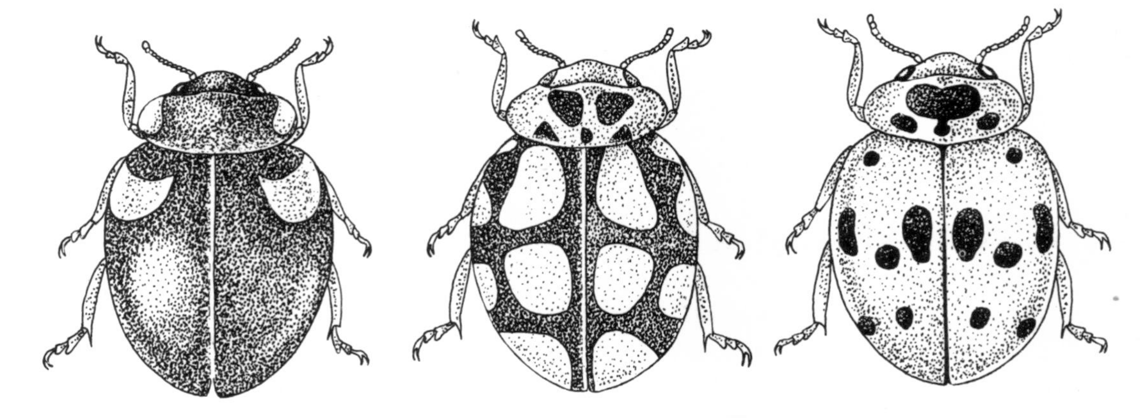

Variation in colouring in *Adalia decempunctata* L. (Ladybirds, Coccinellidae)

for example, the entire body is densely covered with hairs, as in the case of the Weevil of the genus *Lithinus* (Curculionidae) (Figs. 59, 60).

Even most of the greatly flattened species living beneath bark can always be recognised easily as beetles. Some examples are the Hister Beetle *Hololepta plana* (Histeridae) that is 7.5 mm in length but only 0.9 mm in height, and most of the species of Flat Bark Beetles (Cucujidae). In West Africa there is a representative of the Net-winged Beetles, *Chlamydolycus trabeatus* (Lycidae), which has elytra so broadened as to give the beetle a disc-like appearance. Many other species in this family have a tendency toward the discoid form (Figs. 62, 64).

At this point it might be as well to mention that a large number of deformities in beetles have been described. Probably in no case would the abnormality prevent the recognition of the creature as a beetle, but naturally it surprises the observer when he discovers an animal with a forked leg or an antenna deeply bifurcated at the base giving an impression of three feelers. Multiple legs also occur frequently.

What does a beetle look like inside?

In general, it is the external form of the beetle with which people are familiar. Characteristic features are the chitinous integumental coverings (cuticula) of the segments which protect the creature's body in an ideal way from mechanical and chemical influences. The chitinous external skeleton has often been compared with a coat of armour, although the most ingenious constructions created by human hands could never even approximately attain the perfection of form which nature has lent to the insect body.

The mobility of the beetle's body is provided by means of articulated and ball-and-socket joints between the sections of the body and the segments of the legs.

But the cuticle also serves as the point of attachment for a large number of muscles. The activity of the muscles must, of course, be regulated by the nervous system, and beetles have a fairly complicated system of control. Linked to a highly developed brain are the two ventral nerve strands which, in the most primitive form, have a series of knots of ganglia (nerve centres) in each part of the body, between which contact is maintained by transverse nerve fibres. This primitive "rope ladder" nervous system has of course been very much modified, in particular it has become concentrated, and is closely connected with the manifold functions of the sense organs and the internal secretory apparatus. Gaseous interchange with the atmosphere (respiration) is carried out by a system of air-tubes called the tracheal tubes. The external starting point is the series of small respiratory apertures or spiracles (stigmata) which lead into the body by way of a system of ramifying tubes which become progressively finer, whereby oxygen is carried to almost every individual cell. The haemolymph (insect "blood") scarcely plays any part in gaseous interchange but functions inter alia as a means of distributing food and hormones throughout the body and removing the products of metabolism.

Along the back is the tubular heart chamber, which draws in haemolymph through slit-like openings along its sides (ostia) and pumps it forward towards the head. Blood does not circulate in an enclosed system but seeps among the tissues of the whole body, finally to be sucked in again through the ostial valves.

Extending through each beetle from the mouth opening to the anus is the intestinal canal, which is subdivided into three sections, the fore, mid and hind gut. The first and last sections have a chitinous cuticular lining. In front of the mid gut, many species have a gizzard or proventriculus, often furnished with small teeth which serve to grind down and crush food particles (masticatory stomach). At the junction of the mid and hind gut are openings into a number of slender blind tubes known as the Malphigian tubules. They carry out excretion, absorbing the products of metabolism from the blood and discharging them into the hind gut.

A considerable proportion of the volume of the abdomen is taken up by the sexual organs the structure of which is considered elsewhere in this book.

Orientation and Sensory Perception

The head as the control centre

The head is the control centre of the insect. It carries important sense organs and is responsible for sight, taste and smell. The amalgamated neural material which makes up the brain is housed in the head capsule. The antennae and mouthparts are furnished with sense organs. The primary function of the latter is the taking of food.

A remarkable modification of head shape

The most substantial modification and peculiarity of head form is the development of a pronounced rostrum (Figs. 23, 65, 66). In addition to the Weevils (Curculionidae), other families that also exemplify this development, though without in general achieving such spectacular length of snout, are for example the Shrew Weevils (Apionidae), Straight-snouted Weevils (Brenthidae), Bark Beetles (Scolytidae) and Fungus Weevils (Anthribidae) as well as Narrow-waisted Bark Beetles (Salpingidae), Oedemerid Beetles (Oedemeridae), Carrion or Burying Beetles (Silphidae), Net-winged Beetles (Lycidae) and others. Many weevils of the Curculionidae family have a very slender rostrum which exceeds the length of the beetle's body, giving it a bizarre appearance (Fig. 65). The function of the rostrum is to take in food, and sometimes to bore narrow and often deep holes and channels in even a relatively firm substratum, in which eggs are then deposited.

Antennae as olfactory organs

The antennae are more or less densely covered with olfactory sensilla that are stimulated by the vapours of volatile substances. They are capable of perceiving scents of a wide variety of qualities and are therefore particularly important in seeking out appropriate food, in selecting suitable sites in which to settle and most of all in finding a sexual partner. As a consequence of this latter function, the surface area of the antennae is often considerably greater in males than in females. This effect can be achieved, for example, by lengthening. The most striking examples of this are found in the Longicorn Beetles (Cerambycidae). The lead is held by *Batocera kibleri* of the Solomon Islands with antennae that can be as long as 230 mm (Figs. 67, 68). An outstanding example from the fauna of Europe is the Timberman *(Acanthocinus aedilis)* (Cerambycidae). In the male, the antennae can be five times as long as the body, while in the female they are at most twice her body length. Among the tropical species of Fungus Weevils (Anthribidae) (Fig. 69) we find antennae that are several times body length.

In general, beetle larvae have very short antennae. But there is one noteworthy exception: this is found in the larvae of the family of Marsh Beetles (Helodidae) which are unique in having antennae with some 150 segments. The number of articulations increases with each moult, a peculiarity found in very few insects. It is not known whether the long antennae of the Helodid larvae fulfil any special function.

The extension of the surface area of the antennae can be achieved in another way. We see an example of it in the Lamellicorns (Scarabaeidae), whose antennae carry at their extremity three to seven spreading, lamellate organs which can be spread apart by the pressure of the haemolymph. The size and number of these plates, which are furnished with a large number of sensory cells, can vary greatly between the sexes and within the various species. Embranchment of the antennae also brings about an increase in their surface area, as can be observed in the example of the male Click Beetle (Elateridae). The male of the Blister Beetle *Cerocoma schaefferi* (Meloidae) which is widespread in Europe, has an antenna of very complicated construction.

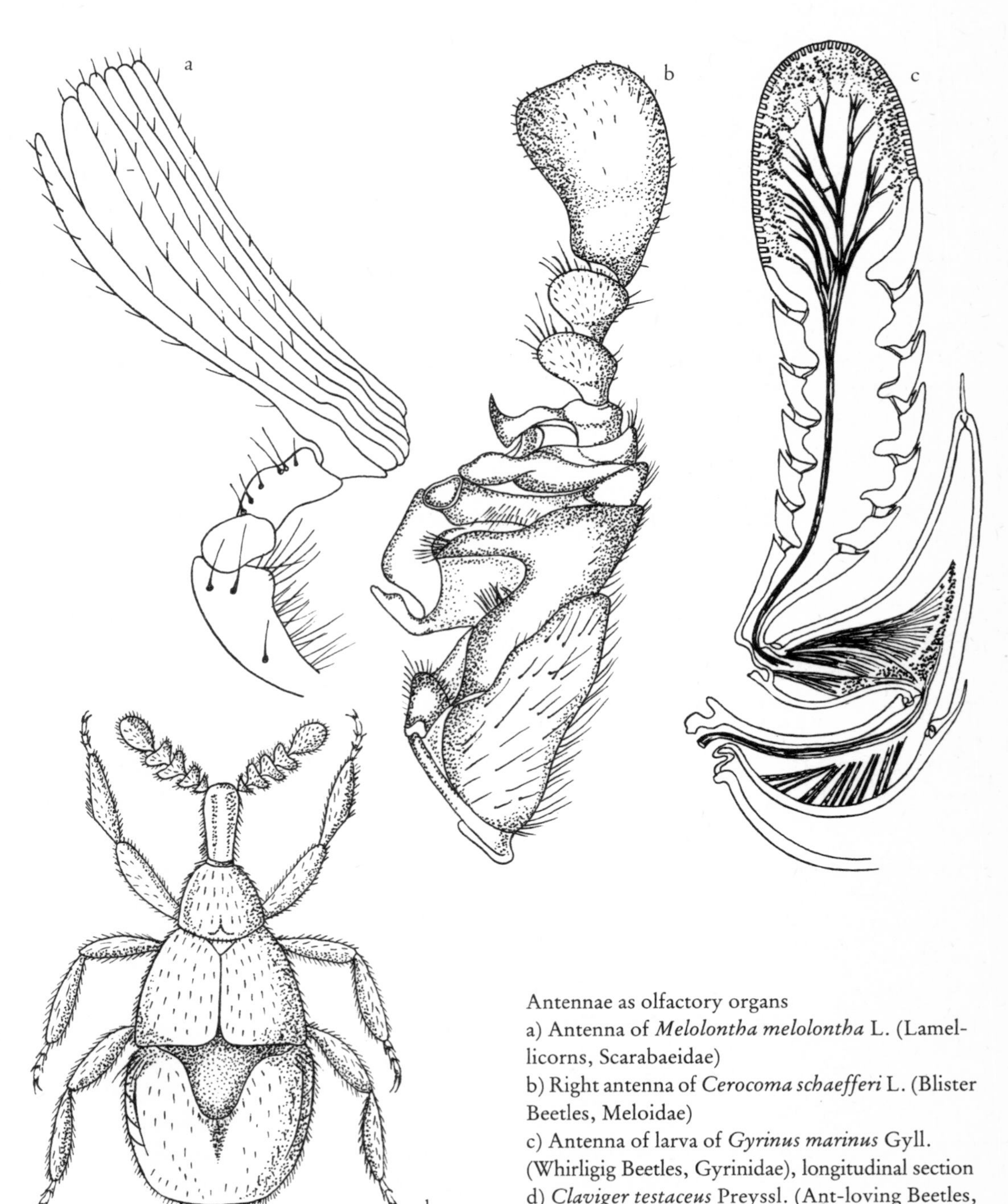

Antennae as olfactory organs
a) Antenna of *Melolontha melolontha* L. (Lamellicorns, Scarabaeidae)
b) Right antenna of *Cerocoma schaefferi* L. (Blister Beetles, Meloidae)
c) Antenna of larva of *Gyrinus marinus* Gyll. (Whirligig Beetles, Gyrinidae), longitudinal section
d) *Claviger testaceus* Preyssl. (Ant-loving Beetles, Pselaphidae)

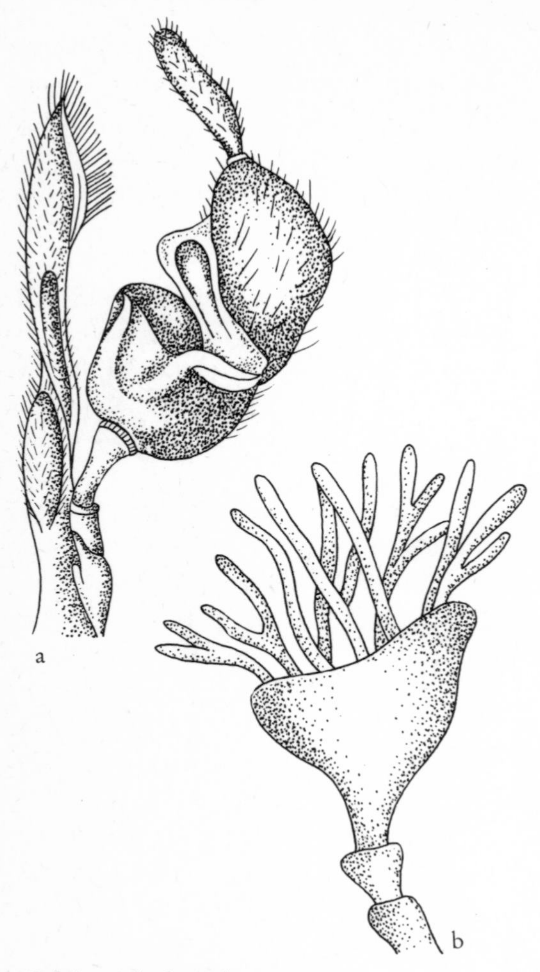

Palpi as substitute for antennae
a) *Cerocoma schaefferi* L. (Blister Beetles, Meloidae)
b) *Hylecoetus dermestoides* L. (Ship Timber Beetles, Lymexylidae)

The antennae of the Whirligig Beetles (Gyrinidae) fulfil a completely different function (see p. 111).

The antennae of the Paussid Beetles (Paussidae) also show considerable specialization. The Claviger Beetles (*Claviger* species) of the family of Ant-loving Beetles (Pselaphidae) are characterized by clavate antennae. From time to time the ants drag the beetles through the nest by means of these "clubs". Apart from this, nothing is known about the functions of these curious antennae. Long-toed Water Beetles (Dryopidae) of the genus *Dryops* have antennae with the second segment expanded in an auriculate shape, but what purpose it serves is not clear. The Weevil *Cercidocerus securifer* (Curculionidae) of Java and Kalimantan (Borneo) has a greatly enlarged, hatchet-shaped terminal antennal segment.

Maxillary palpi as a substitute for antennae

In certain beetles, the maxillary palps support the functions of the antennae. One example of this can be seen in *Cerocoma schaefferi* (Meloidae) mentioned above. In this species, the second segment of the maxillary palp is furnished with a large number of single-celled glands, as are the antennae, and function in the search for a sexual partner.

In various other groups of beetles, the maxillary palpi alone have taken over the perception of smell. This is the case with *Hylecoetus dermestoides*, for example, a species belonging to the family of Ship Timber Beetles (Lymexylidae). Particularly on the second segment of their maxillary palpi, the males have a large number of long lateral branches equipped with olfactory sensilla. By means of these sense organs, the males are able to perceive pheromones secreted by the females.

The Water Scavenger Beetles (Hydrophilidae) have put their antennae to the service of respiration. In this species, the maxillary palpi are enlarged and are extremely elongate. In certain species at any rate they seem to have taken over the tactile functions of the antennae. We also find exceptionally large and to some extent modified maxillary palpi in the Ant-loving Beetles (Pselaphidae).

Fragrant Beetles

In contrast to those secreted by many other groups of insects, the odiferous substances produced by beetles have not been examined very closely. And so we are not able to give a great deal of information about the working of their sense of smell. However, we might first consider the larvae of the Red Poplar Leaf Beetle of the genus *Melasoma* (Chrysomelidae). When touched, they emit a strong-smelling secretion from special glands at the sides of the abdominal segments. This probably has its origin in the salicylic acid present in the leaves of the willows and poplars upon which the larvae feed. The Musk Beetle *(Aromia moschata)* (Cerambycidae) also lives on willows and produces a musk-like scent that is probably also based on salicylid acid. The renowned systematist John Ray writes of the Musk Beetle: "It exhales such a strong scent of musk that one is aware of it even when it merely flies past. The scent is a mild one."

Among the Lamellicorn Beetles (Scarabaeidae) there is the Russian Leather Beetle *(Osmoderma eremita)* that does indeed smell of leather. At mating time, the wingless females of the Drilid Beetles (Drilidae) make their way to low-growing vegetation and emit an unpleasant, putrid odour to which the male is attracted.

There is no doubt that odiferous substances are secreted by many other species of beetle, but only very few of them are perceptible to man.

What can beetles see?

The great Dutch naturalist Antony van Leeuwenhoek (1632–1723) was one of the first to carry out scientific research into the construction of the beetle eye. We do not know which beetle served as his subject. A striking aspect of his work was his attempt to view objects in his environment through a microscope and the cornea of the beetle's eye. But let us hear what the master himself has to say: "I removed the scleroid coat from the head of the beetle and observed, under the microscope, that the eye is not a hemisphere, but is longer than it is wide. At the greatest diameter of the eye, I counted a row of no less than 60 separate optical organs, and 40 at the narrowest point. Related to a hemisphere, that would make 50 eyes per row at the maximum diameter, or for the greatest compass of pairs of eyes brought together as a globe, 100 eyes. From this, the total number of eyes can be calculated. On the assumption that both eyes are hemispheres, the number of individual optical organs is 3181 (Leeuwenhoek's mode of calculation omitted) . . . The tower of the new church in Delft, the dimensions of which I have described in an earlier letter, observed in this way [that is, through the eye of the beetle, the Author] appears no larger than the point of a needle." Nowadays it is even possible to take photographs through the eye of a beetle and obtain a many-facetted picture of the environment. The number of individual facets is very varied, ranging from 20 in the Ant-loving Beetle (Pselaphidae), to 5,000 in the Cockchafer (*Melolontha melolontha*; Scarabaeidae) and as many as 25,000 in the Tumbling Flower Beetle (*Mordella* species; Mordellidae). The diameter of a single visual unit or cone (ommatidium) of the compound eye of the Common Cockchafer *(Melolontha melolontha)* (Scarabaeidae) is 0.02 mm. The smaller the angle enclosed by the ommatidium (the ommatidian angle), the greater is the resolving power and therefore the visual acuity of the complex eye. The June Beetle *(Polyphylla fullo)* (Scarabaeidae) possesses three times as many facets per angle unit as the smaller Garden Chafer *(Phyllopertha horticola)* (Scarabaeidae). Accordingly its resolving power should be three times as great. With the reduction of the ommatidian angle, the intensity of the image decreases, since the quantity of light depends upon the diameter of the cone. By increasing the size of the eye while retaining a constant ommatidian angle, the diameter of the ommatidium and therefore the intensity of image can be increased.

In beetles, the eyes do not show very many striking modifications. But one noteworthy feature is the division of the eyes into an upper and lower eye on each side, such as is typical of the Whirligig Beetles (Gyrinidae) (Fig. 70). Divided eyes are also found in other families of beetles such as the Longicorns (Cerambycidae) (see below). Intermediate stages exist from kidney-shaped eyes progressively through incomplete division (e.g. *Tetropium*) to complete separation of each eye into two (*Tetrops*; sub-genus *Opsilia* of the genus *Phytoecia*). Divided eyes also occur in Scarabaeids (Scarabaeidae), as in the species *Odontaeus armiger* widely distributed over Europe.

Another extreme is the complete reduction of the eyes. We find examples of this among the Feather-winged Beetles (Ptiliidae). There, even within the same species, there are eyeless and eyed individuals.

Reduction of the eyes can also be observed among numerous other families. In particular, beetles leading a subterranean existence are usually blind (beetles living in caves), as, for example, many species of the Ground Beetle genus *Trechus* or the genera *Anophthalmus* and *Aphaenops*, together with some other representatives of the Ground Beetles (Carabidae), Rove Beetles (Staphylinidae), Ant-loving Beetles (Pselaphidae), Rhizophagids

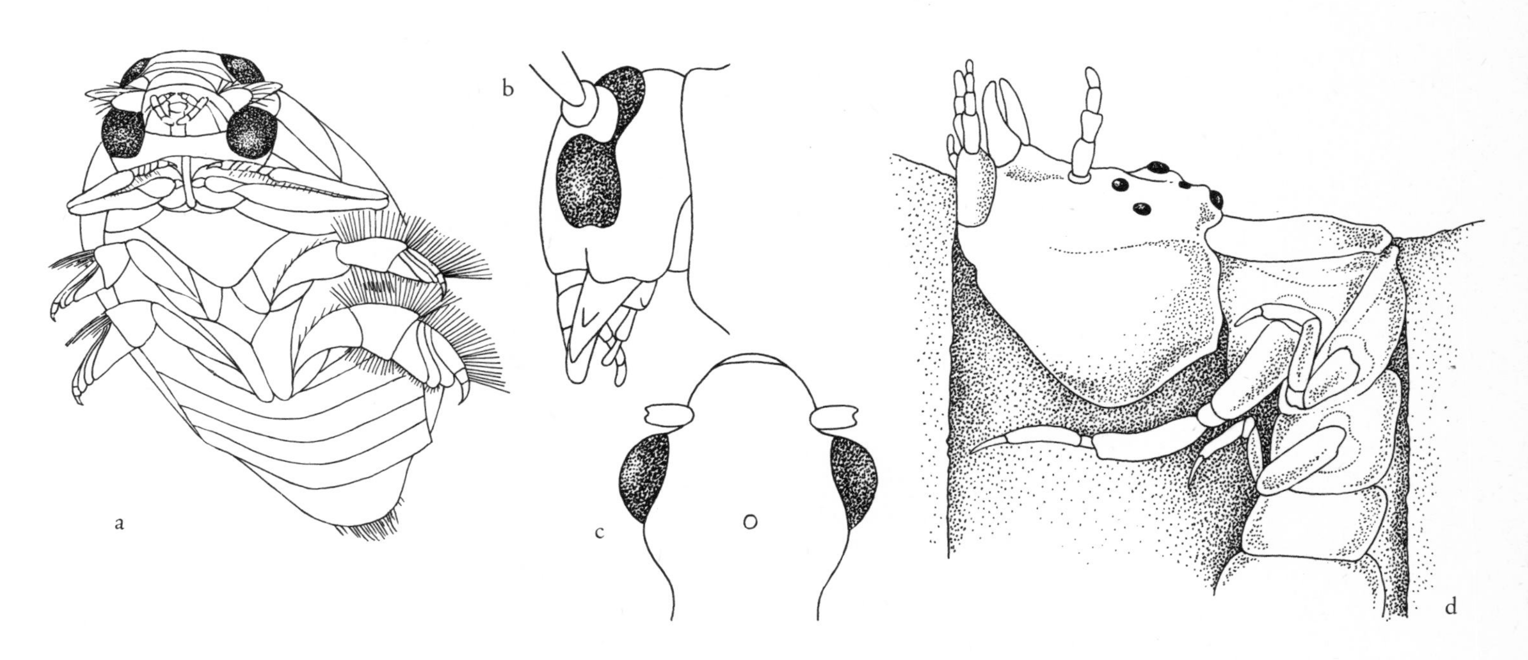

Beetle eyes
a) Whirligig Beetle (Gyrinidae), frontal aspect. The four eyes enable the beetle to see above and below water simultaneously.
b) *Phytoecia coerulescens* Scop. (Longhorns, Cerambycidae), eyes almost completely divided
c) Pineal eye (ocellus) of a Bacon Beetle (*Dermestes* spec.; Dermestidae)
d) Larva of *Cicindela* spec. (Tiger Beetles, Cicindelidae) in its vertical burrow in the ground, with ocelli (stemmata).

(Rhizophagidae), Mammal-nest Beetles (Leptinidae), Predacious Diving Beetles (Dytiscidae) and Catopids (Catopidae).

Apart from the laterally situated compound eyes, some beetles also possess ocelli or simple eyes placed at the top of the head. Those of the Hide Beetles (Dermestidae) are particularly well-known. Ocelli are also found among the sub-family Omaliinae of the Rove Beetles (Staphylinidae), and in the Derodontidae. Particularly in the case of the two last-named groups, it is generally thought that the ocelli fulfil no optic function.

And of what feats is the beetle eye capable? Many beetles are able to find their bearings from the sun. This ability to make use of a "sun compass" has been demonstrated in, for example, some of the river-bank dwelling beetles in the families of Rove Beetles (Staphylinidae) and Ground Beetles (Carabidae). But experiments have shown that the Cockchafer (Scarabaeidae) also has this capacity. In addition, many beetles are capable of direct perception of the plane of polarization of light from the sky even without the sun being visible—an achievement which up to now has been particularly associated with bees. The initiation of activity in crepuscular beetles is dependent upon the intensity of light.

The eyes of Fireflies (Lampyridae) are characterized by a particular lense apparatus consisting of strata of varying optical density which break up the rays of light like a lense cylinder. Nocturnal vision is further improved by the type of construction of the superposed eye.

The lateral ocelli (stemmata) of the larvae of Tiger Beetles (Cicindelidae) contain over 6,300 optic cells each and are capable of binocular estimation of distance. Unilateral removal of one such eye prevents the estimation of distance.

Most beetles are probably capable of colour perception and like many insects, have a particular spectral region, which, compared to that of man is displaced towards the ultraviolet end of the spectrum. A distinct ability to perceive red has been demonstrated for Ground Beetles (Carabidae) of the genus *Carabus*, which still react at 670 nm. A result such as this is otherwise obtained only in the case of a few diurnal butterflies. As far as is known to us, the Red Poplar Leaf Beetle *Melasoma populi* (Chrysomelidae) and the Rose Chafer *Cetonia aurata* (Scarabaeidae) are colour blind.

Peculiarities of locomotion

Thorax as the motor centre

The three segments of the thorax each carry a pair of legs, and in addition, the second and third segment of the thorax each bear a pair of wings, of which, in beetles, only the hind wings are responsible for providing motive power in flight. All organs of locomotion are concentrated in the thorax, so it is not surprising that dissection of this part of the body reveals a considerable concentration of muscles.

Flight organs and flight capacity

The fore wings (elytra) are of only secondary importance in flight. In most species they are held obliquely outwards. There is some movement of flight, but it is very slight. Most of the work is performed by the posterior wings. The large species fly on the dynamic lift principle. But the very smallest of the beetles move through the air on the aeronautic principle of drag. The hind wings of these very small species are greatly reduced in area and are furnished with bristles along the edge. It is a phenomenon of convergence which can be observed in small beetles of many families, but also in small insects belonging to other orders, for example, thrips (Thysanoptera) and hymenopterons (Hymenoptera).

Most species of beetles require a certain amount of time before they are able to take off in flight. They have first to inflate their body with air. This process can be observed particularly clearly in the case of the Cockchafer or May Beetle (Scarabaeidae). Only the Tiger Beetles (Cincindelidae) are capable of instantaneous flight, but in this they are an exception. The purpose of filling the body cavity with air is to obtain the greater quantities of air required during flight. The consumption of oxygen for a Cockchafer when it is at rest is 360 mm^3 per gramme of body weight per hour. In flight is uses 39,700 mm^3. That is more than one hundred times as much. Ladybirds (Coccinellidae) on the other hand increase their consumption of oxygen in flight by only about twenty times.

Whereas all other beetles fly with elytra raised high (Figs. 75–84, 88, 89, 91), Rose Chafers (Cetoniinae) do not open their elytra during flight. The hind wings emerge through a slit in the edge of the elytra (Fig. 85). Included in this sub-family are the Goliath Beetles, which provide a contrast to almost all other beetles in that they have brilliant, metallic coloured hind wings.

Performances achieved in flight vary greatly. The number of wing beats per second is 220 for the Cockchafer (Scarabaeidae), compared with 75 to 91 for the Two-spotted Ladybird *(Adalia bipunctata)* (Coccinellidae). Speed of flight reaches 2.3 m/s for the Spanish Fly *(Lytta vesicatoria)*, 2.2 to 3 m/s for the Cockchafers (Scarabaeidae) and 7 m/s for the Dung Beetle (Scarabaeidae).

Many species of beetles have lost the capacity for flight. In some cases, this is accompanied by a reduction of the elytra. But in other species the elytra have been retained complete, and only the hind wings are reduced. This phenomenon is widespread among Ground Beetles (Carabidae). Even within a single species it is possible to observe a wide range of stages in wing reduction. Also among the Feather-winged Beetles, winged and wingless individuals can be found within the same species.

Organs of flight
a) Wing of *Trichopteryx* spec. (Fringed Ant Beetles, Ptiliidae)
b) Wing reduction in *Carabus clathratus* L. (Ground Beetles, Carabidae), on left, normally developed hind wing, on right much reduced hind wing

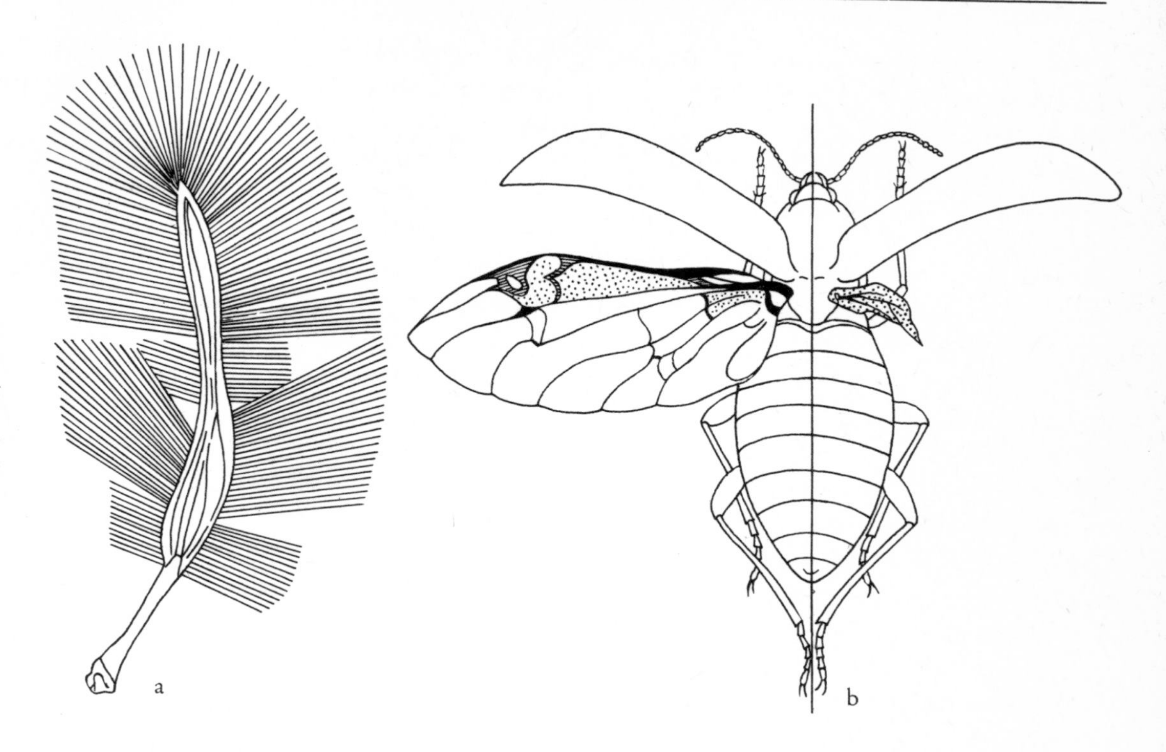

Elytra and their fine structure

Because of the immense variety in their construction and coloration, the elytra more than anything else are responsible for the wealth of forms to be found in the beetle world. In a number of species of beetle, the elytra show secondary reduction. Some examples can be found among the Longicorns (Cerambycidae), the Oedemerids (Oedemeridae), the Rhipiphorids (Rhipiphoridae) and other families, in particular genera of which the elytra are very narrow. Among the large family of Rove Beetles or "Staphs" (Staphylinidae), wing reduction has progressed much further, and the abbreviated elytra always leave several segments of the abdomen exposed. Similar reductions are met with among the Longicorns (*Necydalis* spec., *Molorchus* spec.; Cerambycidae), Oil Beetles (*Meloe* spec.; Meloidae), Carrion Beetles (Silphidae), Soldier Beetles (Cantharidae), Soft-winged Flower Beetles (Melyridae) and Ship Timber Beetles (Lymexylidae). And then there are other groups of beetles in which the elytra are completely absent. We find them among the Mammal-nest Beetles (Leptinidae) and the females of many Fireflies (Lampyridae), Drilidae, Phengodidae, Homalisidae and Hide Beetles (Dermestidae), which have also lost the hind wings.

Even if a beetle has fully developed elytra, it is necessary for the hind wings to be folded up to fit beneath. This is much more difficult when the area of the elytra is much reduced, as it is for example in Rove Beetles (Staphylinidae), and when nevertheless the hind wings are well developed. A complicated folding mechanism has resulted. But there are other species which do not fold their hind wings at all but rather roll them up. The Reticulated Beetles (Cupedidae) provide one example of this. In addition, certain Ship Timber Beetles (Lymexylidae) which also have reduced elytra, are not capable of folding their hind wings. The same is true of Rhipiphorid Beetles (Rhipiphoridae) which have hind wings that are permanently visible beneath the more or less reduced elytra.

Another extreme in the development of the elytra is their tendency to become fused together. This occurs particularly frequently in the Weevils (Curculionidae), Ground Beetles of the genus *Carabus* und various Darkling Beetles (Tenebrionidae). There is one of the Spider Beetles, *Gibbium psylloides* (Ptinidae), in which the elytra enclose the body entirely apart from a small central opening along the underside of the abdomen. Occasionally the fusion of the elytra can be seen to fulfil a biological function. Among the Blister Beetles (Meloidae), the species belonging to the genus *Cysteodemus* carry with them a ball of air beneath the fused elytra, which is believed to afford them some protection from tropical heat and the danger of desiccation.

Gibbium psylloides Czempinsky (Ptinid Beetles, Ptinidae). The elytra encircle the body almost completely.

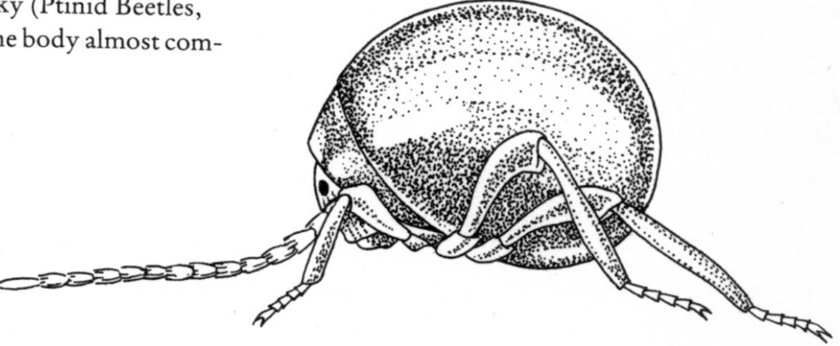

We encounter another curiosity in wing-cover construction in the Reticulated Beetles (Cupedidae), which have perforated elytra. This perforation has been interpreted as the initial stage in the development of the elytra. Chitinous bars have been superimposed upon the longitudinal and transverse veins or nervures which were a primary feature of the membranous fore wings. In the Cupedidae, the wing membrane can still be detected in the interstices remaining (cells), whereas during the course of development in other families, growth outwards from the chitinous bands has closed up the intervening gaps. In various other families, perforation also occurs as a secondary phenomenon, in, for example, some Net-winged Beetles (Lycidae), Soldier Beetles (Cantharidae), Darkling Beetles (Tenebrionidae), Leaf Beetles (Chrysomelidae) and Bark Beetles (Scolytidae).

It is not widely known that many beetles, like butterflies, have scales on their wing cases which are derived from genuine hairs. Up to now, scales of this kind have been observed in 16 families of beetles. Some idea of their often bizarre beauty may be gained from Figure 92 which shows scanning electron photographs of eight different species. A noteworthy feature is that in the Cupedidae, minute scales occur also on the underside of the elytra.

Migration in beetles

Beetles are not essentially migratory insects and yet there are numbers of species that change their habitat periodically. Ladybirds are particularly well known for this; but there are other species as well that are capable of covering quite large distances. For example, swarms of Caterpillar Hunters (*Calosoma* spec.; Carabidae) that came down in the centre of Berlin must have covered a distance of at least ten kilometres. The Rape Beetle (*Meligethes* spec.), only 2 mm in length, belonging to the family of Pollen Beetles (Nitidulidae), sometimes spends the winter 2 to 3 km away from the fields of rape. And sometimes Cockchafers *(Melolontha melolontha)* (Scarabaeidae) will travel as much as 6 km between the egg-laying site and the trees on which they feed.

The universally familiar migrations undertaken by Ladybirds (Coccinellidae) are usually for the purpose of seeking out over-wintering sites (Fig. 33). It is a particularly striking feature of the North American species *Hippodomia convergens.* Making use of wind currents, these creatures fly many kilometres from the valleys of California to their winter quarters at an altitude of some 600 m in the Sierra Nevada. In spring they return again. In their winter quarters the creatures collect into aggregations which can reach gigantic proportions. The number of individuals in one such assembly was calculated and it was found that there were some 42 million beetles crowded together and on top one another. Other Ladybirds carry out periodic movements of this kind, and migrations can be observed on coastal areas of the North Sea and the Baltic. Occasionally vast swarms of Ladybirds have been known to fly from the Continent of Europe to England.

Particular forms of legs

The legs of beetles show considerable variation in construction. Locomotion underground, on the surface of the ground, on plants and in water has produced an extremely wide spectrum of modifications.

Running

Normally all beetles progress in a forward direction, they have developed scarcely any capacity for reverse motion. Only those beetles living in galleries are capable of running backwards, as, for example, Dung Beetles (Scarabaeidae) and Bark Beetles (Scolytidae). The typical running leg is long, and the greatest speeds in running are in general achieved by the long-legged beetles such as Tiger Beetles (Cicindelidae). But even short-legged species can finally reach their goal by dogged persistence. The Weevil *Bothynoderes punctiventris* (Curculionidae), for instance, is reputed to be capable of covering 1 km in a day. Sometimes other reasons make it necessary for the legs to be long. There is a South American species of Stag Beetle *(Chiasognathus granti)* (Lucanidae) in which the enormously long mandibles are directed vertically downward (Fig. 93). The forelegs have been correspondingly lengthened, since otherwise the creature would be incapable of walking.

The Feather-winged Beetles (Ptiliidae) have a curious mode of locomotion. The creatures make a sudden dart forwards at relatively high speed, and within 1 to 2 cm, stand still again just as suddenly. After an interval they dash off again.

Climbing

Beetles are capable of climbing the highest trees. For this purpose, special climbing legs have developed which are characterized by considerable length, the presence of strong claws and in some cases a special adhesive apparatus. Among the Tiger Beetles (Cicindelidae) for example, is the arboreal genus *Collyris*, which has extraordinarily slender legs and a thin, stick-like body. Of similar appearance are the members of the American genus *Ctenostoma* and the species of *Pogonostoma* occurring in Madagascar. All three genera are adapted to catching food on the trees. They are able to run in spirals up and down the trunks and branches with remarkable rapidity. On the ground, the *Pogonostoma* species are incapable of locomotion. Figure 94 shows the South American Harlequin Beetle *(Acrocinus longimanus)* (Cerambycidae), the forelegs of which can be up to 14 cm in length, while the actual body length rarely exceeds 7 cm.

8 The world's largest beetle *(Titanus giganteus)* (Cerambycidae), original size

9 Violin Beetle *(Mormolyce phyllodes)* (Carabidae) from Kalimantan, Java, Sumatra; length of body up to 8.4 cm. The beetle lives under the bark of rotting tree trunks.

10 Male and female of the Great Elephant Beetle *(Megasoma elephas)* (Scarabaeidae), found in Costa Rica, Mexico, Panama; length of body up to about 13 cm. The male is distinguished by cornification and tuberous formations on the thorax and clypeus. Black with velvety, greyish-yellow hairs. Certain species are injurious, often attacking the leaf base tissue of palm plants.

11 A pair of Hercules Beetles *(Dynastes hercules)* (Scarabaeidae), found in Costa Rica, Panama, Nicaragua, Guatemala, the Antilles; length of body ♂ up to 18 cm, ♀ up to 9 cm. In the male, the process on the sternum and clypeus form a vertical, bifurcated frontal horn. Note extreme development of sexual dimorphism.

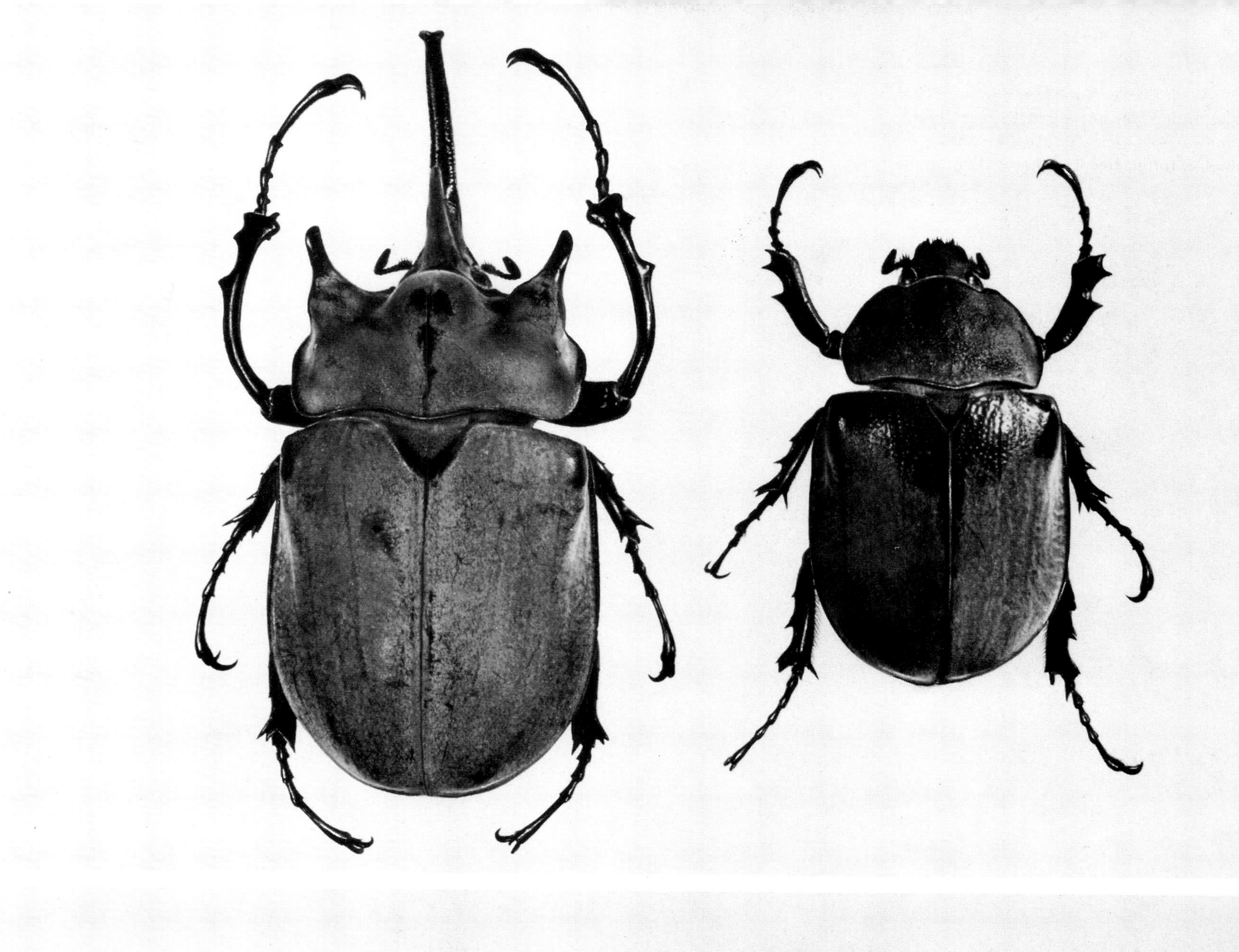

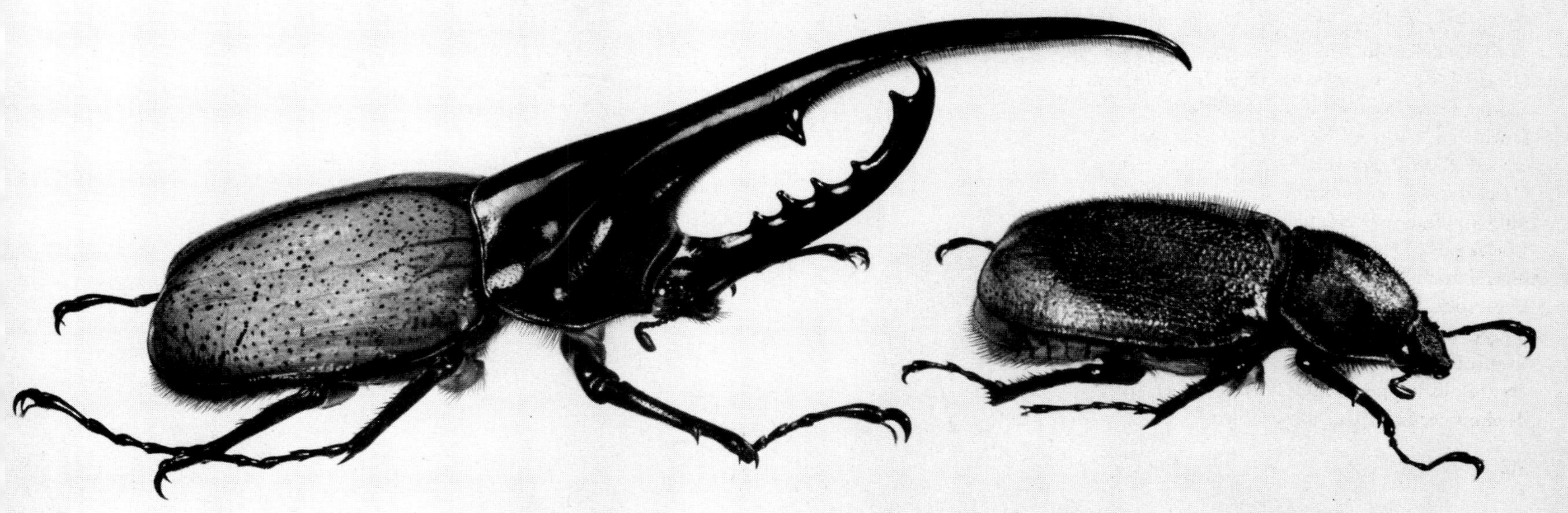

12 Pill-rolling Beetle (Scarabaeidae) with ball of dung
13 A June Beetle *(Polyphylla crinita)* (Scarabaeidae) from California
14 Lamellicorn Beetle *(Chrysophora chrysochloa)* (Scarabaeidae) from South America
15 Goliath Beetle *(Goliathus goliathus)* (Scarabaeidae), from Africa

16 Goliath Beetle *(Goliathus cacicus)* (Scarabaeidae); female, from Africa

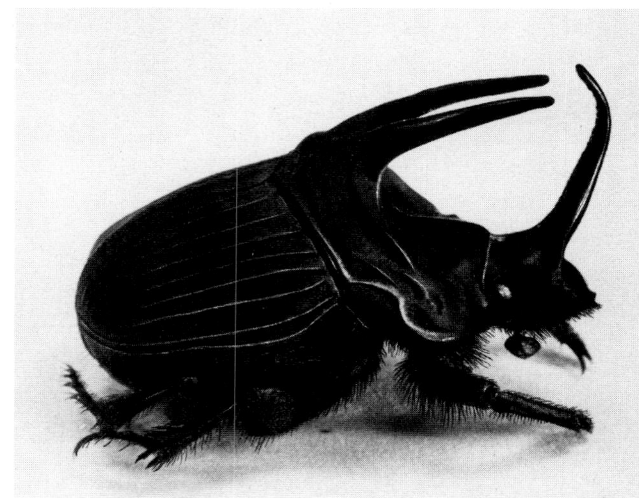

Dung Beetles (Scarabaeidae) and Pill-rolling Beetles with curious ornamentations on the thorax and clypeus, all of them male.

17 *Heliocopris gigas* from Egypt; length of body 4–5 cm
18 *Bolboceras reichei* from Australia; length of body 2.5–3 cm
19 *Copris draco* from Australia; length of body 4–5 cm
20 *Phanaeus velutinus* from Brazil; length of body 2–3.5 cm
21 *Phanaeus bonnariensis* from South America; length of body 2–3.5 cm
22 *Onthophagus rangifer* from Central Africa; length of body 1–1.5 cm

23 Beetles with particularly elongate heads belonging to the families of Straight-snouted Weevils (Brenthidae) and Weevils (Curculionidae).
top row: *Prodector fruhstorferi* from Sulawesi; left female (3.3 cm in length), right male (5.9 cm in length)
Brenthus anchorago from Brazil; left female (2.3 cm in length), right male (4.1 cm in length);
bottom row: *Eutrachelus temmincki* from Kalimantan; left male (7.1 cm in length), right female (4.2 cm in length);
Lasiorhynchus barbicornis from New Zealand; left male (7 cm in length),
right female (4.2 cm in length).
The beetles live in galleries bored by other insects. They are predators and parasites of living space. Their body is well adapted to this way of life.

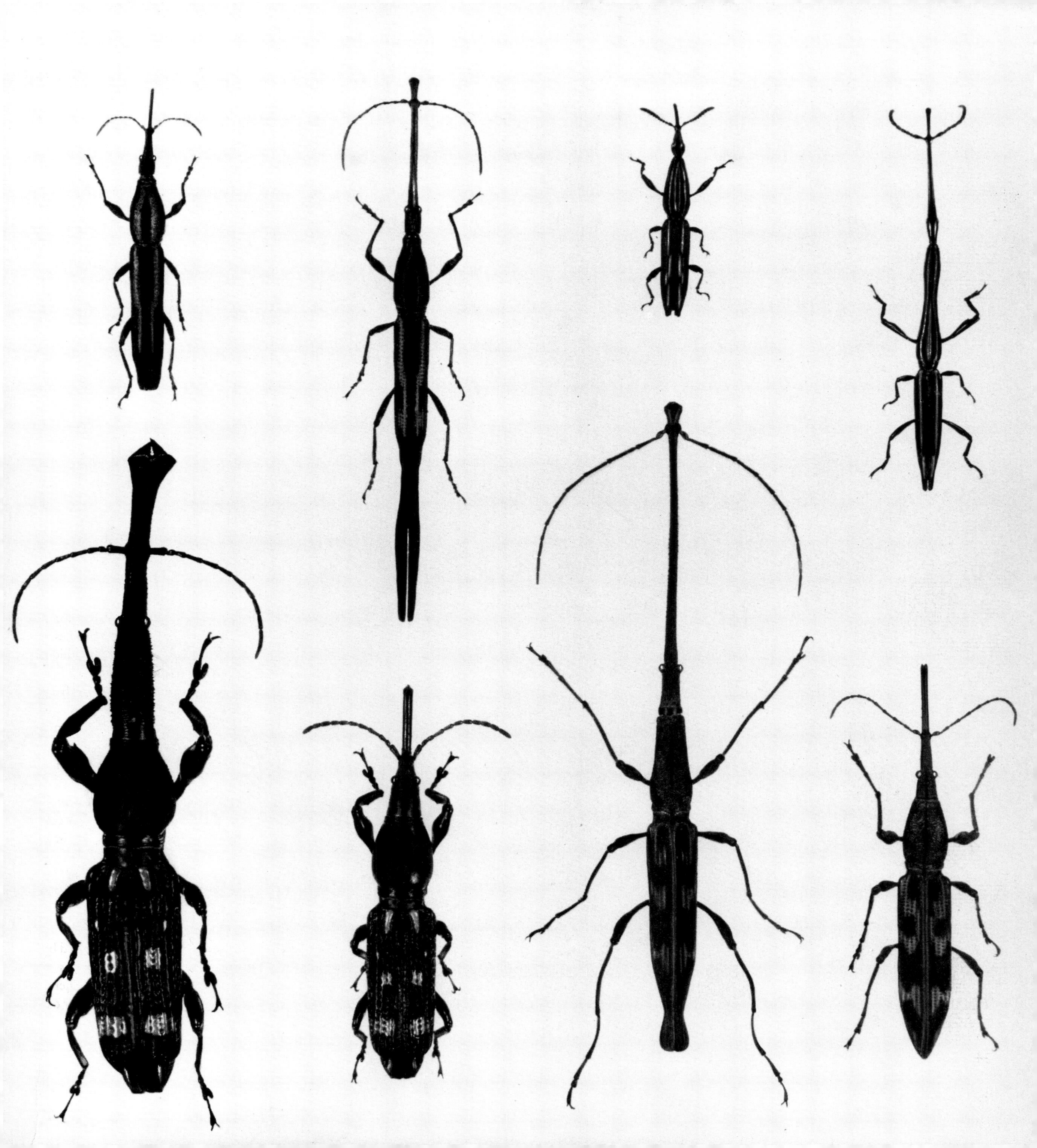

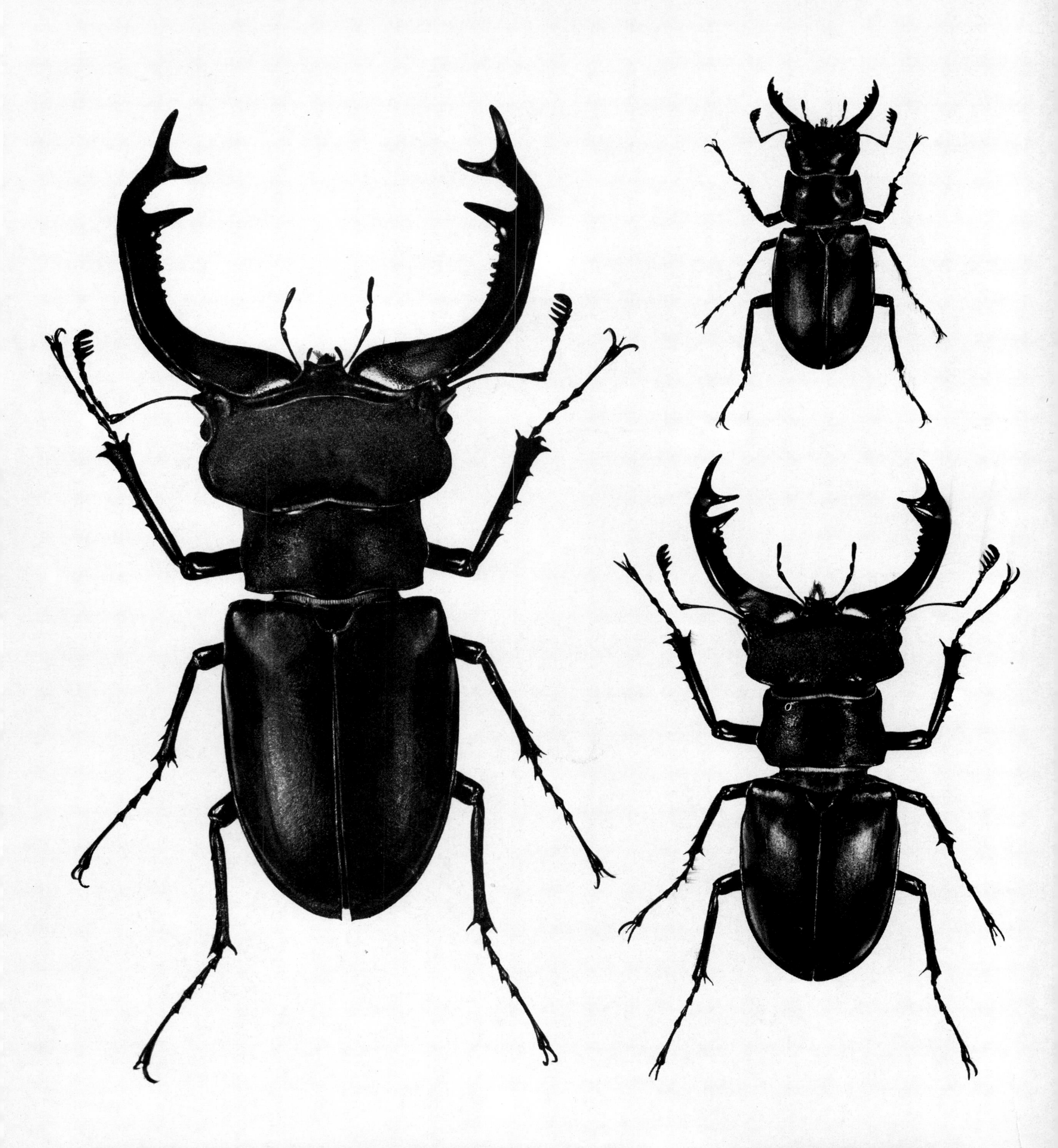

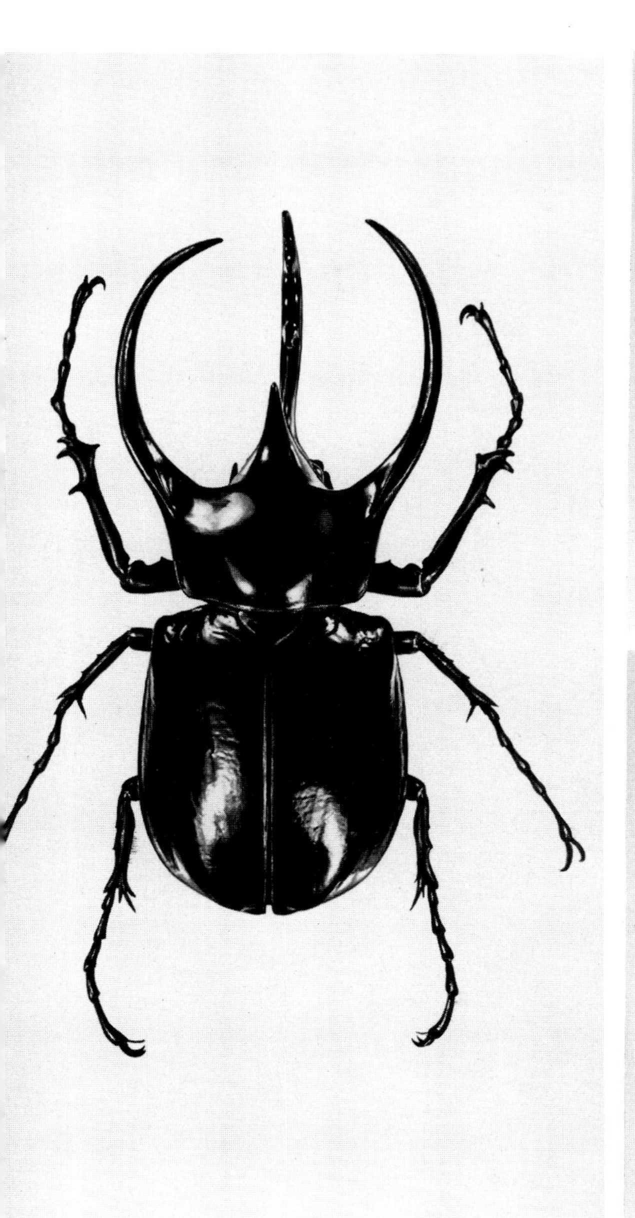

24 European Stag Beetle *(Lucanus cervus)* (Lucanidae). Body size, which varies greatly among males (9.4 cm, 6 cm, 3.4 cm), depends upon the availability of food for the larvae.

25 Atlas Beetle *(Chalcosoma atlas)* (Scarabaeidae) from India, Indonesia; male, length of body up to 12 cm. Note the three large horny processes of the prothorax and the cephalic horn.
26 *Chalcosoma atlas,* male from the East Indies; lateral aspect
27 *Dynastes gideon* (Scarabaeidae) from Java, Sumatra

Following pages:

28 Hide Beetle *(Golofa aegon)* from Ecuador (family of Lamellicorn Beetles, Scarabaeidae). Note the vertical frontal horn and the horny process on the prothorax.
29 *Theodosia westwoodi* var. *westerstradi* (Scarabaeidae) from Kalimantan

30 Lamellicorn Beetles *(Anisoplia ruricola)* (Scarabaeidae) frequenting blossom
31 Checkered Beetle *(Trichodes apiarius)* (Cleridae) frequenting blossom
32 Larvae of the Potato or Colorado Beetle *(Leptinotarsa decemlineata)* (Chrysomelidae)
33 Aggregation of Ladybirds (Coccinellidae) overwintering under bark. The red and black individuals are Two-spotted Ladybirds *(Adalia bipunctata)*, the lighter ones with black markings, present in much larger numbers, are *Synharmonia conglobata*.

34 Tropical Metallic Beetles (Buprestidae)
on left: *Cyphogastra javanica* from Indonesia
on right: *Lamproides viridis* from India

35 Golden Beetle (*Plusiotis* spec.) from Costa Rica (Lamellicorn Beetles, Scarabaeidae)

Tropical Metallic Beetles (Buprestidae)

36 *Julodis klugi* var. *viridipes* from South Africa
37 *Julodis gaviepina* from South Africa
38 *Julodis framica* from Iran
39 *Steraspis squamosa* from Central Africa

Tropical Rose Chafers (Cetoniinae, Scarabaeidae)

40 Two colour variants of *Ranzania bertolinii* (Scarabaeidae) from Africa

41 Cetoniinae *(Dicranocephalus wallichi)* (Scarabaeidae) from Northern India

42 Tropical Rose Chafers (Cetoniinae, Scarabaeidae)

upper row:
Stephanorrhina guttata from West Africa
Heterorrhina sexmaculata from the Sunda Islands
Heterorrhina dohrni from the Sunda Islands
Heterorrhina macleayi from the Philippines

lower row:
Genyodonta flavimaculata from Natal
Heterorrhina imperatrix from Java
Plaesiorrhina cincta from Uganda
Stephanorrhina princeps from East Africa

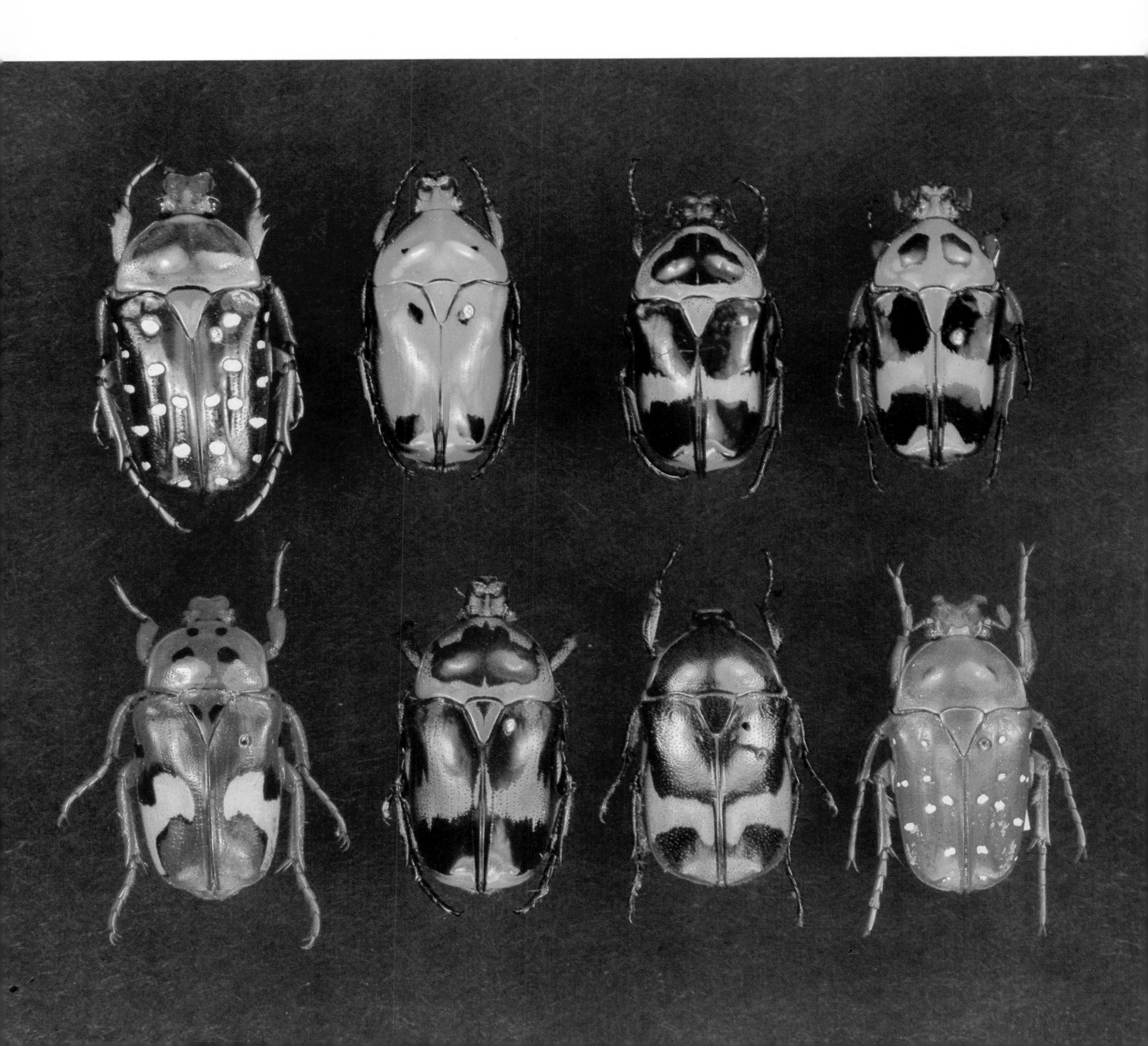

43 *Neptunides polychromus* from East Africa in 8 different colour variants

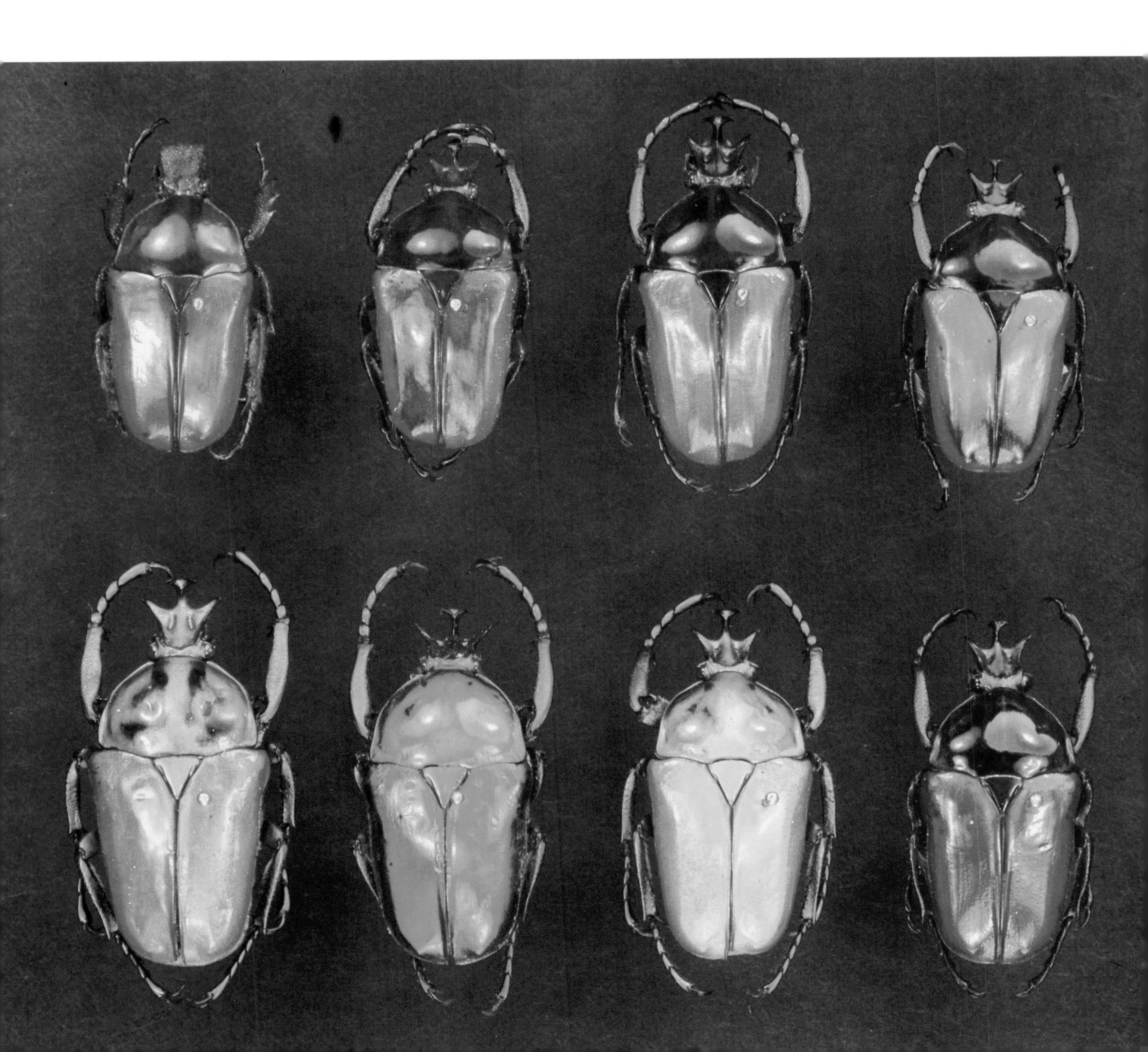

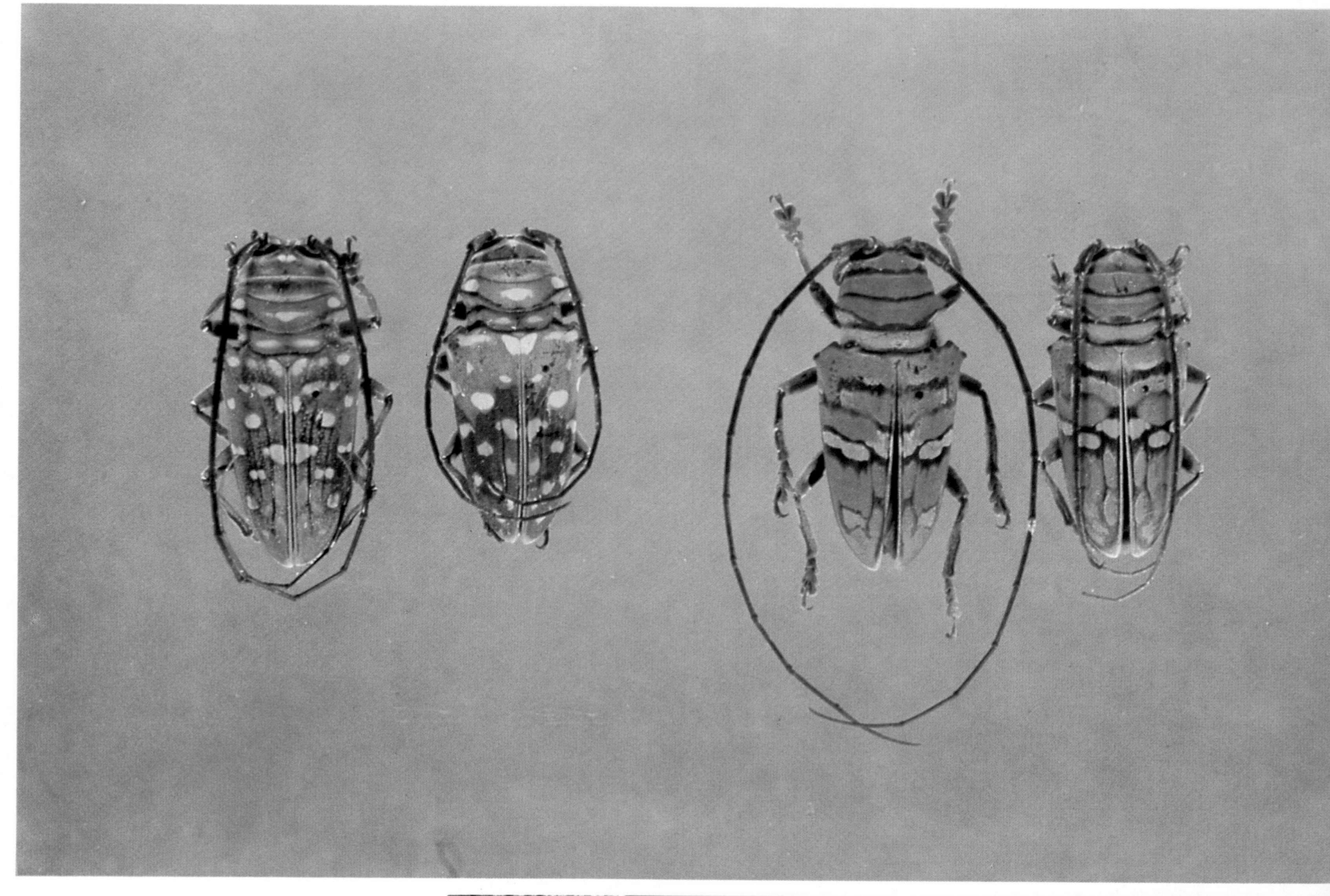

44 Variation in Longhorns (Cerambycidae)
left: Pair of *Sternotomis variabilis* from West Africa
right: Pair of *Sternotomis maculata* from West Africa
45/46 *Batocera browni,* from Melanesia; left: eye, seen from side, right: eyes, seen from front.

47 left: *Aprophata eximia* from the Philippines; centre: *Rosalia lesnei* from Taiwan; right: *Glenida suffusa* from China
48 *Dorcacerus barbatus,* male, frontal aspect of head, from Paraguay
49 *Stenodontes spinibarbis,* head with large mandibles, front aspect, from Brazil

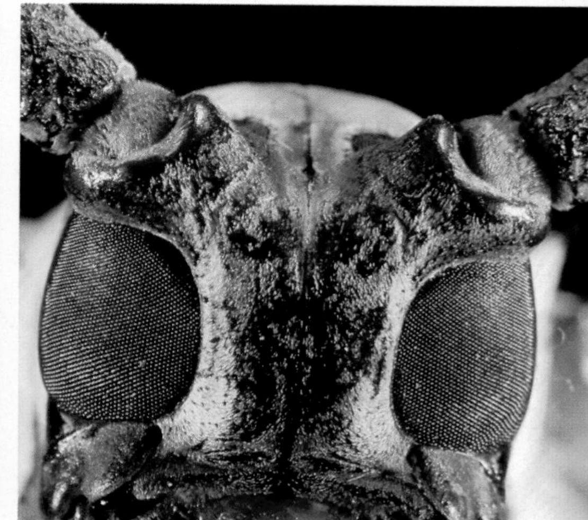

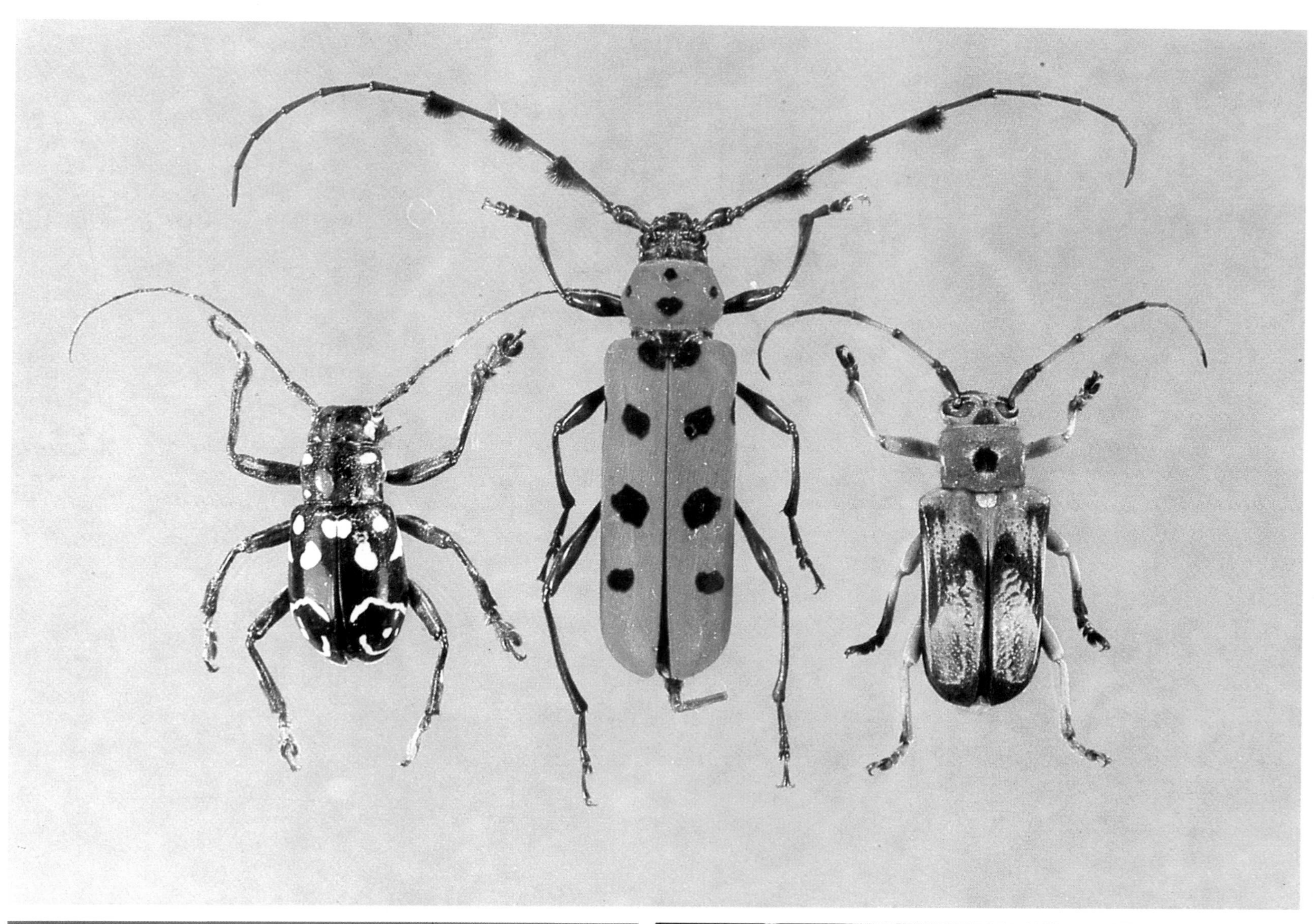

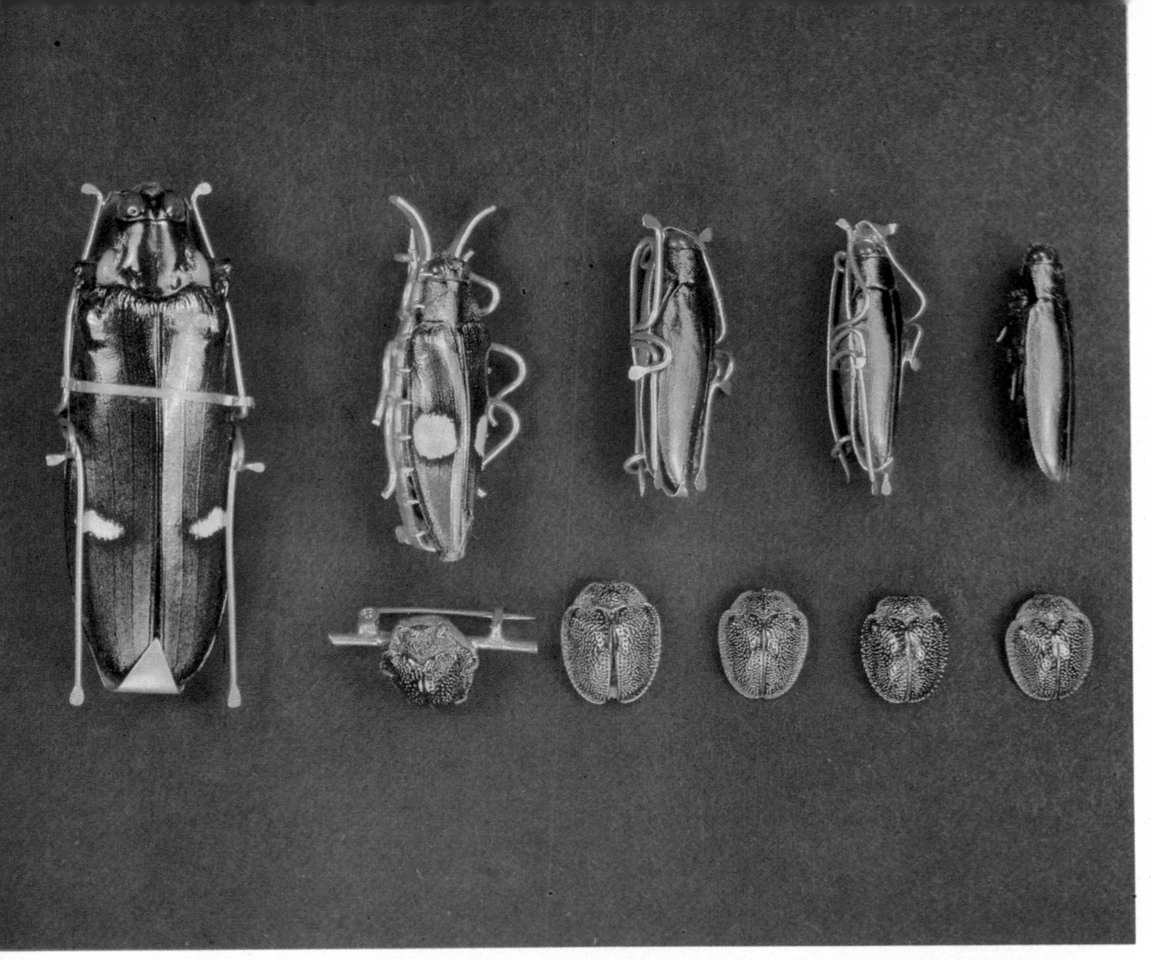

Beetles as ornamentation

50 Beetle brooches
upper row: Metallic Beetles (Buprestidae) from Buitenzorg. The second item is of German manufacture *(Chrysochroa ocellata)*; to the right of it: *Chrysochroa fulminans*; lower row: Leaf Beetles *(Desmonota variolosa)* (Chrysomelidae).
51 Small cover and fragments of cloth from India (about 1890).
Chrysochroa fulminans has been worked into the fabric

52 Leaf Beetles (Chrysomelidae), aggregation upon a plant

Brilliant colouring in Weevils (Curculionidae)

53 *Eupholus schoenherri* var. *faki* from New Guinea
54 *Eupholus browni* from New Guinea
55 *Entimus imperialis*, male, from South America

56 *Eupholus beccarii* from New Guinea
57 *Eupholus benetti* from New Guinea
58 *Entimus splendidus* from Brazil

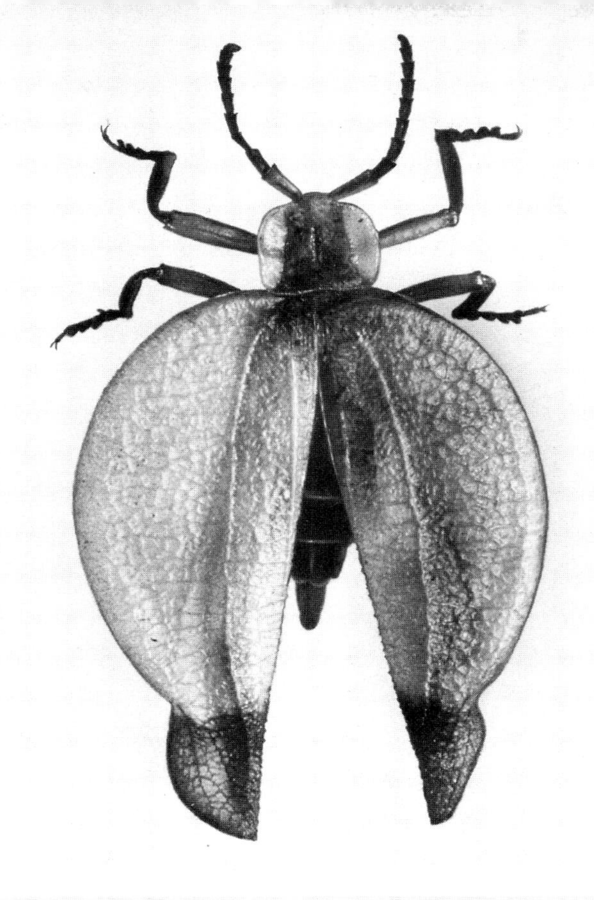

Are they really beetles? The bizarre form of Lichen Weevils (Curculionidae); length of body about 2–3 cm

59 *Lithinus hildebrandti* from Madagascar on a lichinous twig (extreme example of adaptation to shape and colour of environment).
60 left: *Lithinus penicillatus* from Madagascar; right: *Lithinus hildebrandti* without lichen, in order to show the insect's form more clearly.

61 Glow-worm *(Lamprohiza splendidula)* (Lampyridae) from Europe, male
62 Net-winged Beetle *Lycus dilatatus* (Lycidae) from Central and South Africa
63 *Demosis* spec. (Lycidae), female, wrongly designated "trilobite larva," from Thailand
64 *Lycus tunicata* (Lycidae) from South Africa

Extreme deviation in head shape in Weevils (Brentidae)

65 left: *Antliarrhinus tamiae* from South Africa; right: *Clitostylus tenuissimus* from the Philippines. Both beetles are approximately 1.5 cm long.
66 Male with extremely elongated head and female of the leaf-rolling Weevil *(Trachelophorus giraffa)* (Attelabidae) from Madagascar; overall length of male 2.5 cm. The beetles are glossy black with red elytra.

67 Tropical Longicorn Beetles (Cerambycidae)
top row:
Batocera hercules from Melanesia; length of body 7.5 cm
Batocera wallacei from New Guinea; length of body 8 cm
Xixuthrus microceros from Java; length of body 8.2 cm
Many species represent a serious threat to rubber trees.
bottom row:
Macrodontia cervicornis from Brazil; length of body 15 cm. It may occasionally exceed the length of *Titanus giganteus* which is accounted the largest known beetle.
Psalidognathus atys from Ecuador; length of body 5.7 cm
Macrotoma luzorum from the Philippines; length of body 10 cm

Following pages:

68 *Batocera hercules.* The coins give an idea of the considerable dimensions of this Longhorn Beetle.
69 Extreme length of antennae in Fungus Weevils (Anthribidae), above male (2.8 cm in length), below female (2.2 cm in length) of *Xenocerus barbicornis* from New Guinea;
left female (1.7 cm in length), right male (1.8 cm in length) of *Xenocerus semiluctuosus* from New Guinea

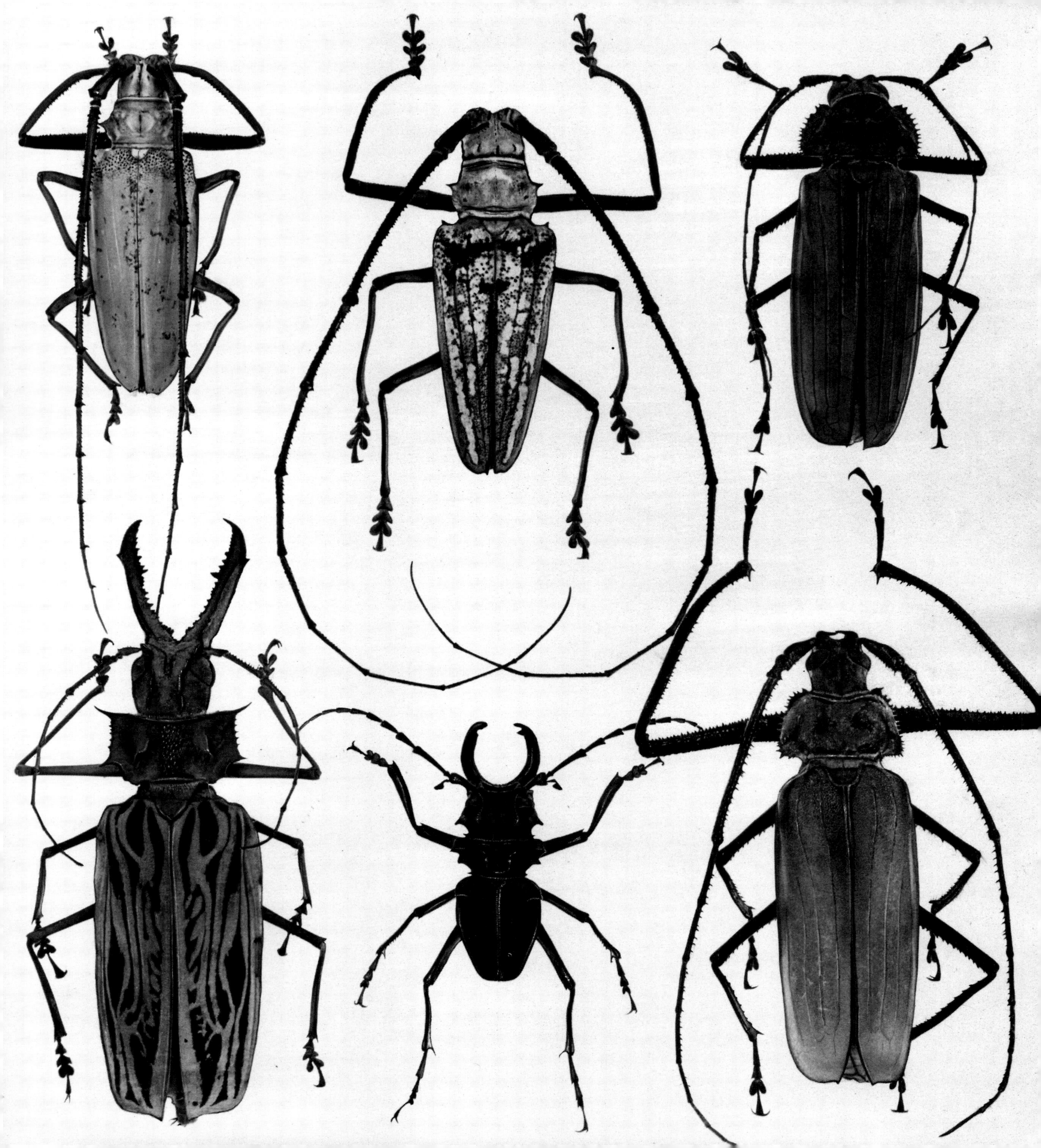

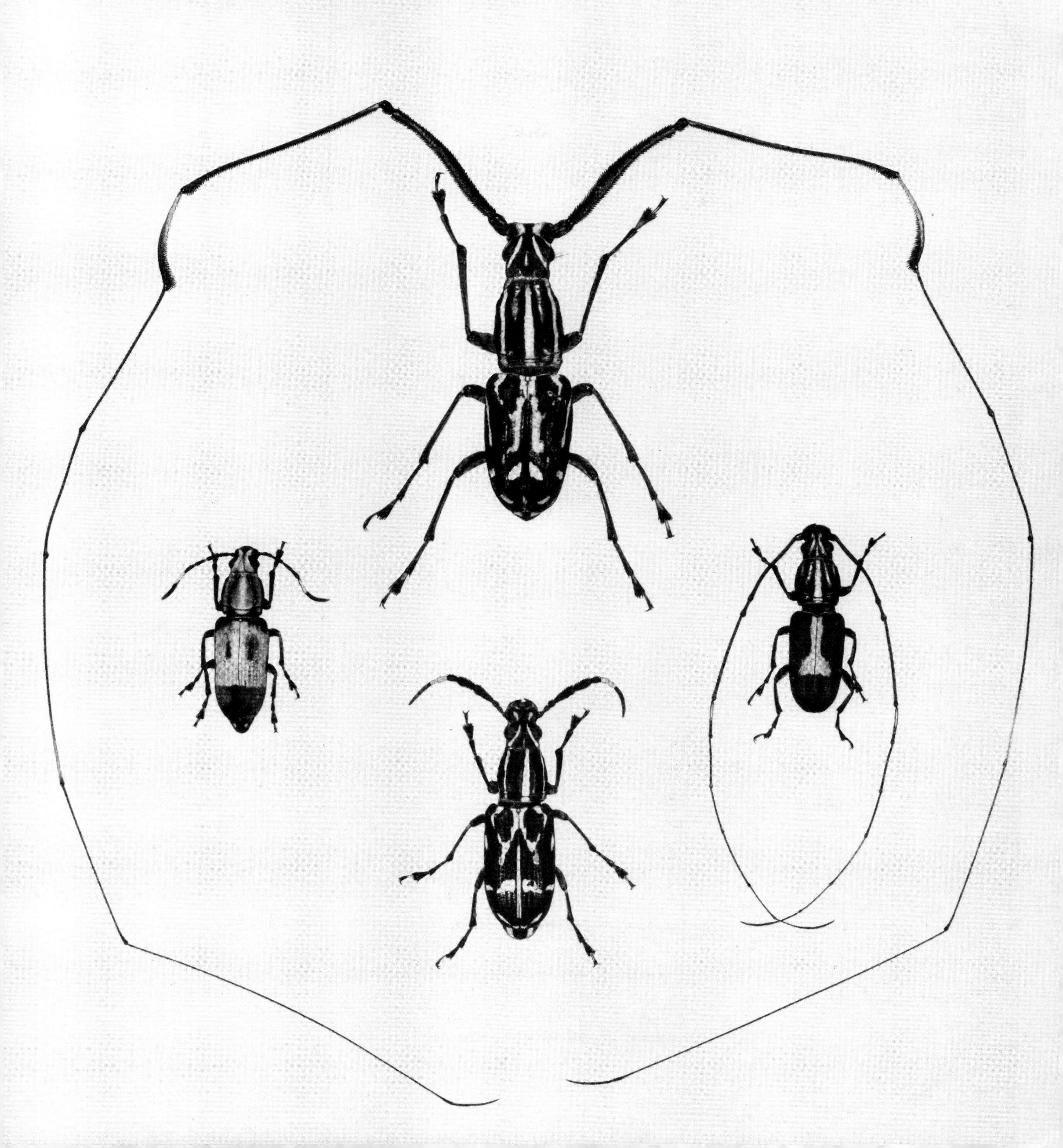

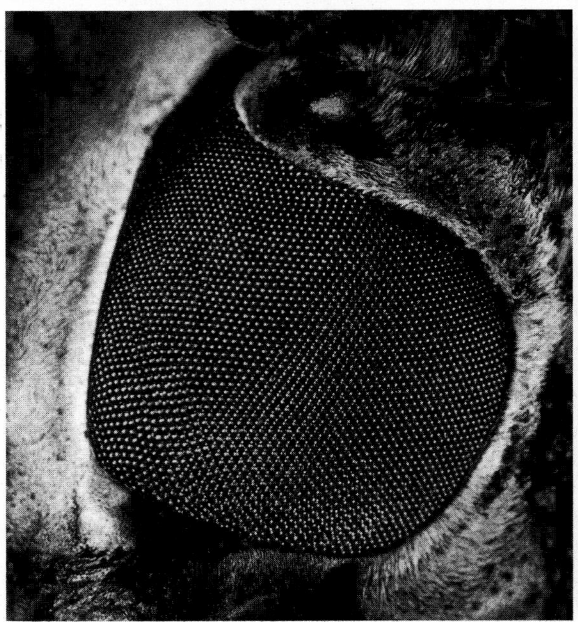

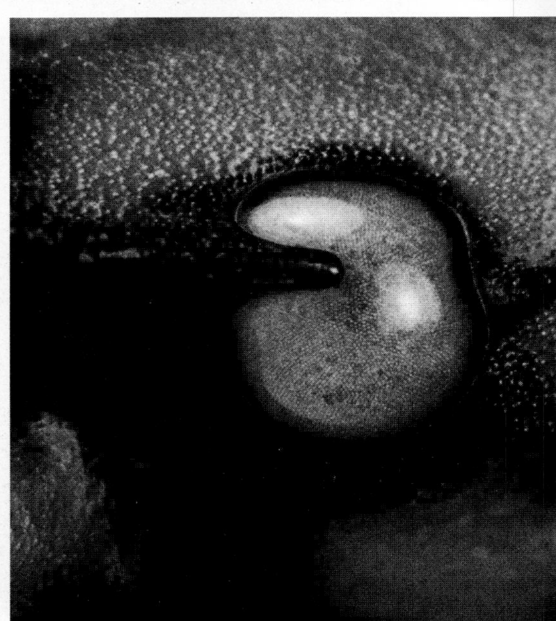

Beetle eyes

70 *Dineutes politus* from the Timor Islands and Java, divided eyes; the water line passes between the pairs of eyes. The upper eye allows the beetle to see objects above the water, the lower, objects under water (Whirligig Beetles, Gyrinidae).
71 *Batocera* spec. from Melanesia, compound or faceted eye (Longicorn Beetles, Cerambycidae)
72 Partial division of the eye in *Homoderus mellyi* (Lucanidae) (male) from Cameroon

These beetles grasp parts of the tree stem with their very long forelegs, while the spurred and curved tibia and tarsus provide a further aid in climbing. Among the Lamellicorns (Scarabaeidae) there is the sub-family Euchirinae, the members of which also have greatly elongated forelegs. The tibia of the foreleg is furnished with spinules pointing inwards and is curved, providing the creature with great facility in climbing. Unusually long forelegs are also a feature of the large Asiatic Snout Beetles (Curculionidae) of the genus *Cyrtotrachelus*. Since the elongation of the leg occurs exclusively in the male, the possibility of its function as an instrument of combat cannot be excluded.

Burrowing

A large number of species of beetles live in the ground. Many of them, particularly the smaller species make use of gaps between soil fragments to move about underground. Others have developed special fossorial legs. In South America there is one species of Longicorn, *Hypocephalus armatus* (Cerambycidae), in which the hind legs have been modified for digging purposes by the considerable thickening of the tibia and femur (Fig. 96).

In most burrowing beetles it is the forelegs which have been modified in this way. Usually the tibia is broadened and frequently furnished with spinules and spikes. Among Ground Beetles (Carabidae), the tribe of Ground Beetles (Scaritini) have fossorial legs of this kind. Both the *Scarites* species, that are up to 5 cm in length, and the *Clivina* and *Dyschirius* species that are only a few millimetres long, are masters in the art of digging. *Dyschirius* species are able to pursue their prey underground. In particular they seek out species of the genus *Bledius* belonging to the Rove Beetles (Staphylinidae). The *Dyschirius* beetles might well be said to specialize in these particular beetles. When a *Bledius* is being pursued, it burrows down into the soil. The *Dyschirius* burrows behind it, extending the gallery made by *Bledius*. The latter's only chance of escape is to switch the line of its tunnel from its initial, vertically downward slope abruptly upwards, and in this way to escape across the surface of the ground.

For a short time *Dyschirius* usually continues to burrow downwards. It is interesting to note that particular *Dyschirius* species specialize in catching particular *Bledius* species. The larger *Dyschirius* species usually concentrate their attacks on the larger *Bledius* species. Other Ground Beetles (Carabidae) also able to dig include *Broscus cephalotes*. Many of the small *Bembidion* species, as for instance those living on beaches, burrow down into the sand before the tide comes in, and only reappear after it has ebbed. Among the Rove Beetles (Staphylinidae), in addition to the *Bledius* species, there are other burrowers, particularly in the subfamily Oxytelinae. Remarkable facility in burrowing is shown by the Heteroceridae in which both the larvae and the adult beetles (imagos) are able to build systems of underground galleries, particularly in fine sand on the banks of rivers. The most skilled of the digging beetles are found among the Lamellicorns (Scarabaeidae); in many of the Dung Beetles, the tarsi are even reduced (Figs. 97, 98, 100, 101). The underground systems of galleries constructed by them represent some of the most striking achievements in burrowing. Dung Beetles also hold the record for the greatest depth attained by the main tunnel shaft; in one instance, the American *Mycotrupes chalybaeus* was observed to build larval chambers at a depth of 3.63 m. Other Lamellicorn beetles are also able to dig, such as the Cockchafer or May Beetle *(Melolontha melolontha)* that lays its eggs some 20 cm beneath the surface of the ground. And it is probably not widely known that the female European Stag Beetle *(Lucanus cervus)* is able to penetrate up to 75 cm into earth where it lays its eggs on the rotten roots of oak trees.

At this point we might well recall that numerous beetle larvae live in the soil, where they feed on such material as the roots of vegetation. They are of various families, for example, Lamellicorns (Scarabaeidae), Click Beetles (Elateridae), Snout Beetles (Curculionidae), Darkling Beetles (Tenebrionidae), Comb-claw Beetles (Alleculidae). All these larvae are very well adapted to burrowing through the soil. To some extent they have developed their own particular methods of progression underground. A good example might be the larva of the May Beetle—the Cockchafer grub *(Melolontha melolontha)* (Scarabaeidae). Its body is c-shaped and cannot be straightened. These creatures burrow down to depths of 1.5 m. How are they able to do this with legs which are short and appear weak? They dig a series of oval caves, in each case filling the previous one with the soil that is produced from excavating the subsequent one. The powerful maxillae are used to transport and to loosen the soil. Fragments of soil broken off in this way are pushed into the curve of the body. Once sufficient soil has accumulated there, the larva inclines its head, braces it against the ball of soil and crawls in a hair-pin curve as it were along its own belly. In this way, the soil is moved to the upper end of the cave. There the larva presses it firm. Curving again in a hair-pin bend, the head returns to the lower end of the cavity and digging continues. In this way, excavation progresses downwards, describing a series of shallow oval curves. In the creature's movements within the cave, the legs play scarcely any part, but rather does it make use of the back part of the abdomen which is provided with bristly protuberances. Thus the curved shape of the body proves itself peculiarly appropriate for movement within the soil.

Adhesion

Many beetles are surprisingly adapt at maintaining a hold on a substratum. Goliath Beetles

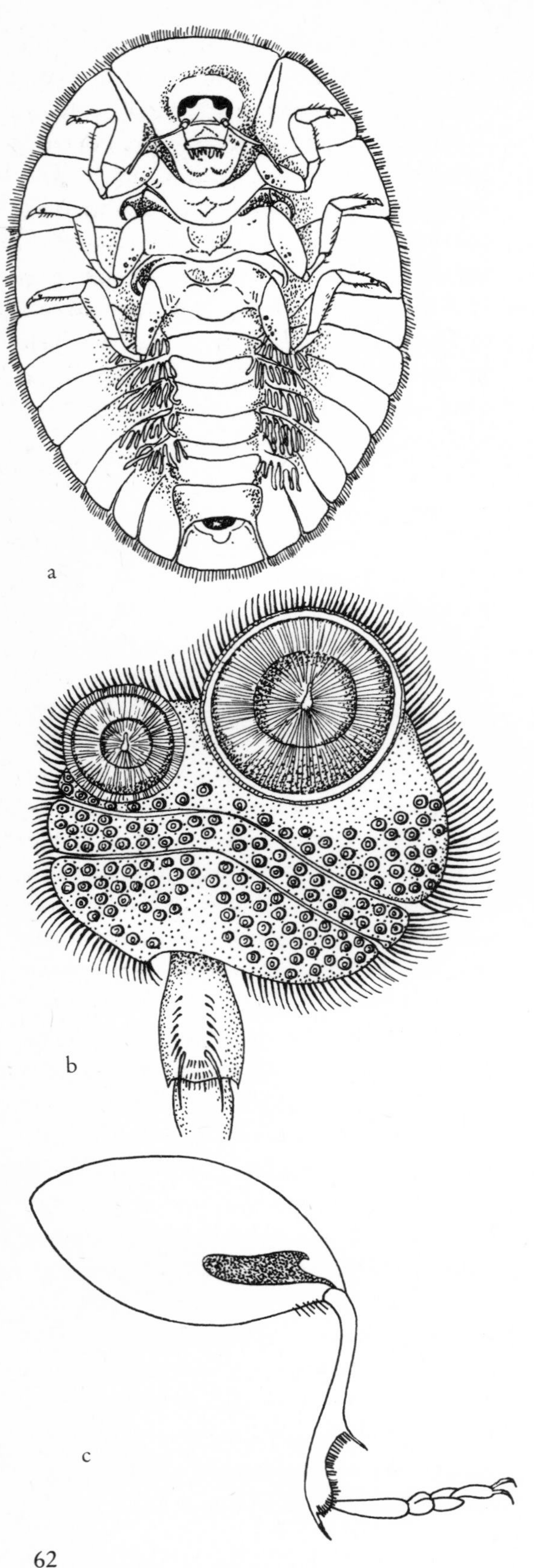

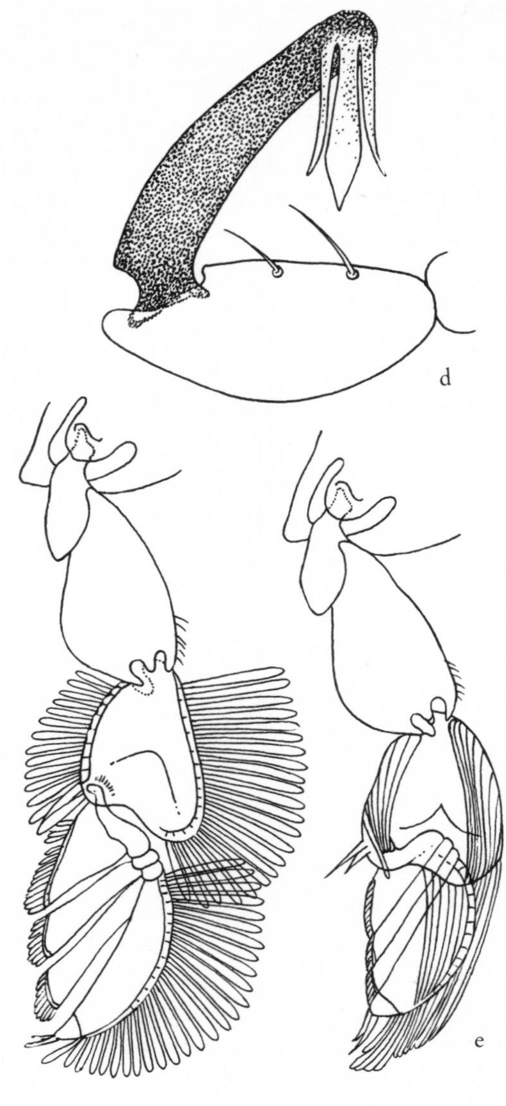

Types of leg
a) Larva of *Psephenus lecontei* (Psephenidae), known as the "water penny," it lives in fast flowing streams, is greatly flattened and has suction pads for adhesion (ventral aspect).
b) *Dytiscus marginalis* L. (Diving Beetles, Dytiscidae). Tarsi of right foreleg of the male furnished with suction hairs.
c) Hind leg of the Flea Beetle *Longitarsus suturellus* Duft, with "jumping organ" (metafemoral apodeme) (dotted). (Leaf Beetles, Chrysomelidae)
d) Claw formation in the triungulin larva of *Meloe proscarabaeus* L. (Blister Beetles, Meloidae)
e) Hind legs of *Gyrinus natator* L. (Whirligig Beetles, Gyrinidae), on left the setae spread to act as an oar, on right the rowing laminae folded in.

(*Goliathus* spec.; Scarabaeidae), for example, are reported to cling to branches as if "forged out of iron." Male Great Water Beetles (Dytiscidae) have dilated tarsal segments functioning as prehensile pads or suckers, used for holding the female during copulation. Long-toed Water Beetles (Dryopidae) and Clawed Water Beetles or Drive Beetles (Elmidae) have very strongly developed tarsi with claws which allow them to hold firmly on to stones and plants, and so live successfully in fast-flowing water.

But probably the most remarkable achievement of all is that of the larvae of certain Psephenidae, known as "Water Pennies," which are able to maintain a hold even in the raging currents of the Niagara Falls and the rivers of the Himalayas. There are several genera capable of these extraordinary feats of adherence, such as *Eubrianax*, *Psephenus*, *Psephenoides* as well as the European genus *Eubria*. The larvae are able to remain fixed in rushing waters and waterfalls because of the flattened, almost scale-like form of the body which gives the currents very little to work against, and particularly because of special sucker-like elements on the underside of the body.

Jumping

Various beetles can jump most efficiently. Very well-known for this ability are the Flea Beetles (Halticinae) belonging to the Leaf Beetle family (Chrysomelidae), which with greatly enlarged hind femora are capable of making powerful leaps. Flea Beetles of 2.5 mm in length can jump a height and distance of 50 to 60 cm. Inside the hind femora is a chitinous body known as the jumping organ or metafemoral apodeme, serving as an additional point of attachment for muscles. The joint principally involved in jumping lies between the femur and the tibia.

Other beetles also jump in a similar way, for instance, Marsh Beetles (Helodidae) of the genera *Scirtes* and *Ora*, Snout Beetles (Curculionidae) of the genera *Rhynchaenus* and *Rhamphus*, and, also belonging to the Leaf Beetle family (Chrysomelidae), the 2 to 3 cm long species of the South-eastern Asian genus *Sagra*. However, the jumping ability of these large creatures is a somewhat controversial question, even though Sagrinae species are popularly called Kangaroo Beetles in Australia. Many representatives of the False Darkling Beetles (Melandryidae), for example, the genus *Orchesia*, can jump actively to a height of 50 cm with the aid of serrate tibial spurs.

Tumbling Flower Beetles (Mordellidae) which have the final abdominal segment produced into a spine, jump in quite a different way. Before a leap is made, the spine is pressed against the base on which the beetle stands. Leverage thus produced, supplemented by spring support from the hind legs, catapults the beetle upwards.

Swimming

Some 7,800 species of beetles live in water and have developed a greater or lesser degree of efficiency in swimming. The masters in this field are the Whirligig Beetles (Gyrinidae) (see p. 111). In the Screech Beetles (Hygrobiidae) the legs, adapted for swimming, are provided with swimming hairs which are distributed in rows and are concentrated primarily on the hind legs. The swimming ability of these beetles is not very great. The swimming action consists of alternate right and left movements. Nor can the Small or Crawling Water Beetles (Haliplidae) swim very well. Their swimming movements are similar to those of Hygrobiidae, and the intensified pubescence is concentrated on the tarsi. The True Water Beetles or Predacious Diving Beetles (Dytiscidae) are distinctly more skilful at swimming. The mid leg and in particular the foreleg have undergone adaptive modification as natatorial legs. They are broadened and flattened, and the tibia and particularly the tarsi are clothed with lateral hair fringes, so that at each oar-like stroke of the leg, they spread out wide and increase the effective surface area pressing against the water. On the recovery stroke, the legs are flexed and drawn forward edge first. In swimming, the legs act synchronously. Sometimes in particularly rapid swimming, only the hind legs are used. When the beetle swims more slowly, mid and hind legs are activated alternately. Small species of Dytiscidae often achieve a higher frequency of leg strokes than large ones. *Hydroporus* species (2.5 to 3 mm long) perform 16 strokes per second, *Ilybius* (17 mm long) 7 strokes per second and the large Great Water Beetle *(Dytiscus)* (35 mm long) 2 strokes per second. The whole body of aquatic beetles is much flattened, offering minimum resistance to the water. There are, however, considerable variations. The genus *Acilius* (Dytiscidae) is particularly well adapted for rapid movement under water. Hydromechanical examination shows that in the construction of its body, it is as perfectly streamlined as a submersible boat. Great Water Beetles of the genera *Dytiscus* and *Cybister* are ideally adapted in terms of fluid dynamics. The maximum speed of which they are capable is some 50 cm/s. Curiously enough, approximately the same result has been obtained for almost all water beetles examined, and is determined by the number of swimming strokes per second related to body size. The expenditure of energy in swimming is relatively slight.

Aquatic larvae are also well adapted for swimming, although in comparison with the adults, they paddle considerably more slowly. In the larvae of *Acilius* (Dytiscidae), a leg action of 3 to 4 strokes per second is found, producing a speed of 2 to 6 cm/s. The larvae are also capable of a quite different form of locomotion. Rapid contraction of the muscles of the abdomen permits the larva to shoot forward some 5 to 6 cm. It somersaults as it goes, and can repeat the process several times. Thus, an *Acilius* larva can cover up to 60 cm.

Other families of aquatic beetles (Hydraenidae, Hydrochidae, Hydrophilidae, Spercheidae) cannot move particularly rapidly in water. The mid and hind legs are only moderately provided with swimming hairs, and in swimming, the legs perform strokes in alternating pairs. Many species of these families possess the ability to run along the underside of the water surface. The larvae of many species can synchronize the swimming action, with each pair of legs consecutively performing a backward stroke, and in this way achieve a speed of 0.6 to 1.3 cm/s.

Phoresy

Whereas up to now we have examined certain modes of locomotion in which the beetles themselves have to exert effort to progress forwards, we might now also mention a few examples of phoresy. By this term we mean the exploitation of other animals for locomotion.

One example we might give is that of the triungulin larvae of Blister Beetles (Meloidae) which allow themselves to be carried by bees to their nests. The tarsi are developed as special prehensile claws. Examples of similar, more or less obligatory phoresy occur in other beetles. Silken Fungus Beetles of the genus *Antherophagus* (Cryptophagidae) sit on flowers until they are able to take fast hold on the legs of bumble-bees. They allow the latter to carry them to their nests, where "in return" for this effortless mode of transport, they lay their eggs. The *Antherophagus* larvae develop in the bee's nest. It is probable that the distribution of Claviger Beetles belonging to the family of Ant-loving Beetles (Pselaphidae), is brought about by ants during their nuptial flight, since the beetles are able to gain a very firm hold with their claws. The comparatively wide distribution of these beetles cannot be satisfactorily explained in any other way, since *Claviger* has very restricted walking ability and in addition is blind.

Not only do beetles allow themselves to be carried about, but they are also used by other creatures as a means of transportation. Dung Beetles (Scarabaeidae), for instance, carry various mites (Uropodidae, Gamasidae). Beetles living in dung also transport threadworms (Nematodes). Other Nematode species make use of Stag Beetles (Lucanidae) and Longicorns (Cerambycidae) in order to move to new habitats. Even pseudo-scorpions are occasionally carried by beetles such as Longicorn Beetles (Cerambycidae).

Some remarkable modes of behaviour

The explosive secretions of Bombardier Beetles
Within the family of Ground Beetles (Carabidae) there exists in Europe the tribe of Brachinini, which have earned their popular name of Bombardier Beetles (*Brachynus* species) from the habit, probably unique within the animal kingdom, of ejecting an explosive mixture of gases. It is scarcely surprising that the activity of the Bombardier Beetles has attracted the notice of observers from early times. The account of them given by Rolander in 1750 is still today one of the most exact descriptions ever made, and well worth reading again. "When first I took up this creature and it straight away gave out a small jet of light blue smoke accompanied by a slight report, this unexpected event startled me so greatly that I let the creature fall from my hands to the ground. Like others of its kind, it was very swift to conceal itself. I was curious to examine this strange feature, since I was convinced that the creature itself had occasioned the smoke and the report, but did not know in what manner. But this time I sought in vain, for it had found a secure refuge. A few days later I found a similar creature, again beneath a stone, which, when it was captured, ejected smoke from its hind end accompanied by a slight report, as when the tinder of a rifle is ignited. So it was clearly of the same genus as the previous one. As often as it was touched lightly beneath the outer end of the wing covers on the upper part of the abdomen with a pin, it fired off an explosion, fully twenty times in succession, so that one could only be amazed that so much air should be contained within so small a body."

How then is this phenomenon brought about? First of all it is necessary to examine the anatomical structure of the apparatus producing the explosion. A pair of specialized pygidial glands are present. From each of the two grape-like gland ducts, a channel leads into a reservoir. In front of each reservoir sac, and linked to it, is a chitinous capsule, the explosion chamber. Between the reservoir sac and the explosion chamber is a valve which can be opened. From each explosion chamber, a short channel leads out to the dorsal side of the final abdominal segment.

A secretion is produced in the pygidial glands consisting of a solution of hydroquinone and toluhydroquinone with 23 percent hydrogen peroxide. This secretion accumulates and is stored in the reservoir. The wall of the explosion chamber is lined with globular groups of single-cell, enzyme secreting glands, which discharge their secretions into the explosion chamber. When the beetle is irritated, as described above by Rolander for instance, the shutter device of the reservoir is opened. The secretal mixture is forced into the explosion chamber, since the reservoir has elastic walls and therefore its contents are under pressure. Catalytic action within the explosion chamber produces the rapid decomposition of the hydrogen peroxide into water and oxygen. The peroxidase oxidizes the hydroquinones to form benzo- and toluquinones. A temperature of 100°C is produced in the reaction. The resulting gaseous pressure of the oxygen causes the forcible ejection of a spray of yellow to violet quinones from the chamber, accompanied by an explosive report. The whole process is illustrated in the accompanying diagram. The beetle is able to fire off 80 times in four minutes.

Paussid Beetles (Paussidae) possess a similar bombarding apparatus, although it is obviously not used against the ants with which they live. However, explosions brought about experimentally proved fatal to a number of ants.

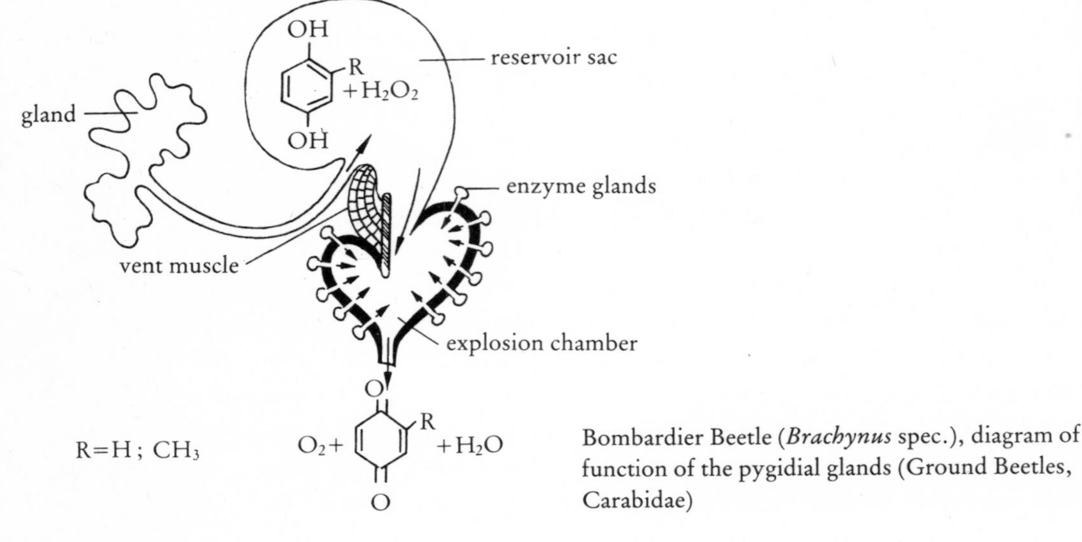

Bombardier Beetle (*Brachynus* spec.), diagram of function of the pygidial glands (Ground Beetles, Carabidae)

Secretions from anal glands
A large number of other species of beetles, particularly in the very numerous family of Rove Beetles (Staphylinidae) are able to produce

secretions from the anal glands. Since these secretions usually have a powerful, offensive smell, the glands are popularly known as stink glands. The secretions appear to provide some degree of protection against predatory insects. In giving off these secretions, the Rove Beetles have the habit of curling the hind body over and forwards in threat, almost like scorpions. The coleopterist Adolf Horion (1882–1977) writes: "If you carefully lift up one of these black Mould Beetles, such as the Devils Coach Horse *(Staphylinus olens)*, which may be over 3 cm long, it immediately gives off a repulsive, brown secretion from its stink glands in the vicinity of the anal opening, and attempts to seize its attacker with its sharp maxillae; it quickly bites right through the skin of your finger so that you quickly let the aggressive predator go."

In many species the foetid anal glands are eversible. In addition to those of the Rove Beetles (Staphylinidae), anal glands are found particularly in the family of Darkling Beetles (Tenebrionidae), for example, in the Churchyard Beetle or Darkling Beetle of the genus *Blaps* (Tenebrionidae).

The discharge of milky secretions by aquatic beetles

When Whirligig Beetles (Gyrinidae) are being pursued, and all their skill in swimming and diving proves inadequate in shaking off their pursuer, they are able to discharge a milky secretion from glands on the abdominal segments. Little is known about the effect this produces, it may be simply that it obscures the vision of the pursuer. Great Water Beetles *(Dytiscus)* also have a gland on either side of the prothorax from which they give off a milky secretion when disturbed.

Jet propulsion across water

Rove Beetles (Staphylinidae) of the genus *Stenus* can run across the surface of the water and, by means of secretions from their pygidial glands, can cause themselves to be projected rapidly forwards over a distance of some 10 to 15 m. The glands secrete surface-active terpenes, the expansion of which drives the insect forwards at considerable speeds that can reach some 0.75 m/s. In this way, the beetles can cover 150 times their own body length per second. (A motor car travelling at 100 km/h manages only 7 times its own length per second.)

Venom glands

Some species of beetles possess venom glands which have their external opening at various points on the surface of the body. The secretions they produce can fulfil various biological functions. On the one hand, they have a defensive role (repugnatorial) in repelling predatory enemies, and on the other hand, they inhibit or prevent the growth of microorganisms. Great Water Beetles *(Dytiscus)*, for example, secrete substances destructive to microorganisms from their paired pygidial glands. The secretion contains benzoic acid (11%), p-hydroxybenzaldehyde (79%), hydroxybenzoic acid methyl-ester (8%) and protein (2%). Outside the water, these substances, together with a paste-like glycoproteid, are smeared over the entire surface of the body affording protection from attack by microorganisms. An example of a similar practice is found among various Carrion or Burying Beetles (Silphidae) which secrete from their pygidial glands a 4.5% solution of ammonia.

The milky secretion from the prothoracic glands of the Great Water Beetle (Dytiscidae) mentioned above provides a defence against predatory enemies. The most important active ingredient it contains is the steroid hormone cortexon (11-desoxycordicosteron), of which a single beetle can store up to 0.4 mg. To obtain such a quantity would require the adrenal glands from more than 1,000 cows. Cortexon disturbs the sodium-potassium balance of vertebrate animals. Predatory fish such as pike or trout that have ingested the secretions of Great Water Beetles, very quickly enter a state of deep narcosis. Similar secretions are also manufactured by other species of Water Beetles.

Many members of the family of Darklings (Tenebrionidae) produce quinones in the pygidial glands, and many species are capable of ejecting these products towards their enemies. The secretions of the pygidial glands of Ground Beetles (Carabidae) contain a wealth of organic substances, so there are wide variations in the chemical character of the different repellents. In those of Ground Beetles there is usually an admixture of lipophile compounds which facilitate penetration of the tissues of the adversary.

The phenomenon of "bleeding" in Ladybirds

Probably every reader will have noticed the amber-coloured drops of liquid spontaneously emitted by a Ladybird (Coccinellidae) when it is touched. This is the haemolymph, corresponding to the blood of vertebrates. There is a small opening in the synovial membranes between the tibia and femur, through which the liquid is exuded. As a response to extreme stimulation, haemolymph is emitted simultaneously from all six articulations (reflex bleeding), but where stimulation is slight, only from the articulations of one pair of legs. Since at the same time the beetles draw in their legs, the liquid can often be seen on the sides of the body, and earlier observers assumed that it was secreted at that point. Incidentally, the capacity to emit haemolymph through pores situated around articulations of the leg is not restricted to Ladybirds. Blister Beetles (Meloidae), many Leaf Beetles (Chrysomelidae) and Soldier Beetles (Cantharidae) are also able to do so.

Much has been written on the significance of "bleeding" in Ladybirds. It has been suggested that there is a toxic effect, that the "blood" has repellent properties and the smell has been described as nauseous. It is said that it acts as a deterrent to potential enemies of the Ladybird, such as spiders, "masked hunters" (reduviids), bugs, robber flies (asilids), predatory beetles, toads, frogs, lizards, birds and shrews. But in fact, the Ladybird figures more or less prominently in the diet of many of these potential enemies. So far, the theory of a repugnatorial function has not been proved beyond question.

Sexual pheromones

Aromatic attractant secretions or pheromones are widespread among insects, and they have probably been most closely examined in butterflies. They are effective in minute concentrations and often over very great distances. Pheromones are also found widely among beetles, the best known example probably being that of Bark Beetles (Scolytidae), in which the males, having completed construction of the nuptial chamber (see p. 177), secrete pheromones which attract the females. We find something similar in the case of Necrophores (Burying Beetles, Sexton Beetles or Gravediggers) (*Necrophorus;* Silphidae). If a male finds itself alone on a suitable piece of carrion, it climbs up to an elevated situation, probably on part of the carcase. There it stretches its hind body diagonally upwards and performs swaying movements back and forth. As it does so, a sexual attractant is emitted. The male usually persists in this action until joined by a female.

The saltatory powers of Click Beetles

The first reasonably detailed description of the leaping ability of Click Beetles (Elateridae) and an attempt to explain the process is that given by the Swiss entomologist Weiss, an extract from which reads as follows: "On the prothorax there is a powerful process (Fig. 1 a), which is situated on top of the thorax (a) like the pommel of a saddle and which fits neatly into a kind of cavity (b) in the body (c).

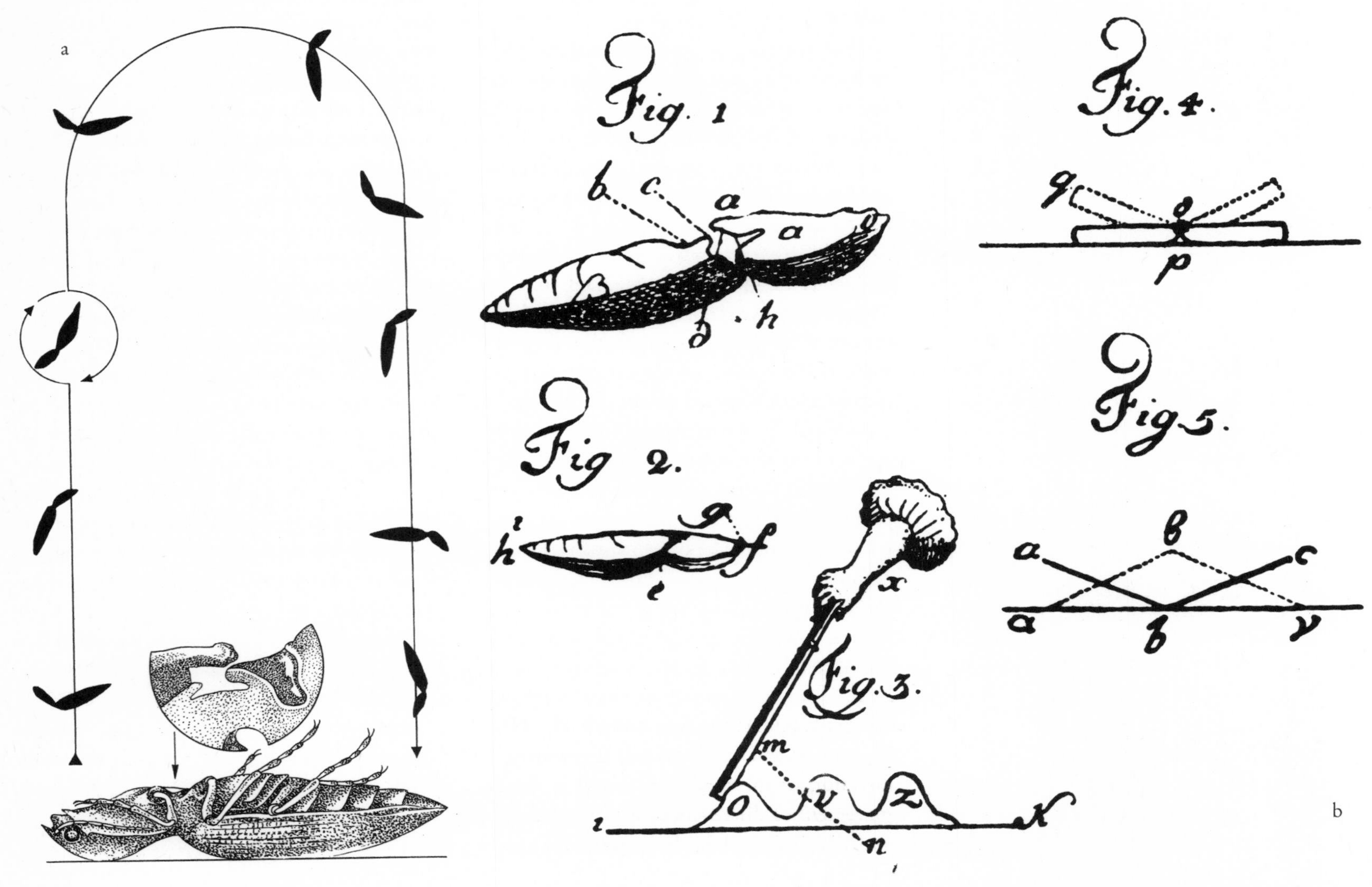

When the creature wants to leap up from a position of lying on its back, it bends itself upwards until point e of the process touches part d, the edge of the cavity, and it presses these two parts hard against one another. It continues to bend itself until the front end is moved from f to g and the hind end from h to i (Fig. 2). Then it rises above the height of c, and the process is driven with force into the cavity. The jolt thrusts the back of the insect against the ground, and it rebounds into the air. The observer can easily convince himself of the force imparted by this movement by holding the prothorax with one hand, and the body of the beetle with the other, and pressing the process gently against the edge of the cavity."

The leap of the Click Beetle (Elateridae)
a) Diagram of the leaping process after Sedlag (1978)
b) The mechanism of the Click Beetle's leap (after Weiss, 1755)
c) Underside of the forepart of the body of a Click Beetle (Elateridae)

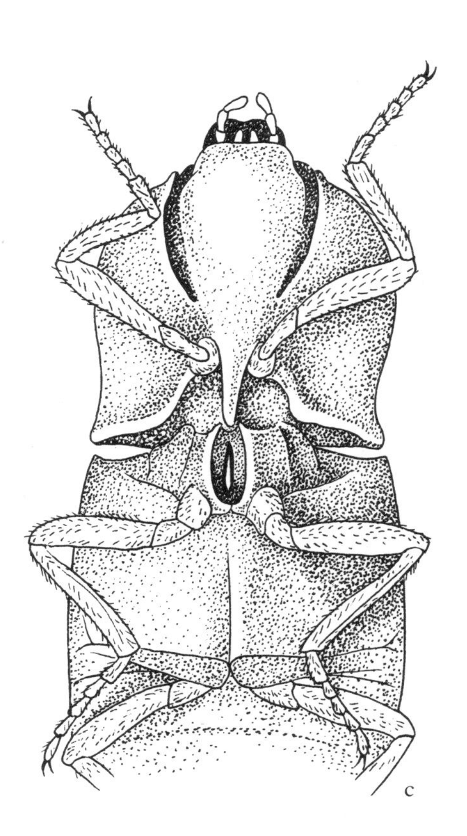

This ability of the beetle has always attracted the notice of observers, as the popular name of "Skipjack" shows, and the clicking sound that accompanies the driving of the prosternal process into the mesosternal cavity has provided the vernacular name of "Click Beetle." The beetle can leap in this way from an initial position either on its back or on its front. The trajectory described is usually semicircular and reaches a maximum height of 30 cm, achieving in the process an acceleration greater than that of any other leaping animal. The attendant clicking noise can be produced even when the beetle is taken in the hand and held fast.

The leaping apparatus consists of three parts and is situated on the pro- and mesosternum. Its most obvious component is a peg-like process on the underside of the prothorax. This spine corresponds to a cavity (pit) on the underside of the mesosternum. In addition to these more obvious elements of the click apparatus there are two triangular knobs on the underside of the prothorax called snappers. These snappers fit into two depressions below the rim of the elytra on the mesothorax. Finally there is the catch (peg), a semicircular projection on the forward side of the mesothorax immediately below the scutellum. Corresponding to it is a furrow on the underside of the prothorax. The act of leaping is a very complicated one which so far has not received a satisfactory explanation. The prothorax has a powerful, widely extended longitudinal muscle, the snap muscle (median dorsal muscle). The contraction of this muscle causes ventral bending of the beetle's body, in which the prothoracic peg snaps into the mesothoracic cavity. As this happens, the fore body is lifted from the ground and the hind body is drawn in the direction of the head. The result is the displacement of the centre of gravity of the fore and hind body and the development of a counter thrust that shoots the creature high into the air. In flight, the beetle rotates several times around its lateral axis and in some 75% of all cases, lands on its feet. Illustrated is a diagrammatical representation of the leaping apparatus. The beetle's inclination to make use of the apparatus and the performance achieved is very variable among the species. We still know very little about the process involved in the beetle's leap from a prone position.

Even today, opinions differ on the biological significance of the saltatory power. Turning over from a prone to a dorsal position which presents much difficulty to many beetles is not particularly difficult for Click Beetles, since they are able to do it quite well by extending their wing covers. Perhaps the leap can be interpreted as a flight reaction, for example, to avoid the attack of a bird. But this is also very doubtful, since a hungry bird is unlikely to be deterred by the leap. It has been observed that even without making a leap, the beetles can produce the characteristic clicking sound, sometimes in a definite rhythm. Could it be an example of sound produced as a mating call? Other workers believe that the leaping mechanism may serve in the process of respiration, since the large pronotal stigmata lie between the pro- and mesothorax. And one more variation in interpretation might be quoted. In comparison with beetles of similar size, the legs of Click Beetles are relatively weakly developed. All Click Beetles pupate in a more or less solid substratum, for example, wood or soil, and must be able to work their way out into the open. In this activity, they are undoubtedly greatly aided by their ability to leap, since their legs are certainly too weak for the purpose.

Another family, the False Click Beetles (Eucnemidae), which is very closely related to Click Beetles possesses a reduced saltatory power and has a similar click-producing apparatus.

A curious turning reflex

Male Whirligig Beetles (Gyrinidae) make use of a highly original method of turning over. They are able to turn themselves on to a ventral position by making use of their extended aedeagus, the organ of copulation, and aided by one of the forelegs. But many other beetles, once on their back, experience the greatest difficulty in turning over. Observation will show that Cockchafers, Dung and Stag Beetles are quite incapable of this manoeuvre. Indeed, they die on their back.

The ability to roll up into a ball

Many arthropods (Arthropoda), such as woodlice, are able to roll their body up completely. It is less well-known that the ability to roll up in this way also occurs in beetles, and yet there are several groups capable of doing so. First we might mention the family of Clambidae, of which some ten species occur in Europe. They are exceedingly small creatures, 0.5 to 1.5 mm in length and very convex in shape. Head and pronotum can be folded downwards, the legs drawn in, and the result is a neat little ball. Representatives of other families, such as Calyptomeridae and Liodidae (Round Carrion Beetles), particularly members of the genus *Agathidium*, can roll themselves up more or less completely. This feature is also found among Snout Beetles (Curculionidae). Particularly noteworthy are the species of the genus *Orobites* which live on violets.

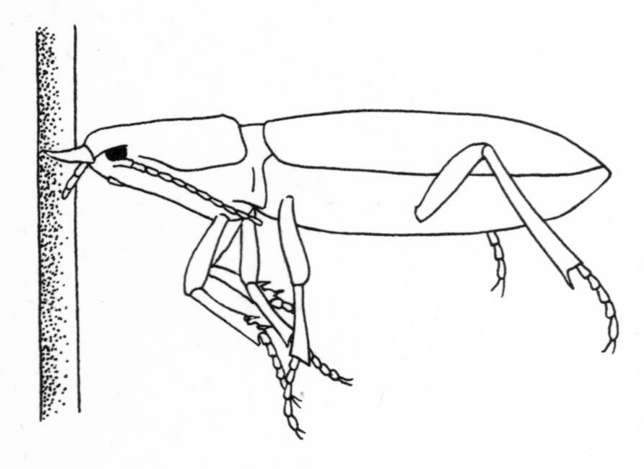

Thanatosis in *Broscus cephalotes* Panz. (Ground Beetles, Carabidae); diagram

Thanatosis

The first observation on thanatosis, the reflex action of the assumption of an appearance of death, is found in Aristotle. "A clear example of this is seen when the creatures known as cantharids are touched, for, if they are frightened, they become motionless, and their body becomes rigid." Such reflexes in which the creature feigns death are widespread among beetles. Usually in thanatosis, the muscles are contracted. In many beetles, this is associated with the drawing in and folding of the legs and antennae. Such is the reaction, for example, of Hister Beetles (Histeridae), Ladybirds (Coccinellidae), Pill Beetles (Byrrhidae), Hide Beetles (Dermestidae) and Colorado or Potato Beetles) *Leptinotarsa decemlineata*, (Chrysomelidae) (Figs. 104, 105). In various species, (Ladybirds, Blister Beetles) haemolymph is excreted during thanatosis. A relatively small number of species stretch out their legs stiffly from the body during the period of rigidity. Various species of Darkling Beetles (Tenebrionidae) are known to do this, for example, many species of the genus *Eleodes*, which stand on their head during thanatosis. The reflex of feigning death takes on a very striking form in the Carabid beetle *Broscus cephalotes*. This beetle opens its maxillae wide and stretches its convulsively rigid legs out from its body. While the entire body remains in a state of rigidity—as is usual in thanatosis—the maxillae remain mobile. If a thin twig is placed between them, they close and from then on, participate in the general state of thanatosis. The stiffened beetle can be carried about hanging freely from the wood, without altering its condition. Only gradually does the thanatosis abate and the capacity for motion returns.

A special form of the death-feigning reflex is the ability of many beetles to roll up into a ball, described above. Thanatosis is undoubtedly a useful means of diverting predatory animals which react to moving prey. It can be brought about artificially in many species, a procedure which is sometimes described as hypnosis in popular literature. The Stag Beetle (Lucanidae), for example, if it is stroked on the upper surface of the body, will rear up and remain rigid in this position.

Sagittate hairs

The larvae of *Anthrenus* belonging to the family of Hide Beetles (Dermestidae), are invested with arrow-like hairs at the end of the body arranged in tufts, which can be raised and vibrated at will if the creature is disturbed. Horion (1949) describes them very clearly. "The individual sagittate hair consists of an extraordinarily fine central axis on which there are small, four-pronged coronets, which, viewed from above, have the appearance of an inverted triangle. The uppermost coronet is the largest and terminates in four inward-curving barbs. Then there is a short, free length of the central axis, followed by the arrow head." These sagittal hairs break off very easily, and because of their construction, cling persistently particularly to chitinous surfaces. When a predatory insect attacks the *Anthrenus* larva, numbers of these bristly hairs adhere to its mouthparts, and it takes a considerable time to remove them.

Larvae "in disguise"

The larvae of many beetles cover or envelop their body. The function of such an action is to create a specific microclimate and to obtain protection from strong sunshine. On the other hand, the enveloping of larvae is said to afford protection from parasites and predators (birds), but it scarcely seems to have this effect. We find disguised larvae among *Cionus*, a genus of the Curculionidae family (Weevils), which envelop the entire body with a viscous secretion. The larvae of many Ladybirds of the

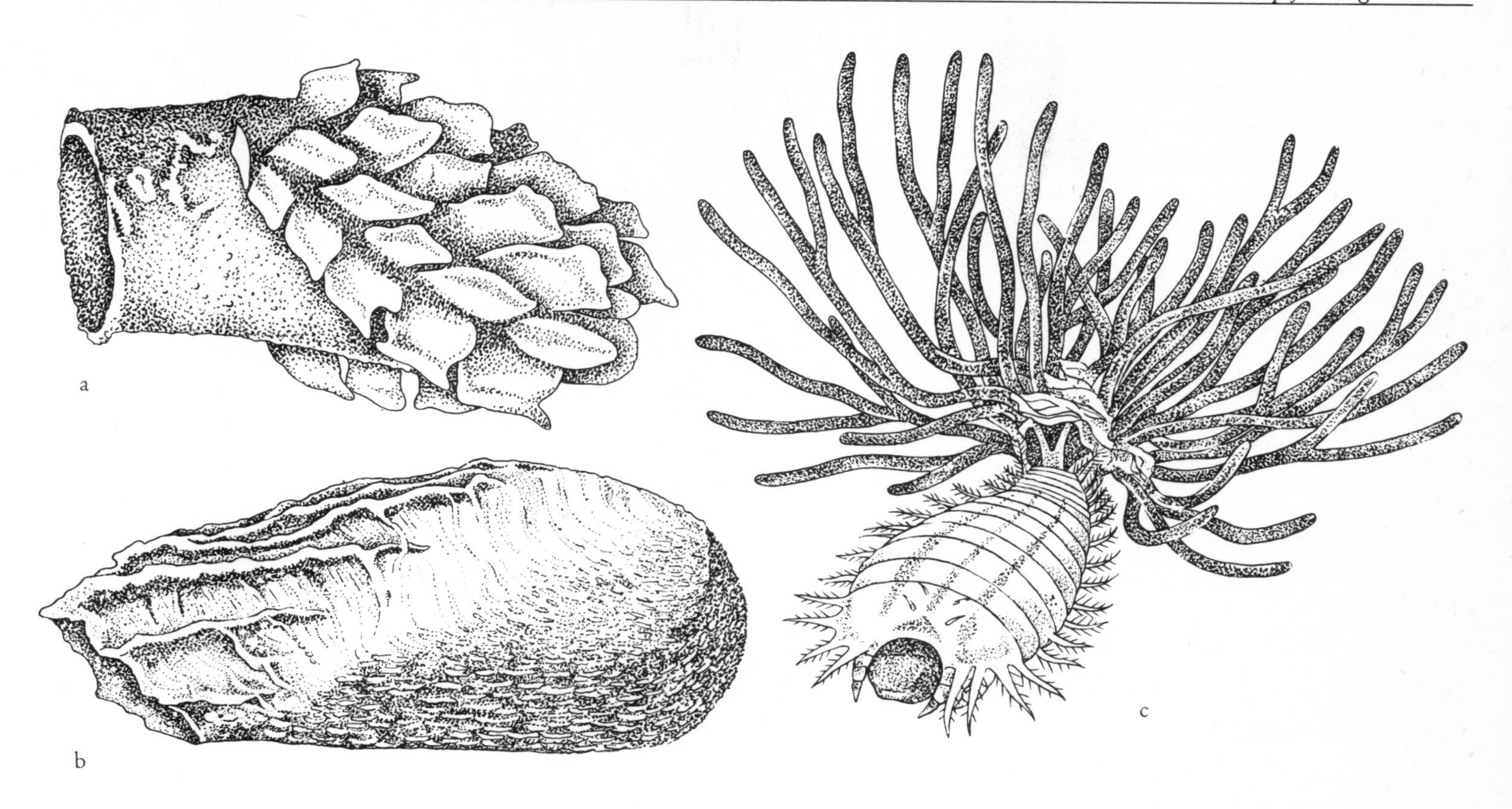

Larvae "in disguise"
a) Larval case of *Cryptocephalus bipunctatus* L. viewed from side (Leaf Beetles, Chrysomelidae).
b) Shell of excrement covering the fully-grown larva of *Clytra quadripunctata* L., seen from side (Leaf Beetles, Chrysomelidae).
c) Larva of *Batonota* spec. with excreted matter as an antler-shaped structure attached to the cast skins of earlier stages, which can be moved forward across the back or retracted (Leaf Beetles, Chrysomelidae).

tribe Scymnini have a conspicuous covering of white wax (Fig. 111). Many Leaf Beetle larvae (Chrysomelidae), such as those of Lily Beetles *(Lilioceris)*, Asparagus Beetles *(Crioceris)* and Cereal Leaf Beetles *(Lema)* conceal their body with coverings of excrement. In these larvae, the anal aperture has been displaced on to the back, and lies on the upper side of the hind abdominal segment, the opening being directed forwards. Since the anus is in this position, the entire faeces are excreted on to the back, covering the larva completely. The great French physicist and zoologist René Antoine Ferchauld, Seigneur de Réaumur (1683–1756) observed how the larvae of Tortoise Beetles (Chrysomelidae; sub-family Cassidinae) enclose their body in a layer of excrement (Fig. 110). He gives a detailed description of the process. "The faecal matter does not lie directly on the body, but a little away from it, and is used by the creature in the manner of a roof or sunshade, which it can raise and lower at will ... Here [at the end of the body, the Author] there are two horn-like, gradually tapering processes which together form a fork, the position of which the insect can alter at will. Usually they are held parallel with and above the body. Excrement is secreted from the anus directly on to this forked process, accumulating along its length to form the aforementioned roof."

Another remarkable phenomenon can be observed among larvae of the sub-families of Leaf Beetles Clytrinae and Cryptocephalinae (Chrysomelidae). First of all the eggs are covered with a layer of excrement by the adult female. When the larvae have hatched, the end of the hind body remains in this covering, which forms the basis of the larval case in which the larvae remain concealed for the whole of their life. The larval case is extended and lengthened in parallel with the growth of the larva. The cases are composed of a mixture of larval excrement and earth. The form of the larval case is so highly characteristic of species that it is of particular taxonomic value. This total enclosure of the larva is a feature that can be observed among a wide range of insects, for example, Caddis Flies (Trichoptera), various butterflies (Psychidae, Coleophoridae) and certain dipterons (Diptera).

Group feeding in larvae

Beetle larvae may well be considered to be ungregarious. And indeed this is true of the majority of species, but there are certain Leaf Beetle larvae (Chrysomelidae) which, after they have hatched from the eggs, remain together for some considerable time and feed communally on leaf material (Fig. 113). For this purpose they sit close together and eat their way forward on a broad front. Similar behaviour is observed among various species of Bark Beetles (Scolytidae), for example, the large Central European species Spruce Bark Beetle *(Dendroctonus micans)*. The female lays the eggs at the end of the egg tunnel. After hatching, larvae remain together inside the wood and, moving in closed ranks, eat out a considerable area under the bark. If this compact front of larvae comes up against obstacles, such as side branches, the larvae separate into two groups and make their way round them. It is interesting to note that not all the larvae feed simultaneously. One section of the group is always engaged behind the lines carrying away the excrement and shed larval cuticles of their brothers and sisters, and pressing them compactly into the boring-dust deposits. After some time, they again force their way to the "front line of attack" and other larvae that have been crowded out by them, take over the tasks at the rear. The larvae remain together until pupation.

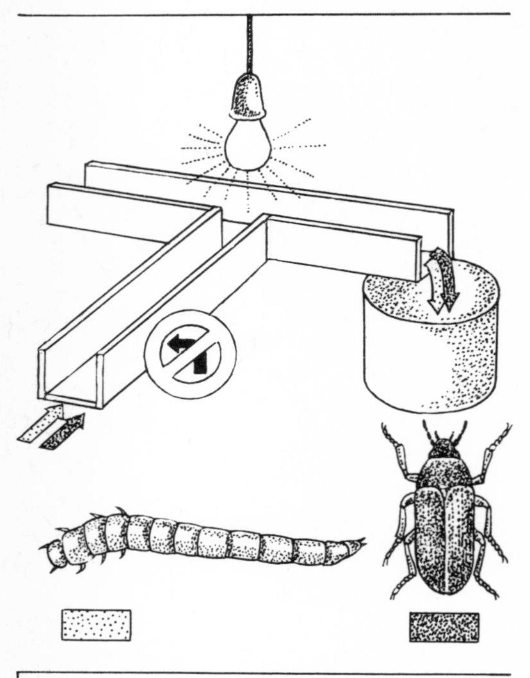

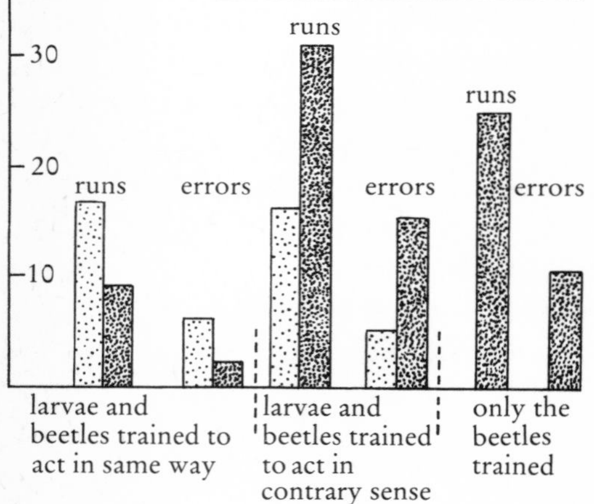

Memory and training
Average number of runs required and average number of errors made before correct performance of the training task (a predetermined sequence of correct decisions) by trained Mealworms and Meal Beetles (*Tenebrio molitor* L.). A correct decision gives the insect access to its breeding jar, after an incorrect decision, the run has to be repeated from the start.

The larvae provide in advance for the emergence of the imago

There are many examples which illustrate how beetle larvae, living in more or less solid substrata, make certain provisions in advance in order to allow the imagines to force their way out of the larval medium (Fig. 116). One example is that of the Pea Beetle *(Bruchus pisorum)* belonging to the family of Pulse or Seed Beetles (Bruchidae). The larvae of this beetle live inside peas, where they also pupate. But beforehand the larva gnaws through the skin of the pea to form a semicircular slit. Later on, the emerging beetle is able to burst the covering by the pressure of its body and so emerge into the open. Its own mouthparts would be inadequate to open up the pea from inside. The larva of the Willow Weevil *(Cryptorhynchus lapathi)*, one of the Weevils (Curculionidae) takes the precautionary measure of extending the calibre of the larval burrow by gnawing to form a pupal cell, without which it would be impossible for the newly emerged beetle to perform its turning movements.

Intoxicated beetles

It has sometimes been found that beetles react to alcohol ingested during experiments. But occasionally this also happens in natural surroundings. In particular, it is said that the food eaten by Stag Beetles (Lucanidae), the fermenting, sappy secretions of oak trees, may contain alcohol. Horion (1949) describes the affected beetles as follows: "At first they begin to stagger, then they tumble down from the trees and attempt to stand, now on one leg, now on another, in the most comical fashion; they topple over repeatedly until they have finally slept off their intoxication."

Memory and training in beetles

Although many species of beetles have a highly developed nervous system, as evidenced by their complex behavioural patterns, their capacity for learning is very slight. Experiments in training have been carried out to discover whether beetles possess any faculty of "memory" at all. Great Water Beetles *(Dytiscus* spec.) "learned" a Yes-No response. But they were unable to "remember" it for long. Meal Beetles (*T. molitor*; Tenebrionidae) are capable of "learning" to make a Right-Left decision. Experiments suggest that beetles emerging from larvae that have already been trained, make fewer mistakes, that is, they are more rapidly trainable. If however, the larvae have been trained in the contrary direction, the beetles are found to make an exceptionally large number of mistakes. In the training of those beetles, the larvae of which had not been involved in the experiments at all, it was found that they made more mistakes than the larvae trained in the original response, but less than those trained in the opposite way.

Edible and curative beetles

In every age, insects have played a greater or smaller part in providing food for human beings. Analysis shows that insect protein has a composition which is of great value to man. The same is true of insect fat. So insects have been and still are an important source of nourishment. Although the best-known instances of this are probably the consumption of grasshoppers or particular species of ants, beetles too have provided and will continue to provide a source of food, particularly in their larval form.

It is generally accepted that in primitive societies, insects were a valuable item of diet. It was probably the large larvae of Longicorn (Cerambycidae) and Lamellicorn Beetles (Scarabaeidae) which were principally eaten. The earliest historical reference to the eating of beetle larvae comes from Ancient Rome. There, at the time of the Roman Emperor Tiberius (42 B.C.–A.D. 37) and of Pliny, the larvae of the Cerambycid genus *Cerambyx* was consumed as a delicacy. The Romans called it *cossus*. This name is used today to denote certain butterflies, but the historical description makes it perfectly clear that the larvae in question were those of Longicorn Beetles. In order to catch and sell them, it was necessary to obtain special authorization. The larvae of Stag Beetles (Lucanidae) were also eaten in Ancient Rome. Indeed, they were specially fattened with spiced meal for this purpose. Jean Henry Fabre (1823–1915) once prepared longicorn larvae in the Roman manner and served them to his family and guests. It was generally agreed that the unusual dish tasted quite delightful, being somewhat reminiscent of roasted almonds with a slight aroma of vanilla.

Even today in many parts of the world, insects are prized as a valuable food. A completely illogical, purely emotionally based aversion to the idea of eating insects is in essence to be found only among Europeans, although Linné in his *Systema naturae* remarks: "Larvae assate in deliciis habentur." (Roast larvae are considered a delicacy.) In Africa, for example, the larvae of a large weevil of the genus *Rhynchophorus* (Curculionidae) and of some species of Rhinoceros Beetles (Scarabaeidae) that are up to 8 cm long are a popular item of food. In Southeastern Asia, the larvae and pupae of Metallic Beetles (Buprestidae), Predacious Diving Beetles (Dytiscidae) and of beetles related to the Cockchafer (Scarabaeidae) are eaten. Here too, the larvae of various species of Rhinoceros Beetles *(Oryctes)* (Scarabaeidae) are particularly favoured. Aelianus tells of an Indian king who had roast larvae "of the most delicious and the finest kind" served as dessert to his Greek guests. In Japan, the larvae of large species of Longicorn Beetle (e.g. *Prionus insularis*) (Cerambycidae), of Diving Beetles (Dytiscidae), Lamellicorn Beetles (Scarabaeidae) and Stag Beetles (Lucanidae) are eaten. For the Aborigines of Australia, the large larvae of Longicorns (Cerambycidae) and Lamellicorns (Scarabaeidae) represent an essential item in their diet. In many regions of South America, the larvae of the Palm Weevil (*Rhynchophorus* species) (Curculionidae) fried in hot fat and then seasoned make a popular dish. The larvae of large Lamellicorns and Longicorns are prepared in a similar way. In Brazil, the larvae of large beetles which have developed inside babassu nuts are fried and eaten. Other beetle larvae found in the stem of the Pataua Palm are also prepared as food. In Surinam, Palm Weevil larvae (Curculionidae) are roasted on small wooden spits and seasoned with pepper, breadcrumbs and nutmeg which in cooking produce a crisp outer covering. Before serving they are given a dressing of orange juice. Maria Sibylla Merian described these larvae as a "zeer delikate spys" (a very delicious food.

In the uplands of Mexico, Longicorn larvae (Cerambycidae) are cooked in rice. Also in Mexico, a stimulating drink is prepared from Tiger Beetles (Cicindelidae) which are soaked in water or alcohol and fermented. The North American Indians use various Darkling Beetles (Tenebrionidae) as seasoning for food. In Europe, Cockchafers (*Melolontha* spec.; Scarabaeidae) in particular have been prepared in various ways. In the best French restaurants, even toward the end of the last century it was still possible to eat Cockchafer Bouillon. The raw material used was generally the abdomens, although other opinion specified the thorax. Cockchafer Bouillon was said to strengthen the nerves. In an old cookery book, the recipe can be found for Cockchafer soup which is recommended in a special diet for anaemia. "Take 1 pound of cockchafers, remove the wing cases and legs, fry bodies in 2 ounces of butter until crisp, add chicken stock and boil; add a small quantity of sliced calf's liver and serve with chopped chives and croûtons."

It seems fairly clear that the use of insects, and beetles in particular, for human consumption is closely linked to their use in folk medicine. And one could reasonably assume that the discovery of an actual or imagined curative effect followed from the original use as an ordinary item of food. In many instances, an element of autosuggestion plays a part, as for example, in South America and Africa, when Hercules Beetles of the genus *Dynastes* or Rhinoceros Beetles of the genus *Oryctes* (Scarabaeidae) are eaten because it is assumed that the "gigantic powers" of these beetles will thereby be transferred to the humans who consume them. Starting out from their use as a food, a cultic reverence developed until finally a wide variety of curative powers came to be ascribed to a large number of beetles. These therapeutic effects may be without any material basis whatsoever, and the "successes" achieved may be brought about entirely by psychological factors or have completely different causes. On the other hand, there are cases in which a curative effect is achieved based on particular substances contained in the beetle. Probably best known for their widespread use in medication are the Blister Beetles (Meloidae) that yield the pharmaceutical product cantharidin (see p. 73). But here we shall consider some other beetles which have been used rather more rarely as remedies.

Toothache has always been an unpleasant and distressing ailment. In earlier times, pain of this kind was attributed to worms boring inside the teeth. This belief led to the idea that the use of various beetles placed either directly or as a decantation onto the tooth would have the effect of killing the worm that was causing the trouble within the tooth. Ground Beetles (Carabidae), Leaf Beetles (Chrysomelidae), Weevils (Curculionidae) and Ladybirds (Coccinellidae) were used for this purpose. Pulverized Ladybirds were sold by the medieval apothecary under the name of "Pulvis dentifricius" (tooth powder). The larvae of Weevils of the genus *Larinus* (Curculionidae), which inhabit thistle-heads, were also believed to be a remedy for toothache. The sufferer had to carry the larvae in a calamus worn around his neck, but it was essential that there should be an uneven number of larvae, otherwise the remedy would prove useless. Of course, all these remedies for toothache were ineffective in any real sense.

The Stag Beetle *(Lucanus cervus)* (Lucanidae) was widely used in folk medicine. In the Middle Ages, it was found that an extract of Stag Beetles could be used to induce fever artificially. In these early times, a deliberately created febrile condition of this kind became part of the treatment for certain illnesses, particularly mental disorders. The French physician and mathematician Antonius Mizaldus is said to have used such a therapy as early as the 16th century. It was he too who gave us the first prescription for producing fever artificially. This prescription was widely publicized later by the Augsburg physician and mathematician Georg Heinisch whose instructions ran as follows:

> "Man kan ein Feber anzünden / wann die hörnichte Kefer /
> welche Schröter heissen / in einem Oel gekocht werden /
> und damit den Pulß gesalbet."
> (A fever can be kindled / if the horned beetles /
> known as stag beetles / are boiled in oil /
> and the pulse anointed therewith.)

Artificially induced fever was alo recommended for use in cases of convulsions, gout and "other maladies." The Paracelsian Wolfgang Hildebrand gives this prescription in his *Magia naturalis* which appeared in 1616. Later on, the practice of fever therapy declined, probably because at that time physicians had at their disposal few means of controlling the fever.

The use of beetles for the preparation of "love potions" (aphrodisiacs) is extremely widespread. In addition to those beetles containing cantharidin, numerous others have been used for the same purpose. In various Alpine countries, for example, a decoction of Whirligig Beetles (Gyrinidae) is reputed to increase the libido. The large, conspicuously horned, tropical relations of the Rhinoceros Beetles (Scarabaeidae) have also served as aphrodisiacs, and belief in the efficacy of such a draught was doubtless encouraged by the creature's exaggeratedly developed horns. For the same reason, many of the prescriptions recommend that the horns alone should be taken in water. It would perhaps be appropriate here to point out that right up to the present day, the horns of Rhinoceros Beetles (Scarabaeidae) have continued to be used in the preparation of aphrodisiacs. The ashes of Stag Beetles added to other foods are believed to have aphrodisiac powers (the Upper Palatinate, Mexico). A Javanese Click Beetle *(Oxynopterus mucronatus)* (Elateridae) is considered to be a particularly invigorating tonic. The price paid for such a beetle is said to be about the equivalent of that for a hen. These few examples may suffice to illustrate the phenomenon.

We are particularly well informed on the use of insects in Japanese folk medicine. J. Umemura (1943) cites 21 species of beetles to the families of Longicorns (Cerambycidae), Blister Beetles (Meloidae), Tiger Beetles (Cicindelidae), Fireflies (Lampyridae), Water Beetles (Hydrophilidae), Diving Beetles (Dytiscidae), Lamellicorns (Scarabaeidae), Stag Beetles (Lucanidae) and Whirligig Beetles (Gyrinidae) which were used in the treatment of skin diseases, for the purpose of staunching bleeding, in cases of pulmonary disease, renal disease, tumours, gynaecological illnesses, convulsions, hydrophobia, asthma, gastric disorders, fever, paralysis, diphtheria, cancer, smallpox, warts, haemorrhoids and whooping-cough. The same situation no doubt also exists in other cultures, but of these no such thorough study has yet been made. Nor has research been carried out to discover the rational basis, if such a thing exists at all, of the majority of these prescriptions dispensed in folk medicine.

The use of cockchafers (*Melolontha* spec.; Scarabaeidae) as a folk remedy is widespread. Pulverized cockchafers were believed to help in the treatment of epilepsy, while boiled in wine they were a remedy for greensickness. Biting off the head of the first cockchafer of the year said to provide protection against fever for a twelvemonth. Oil made of the larvae of cockchafers was used to cure rheumatism. One curious use of beetles (and ants) in surgery is obviously very old. Since the Middle Ages until the present day (among the South American Indians) beetles have been used to close wounds. The beetles are held against the edges of the wound which have been drawn neatly together, and allowed to bite into them. When they have taken a firm hold, the rest of the body is separated from the head and removed. The head remains to hold the wound together until it has healed.

It is not unusual to find the use of beetles recommended as a cure for some ailment or other, which seems utterly without any possible foundation. The following are some examples of this. According to Pliny, the June Beetle *(Polyphylla fullo)* (Scarabaeidae) tied between two lizards is a remedy for four-day fever (a form of malaria). Even if it is cut half and each part tied on the arm, it is said to be helpful. The book *Ortus Sanitatis* dating from the end of the 15th century recommends the medicinal use of the mandibles of the Stag Beetle (Lucanidae). In Vorarlberg they were hung round the neck of children who suffered from convulsions, which practice provided the popular name common in that region of "Krampfkäfer" (convulsion beetle), a name already familiar in ancient Rome. Stag Beetle "antlers" were sold for 10 silver groschen or more. Magic powers were also attributed to the Hercules (*Dynastes* spec.; Scarabaeidae), but it cost 50 to 100 thalers. Schwenckfeld recommends using Stag Beetles in oil for ear-ache, and hanging the "horns" round the necks of small children to prevent bed-wetting. The horns of the three-horned Dor Beetle *(Typhoeus typhoeus)* hung round the neck are said to help to cure many illnesses, Dung Beetles (Scarabaeidae) to bring relief in cases of ear-ache, bladder-stone and dropsy. Even the balls of dung rolled up by Scarab Beetles (*Scarabaeus* spec.; Scarabaeidae) were used to manufacture very costly medicaments. It was believed that horses which had eaten a plant infested with larvae of *Lixus paraplecticus* (Curculionidae) would become lame.

Poisonous beetles

There are two groups of beetles that have been variously used since early times both as remedies and also as poisons: they are the Meloids that contain cantharidin, and certain beetles that provide arrow poison. First of all, cantharidin. It is the internal anhydride of a monobasic acid with the molecular formula $C_{10}H_{12}O_4$. In the various species of Blister Beetles (Meloidae) it constitutes from 0.25 to 0.5 per cent of the body substance (Figs. 73, 182, 183). The presence of cantharidin is said to be restricted to the haemolymph, the accessory glands of the sexual apparatus and the ova. It is very stable and is secreted in an unaltered form through the kidneys. Of animals that have been poisoned by cantharidin, even the flesh is poisonous. The fatal dose for an adult human is said to be 0.03 g.

Cantharidin is still mentioned in various modern pharmaceutical works, as for example, in the Second Pharmacopoeia of the German Democratic Republic. There, the cantharidin content of the Blister Beetle *Mylabris cichorii* is given as 0.7 to 1.3 percent calculated for the substance dried at 105°C. The entry is accompanied by the observation: "The material is intended for use in veterinary medicine only."

In H. Diener's *Drogenkunde* (Pharmacognosy) published in 1958, the following note on its use may be found: "In earlier times as an aphrodisiac, today only rarely as acrium for ointments, plasters; for the preparation of the tincture; particularly in veterinary medicine. An ingredient of hair restorers."

In Haeger's *Handbuch der Pharmazeutischen Praxis* (Handbook of Pharmaceutical Practice), 1949, there is a description of its use and effect. "Cantharidin has a highly stimulating effect on the urinary passage. Even quite small quantities can result in grave poisoning, together with albuminuria, haematuria, cystitis etc. leading to dysuria, stranguria and painful erections. In serious cases it leads to respiratory disturbances, convulsions and acute gastroenteritis. At one time taken internally as an aphrodisiac and diuretic, it is no longer used as such today because the apparently erotic effects thus achieved were nothing more than an indication of a serious disorder of the urinary passage.

73 The poisonous Spanish Fly *(Lytta vesicatoria)* which is gleaming metallic green in colour (Blister Beetles, Meloidae).

Externally, mainly in the form of plasters, also as ointment, tincture and colloid, as a vesicant for pleurisy, pneumonia, articular rheumatism, neuralgia, rheumatic odontalgia, inflammation of the eye, as an ingredient in hair tonics etc. Use in treatment of humans now obsolete."

The effects of cantharidin are described as follows: "Applied to the human skin, cantharidin produces rubifaction within 1 to 3 hours. After this, small pustules appear which, after about 8 to 12 hours, combine to form one large blister. If left to take effect for a correspondingly longer period, or else if application is made to a damaged part of the skin, inflammation and ulceration are caused, followed by suppuration. Taken internally, it causes heartburn, an increased urge to urinate and tingling at the urethral orifice. A larger dose causes a feeling of burning in the mouth, throat and stomach, increases the flow of saliva, sometimes with swelling of the salivary glands, impedes speech and makes swallowing difficult, and as a result of dysphagia and hydrophobic reactions, produces excessive thirst. These symptoms are followed by vomitting, in some cases mucous-sanguinolent diarrhoea, excessive urge to urinate (stranguria), sometimes difficulty in discharging urine accompanied by pain in the region of the kidneys and bladder. Often there is painful priapism; pregnant women suffer haemorrhage from the uterus sometimes resulting in abortion. In addition there is usually debility, severe headache, vertigo, trembling and convulsions, coma and finally death." It is scarcely surprising that the severe effects of cantharidin were already known in early times and were employed by medical practitioners. In the Papyrus Ebers, there is a description of what was probably the earliest Blister Beetle plaster. The physicians of classical antiquity prescribed cantharidin for the treatment of many different illnesses. The Hippocratic Collection (Corpus Hippocraticum), for instance, gives "cantharis" as an ingredient of ointments and suppositories for external application, and of medicinal potions for internal use. Instructions for the preparation of the physics recommend the use of three, four or five Blister Beetles, in every case without head, legs and wings; they are to be ground or pounded and in each case combined with different additional ingredients. The medicament obtained in this way is to be applied as a healing ointment. Quite often, a suppository containing Blister Beetles is prescribed, being used in gynaecological practice for the purpose of "female purgation," and is also said to be a cure for infertility; it is to be used in the case of suppressio mensium, to precipitate the afterbirth or to bring about the expulsion of a dead foetus.

Blister Beetles will also help to cure these same complaints if taken internally, for which purpose a draft is to be prepared, using the trunks of three or four of the beetles, ground and mixed with wine, together with certain other substances. And finally, a Meloid draft is efficacious in the treatment of dropsy (hydrops) and jaundice. The adherents of Hippocrates were well aware that the ingestion of Blister Beetles can bring about pain and stranguria. To counteract these effects they recommend hot baths and a soothing drink of honey and water. In his treatise *On the characteristics of animals,* Aelianus writes about a Blister Beetle, although to which species this particular one belongs is still not clear today. "The Buprestis is a creature which, if swallowed by a cow, causes such grave inflammation that within a short time the cow bursts and dies." Pedanios Dioscorides, a Greek scholar who lived in the middle of the first century A.D., recommends the use of Blister Beetles in the treatment of cancer, leprosy and pernicious herpes. Let us hear what he has to say in an extract from his *Materia medica.* "Suitable for preservation are the cantharides gathered from grain. Toss them into a pitcher that has not been treated with tar, cover the opening with a cloth of pure linen, loosely woven, turn it over and agitate it above steam rising from boiling vinegar, and persist in this until the beetles are suffocated; then grind them down and store them. The most efficacious beetles are those with crosswise yellow stripes on the wings and a longish body, which are bulky and rather oily like cockroaches. Those of a single colour are ineffective." Dioscorides deals at some length with the subject of antidotes to cantharidin poisoning. "The most severe symptoms appear in those to whom cantharidin has been administered. Virtually the entire body from the mouth to the bladder seems to be eaten away, and there is a taste of pitch or else cedar-resin. They experience inflammation of the right side of the lower abdomen and suffer painful retention of urine, they also frequently pass blood with the urine, and within the belly they feel pains similar to those of dysentery; they are afflicted by fainting spells, nausea and vertigo with loss of vision, and finally they lose their reason. And so, before this occurs, it is essential to force them to vomit by giving oil or another of the afore-mentioned remedies, and after the greater part of the substance has been removed by vomitting, to administer a clyster consisting of gruel made from wheat, rice, groats or barley or of a decoction of mallows, linseed, carob or of root of althaea which the Romans call hibiscus. At the same time they must be given bicarbonate of soda with water-meth in order to purge and flush away anything that has remained in the stomach or intestines. If this does not prove cathartic, it is necessary to cause evacuation by introducing honey-meth with bicarbonate of soda giving at the same time wine or sweet wine mixed with ground cedar nuts and cucumber seeds or milk or hony-milk or goose-fat melted and mingled with sweet wine. Wheatmeal boiled together with honey-meth must be placed on the inflamed parts."

The dangerous nature of cantharidin is confirmed by Pliny in his reference to the Roman knight Cosinus for whom a Blister Beetle potion prescribed by his physician proved fatal. The Roman historian Valerius Maximus (in about A.D. 32) describes the scornful reply of Theodor of Cyrene to King Lysimachus (355–281 B.C.) who is threatening him with death. "Forsooth, any of the cantharides can do that just as well!" In Greece, Blister Beetles (probably of the species *Mylabris*) were used instead of the hemlock cup as the means of execution.

In medieval texts there are also descriptions of the use of cantharidin, as, for example, in the writings of Konrad von Megenberg (1309–1374). "The worms are green, but when the sun shines, they are of a golden colour, and therefore people call them golden worms. The worms are collected at night, round about August, and soaked in vinegar. When they are dead, wine is poured over them and they are applied to a limb, it might be a foot or a hand, or some other limb, beneath a small waxen vessel, and so they make a blister at that place. When the blister is pierced at many points with a golden needle or with a hook, all the malignant humour that is in the limb emerges, just as from a cauterizing, and it is as good as many a cauterizing which lasts for a whole year."

Ortus Sanitatis by Johannes Wonnecke of Caub published in about 1480 also contains directions on the use of Blister Beetles. "The cantharides with saffron-yellow wing bands, which are obtained from fields of grain, are suffocated in the evening by means of vinegar vapours, and then they are very useful for many purposes. They remove both the horn and the leprous scale from bad nails. They improve the state of health and have an unusually strong diuretic effect. Some even make up uretic medicine by the addition of a quite small number of cantharides.

In 1548, the Italian scholar Pietro Andrea Matthioli (born 1501) wrote at length on the subject of Blister Beetles, including the following observation. "They heal skin eruptions as well as scabies, and combined with corrosive liquids, they remove corns."

Thomas Mouffet published his own observations on Blister Beetles, and they are well worth noting. "At the slightest touch, the female gives off drops of oily liquid, but the male is always found to be dry. They copulate with their heads facing away from one another, a feature I have often observed in the region of Heidelberg. In copulation, the female drags the male along with her, so that the latter is obliged to crawl backwards. The entire body is soft and black with a bluish shimmer. From the shoulders, two wing rudiments project, but they can be used neither for flying nor as an aid to walking. In young beetles, the segments of the abdomen are a shimmering greenish colour, in older ones, bluish . . . It feeds on the leaves of violets and tender grasses. They are rarely seen at any other times than in the month of May. The rest of the year they live in darkness, or else they die, after having deposited their seed in pills of dung. In Heidelberg and Frankfurt, I have often found them in fields, meadows, gardens and on paths, but so far I have not found a live one in England. Only Agricola describes them as four-legged, whereas in reality, they have six legs. Perhaps his specimens had had two of their legs torn off at some earlier time."

Whereas the observations made by Mouffet were fairly accurate, some of the interpretations published at about the same time were considerably faulty, such as the observations made by Caspar Schwenckfeld. "They develop out of caterpillar-like maggots, which for their part originate from the sap that adheres to the leaves of the ash and poplar tree and to corn. They mate and occasionally give birth to young, although they do not produce beetles but vermicules. In this country they are but rarely found, sometimes in fields of grain, also sporadically on ash, poplar and willow trees, upon the leaves of which they feed. This year they have been very numerous. It is generally believed that they occur in large numbers every seventh year."

It is interesting that in the Middle Ages, cantharidin was also used as a remedy for epilepsy. Its potential use for this purpose had already been known in antiquity. The writings of the Persian physician Avicenna (Ibn Sina) (980–1037), which exerted a very strong influence on European medicine contain what is probably the first mention of Blister Beetles as a remedy for rabies. Their use in the treatment of rabies and of bites in general, even snake bites, is clearly a very ancient one in folk medicine. Use of the beetles as a cure for rabies was given wide publicity in particular by Frederick the Great (1712–1786), who was said to have bought the secret of the preparation of a remedy for this illness from a Silesian peasant for a considerable sum of money, and then to have made it known to the public. The preparation of "potio antilyssa", the potion for rabies, specifically requires the use of the oily haemolymph exuded from the legs. In addition, the creatures are to be held over a honey jar while their heads are cut off, so that the "blood" that trickles out may not be lost. On a portrait of Professor Christian Wilhelm Büttner of Göttingen, who taught from 1763 to 1783, an Oil Beetle *(Meloe proscarabaeus)* is depicted with the legend "Salifa infectos sanat" (healing infections by saliva). It has been assumed that Büttner taught the use of *Meloe* in the treatment of rabies.

There is documentary evidence that Blister Beetles were used for chronic skin diseases and in cases of hydrophobia, gonorrhoea, kidney or bladder stone, and as a vermicide; they are also listed as an abortifacient and an aphrodisiac. Their use as a sexual stimulant, administered in the form of love philtres or powders, is widespread in popular and folk medicine. Mixed with honey, the insects provided one of the most widely known love potions. But at the same time, a warning voice on this subject was raised by an Augustinian friar, Hieronymus Ambrosius Langemantelius in the year 1688, who wrote: "A young man of 24, who had drunk two drams of Spanish fly in wine in order to increase his libido, was delivered to hospital almost unconscious. He suffered great pain, but after the administration of various antidotes, was able to be discharged next day." And yet in the eighteenth century in France, "Pastilles à la Richelieu" and "Bonbons à la Marquis de Sade" were available to increase sexual performance. Obviously, the idea, expressed in the name "love potion," that Oil Beetles had a sexually stimulating effect, was very widespread. In many places, the custom existed for a girl to bite off the head of an Oil Beetle and cook the body in with food to be served to her beloved. A household calendar of 1856 advises: "Too much of it should not be used, or else the woman may lose her reason."

And finally, to the list of illnesses for which Oil Beetles were used, can be added sterility, hydrops, icterus, colic, asthma, rickets, gout and very frequently, particularly from the seventeenth century onwards, rabies. For centuries, almost all vesicant or blistering plasters were made from these beetles, which for this reason were given the name of Plaster Beetle or Blister Beetle. In addition, they are "to be highly recommended in cases of madness and have rendered great assistance."

In the Middle Ages, several distinct species of Blister Beetles were recognized, at least two, the Spanish Fly *(Lytta vesicatoria)* and the Oil Beetle *(Meloe)* going back to Paracelsus (1493–1541). Until this time, it was primarily the Spanish Fly that was used. But from now on, Oil Beetles are also introduced. Nor do they prove disappointing. They are used in cases of gonorrhoea and dropsy and as a cure for gout and stone, and they are frequently employed and recommended in cases of long absence of periods in women, and in related maladies. They are said to be an ancient cure and for many years "well known to country people as a reliable aid in combatting the dreadful consequences of the bite of a mad animal." Very often directions are given for the beetles to be dried, pulverized and the powder mixed with wine and taken as a drink. Another prescription requires the Oil Beetles to be soaked in honey or oil, and the tincture to be taken sometimes together with and sometimes without the beetles. The *Meloe* have been given various vernacular names such as May Worms, Oil Beetles, Dripping Beetles, Piss Beetles. The name May Worm comes from its natural habit of making an appearance primarily in May, and also refers to the worm-like form of the female, while the name Oil Beetle is an allusion to the oily secretions containing cantharidin given off by the insects. They were given the name of Dripping Beetles because in earlier times, in the manufacture of salves or blistering plasters, dripping was used as the ointment base, and the name Piss Beetle refers to their diuretic effect. But over and again, warnings are given of the dire consequences that may result from their use, often accompanied by very realistic descriptions. "On the surface of the skin, they produce inflammation and blisters; absorbed through the skin into the blood, they affect the urinary passages, causing inflammation and the passage of blood-tinged urine, lunacy, convulsions and death . . . Taken internally, they cause the urinary passages to become even more gravely inflamed and finally prove fatal." "A man of 43 years of age consumed a whole Meloe beetle . . . Four hours later, the patient experienced a violent griping and stabbing pains in the lower abdomen. The pain, which increased with every moment that passed, affected

74 The velvety-black Rove Beetle of the genus *Staphylinus* from Europe, with reddish-brown elytra.

in particular and most violently the bladder and the rectum. The fearful suffering seemed to render the patient quite insane; he rolled about in his bed, standing now on his head, now on his feet, and had a constant urge to pass water or evacuate the bowels, but was entirely unable to do so. He seemed to have taken leave of his senses and raved in delirium. His face looked pale and was puffed up; his eyes were wild and started from his head . . ."

In Peru, species of the genus *Pseudomeloe* are still used today to remove warts. The warts are scarified and Meloe pulp is applied to them. A blister develops and by the end of seven days, the wart has been destroyed.

It is well known that the bushmen of southern Africa make arrow poison from the larvae of various species of Leaf Beetles (Chrysomelidae) of the genus *Diamphidia (D. simplex, D. locusta)*. In some cases, the larvae remain alive for several years and can therefore be dug up as required. Larvae of the Leaf Beetle *Blepharida evanida* are also used. The poison is a sapotoxin (toxalbumin) that appears to originate from the food plant, the poisonous shrub *Commiphora africanum* which has the lethal effect of breaking down the red corpuscles of the blood. The poison begins to take effect as soon as it enters the blood stream. Once an arrow has been prepared by immersing its point in the body liquids of the larva, it need only make a very small wound. An arrow treated with the dried poison retains its toxicity for a considerable time.

There are other species of beetles which are also poisonous. As an example, we might mention certain species of the family of Oedemerid Beetles (Oedemeridae); of these it is said that in the Pacific Islands, they sometimes poison the palm wine by falling into it. An American Rose Chafer *(Macrodactylus subspinosus)* (Scarabaeidae) is also reputed to be poisonous, and to cause considerable losses, in poultry farms in particular. In this context, it is worth mentioning that even the familiar Cockchafer is not free of irritants. The genus *Paederus* belonging to the family of Rove Beetles (Staphylinidae) secretes a poison that can cause inflammation of the skin and sores that heal only with difficulty. These can be seen on pigs and poultry that have been affected in this way. The barbed hairs of the larvae of Skin Beetles (Dermestidae) are said to cause irritation of the skin as well as of the respiratory tract, and possibly allergies. It is also quite likely that allergies can be triggered off by dust from finely broken down chitinous body-parts of beetles.

Phylogenesis and Classification

Phylogenesis of beetles

Geological age and the earliest fossils
The oldest insects that have been described came from the mid-Devonian, that is, they are 360 million years old. The earliest fossil insect to have been found so far is a representative of the order of Springtails (Collembola). Beetles are "much" younger. The earliest fossils to have been categorized as beetles come from the lower strata of the Permian period, and are thus some 270 million years old. From these strata, some 15 species are known so far, and they have been placed in seven different families. Considering the fragmentary nature of fossil finds and the very slight opportunities for fossilization that existed among many groups, beetles occur in a variety of species even in the Lower Permian. From this, as well as from other evidence, many workers have assumed that beetles originated as early as in the Carboniferous period, that is, 325 to 285 million years ago. Certainly one of the oldest and perhaps the oldest fossil beetle *(Tshekardocoleus magnus)* (Tshekardocoleidae) is illustrated here.

Probable related group and the lineage of beetles
The most widely varied theories have been proposed on the question of which group of insects can be considered most closely allied to beetles. There are very many reasons to support the assumption that the closest relations of the beetles have become extinct and that therefore a very great distance separates the beetle from its nearest relations living today, making it very difficult to recognize the existence of any close degrees of kinship. In the light of present knowledge, it seems probable that the Neuropteroidea (Drone Flies) (Megaloptera), Snake Flies (Raphidioptera), Tangle-veined Flies (Planipennia) or a partial group belonging to them may be the beetle's closest relations. In favour of this view, in addition to the possession in common of a number of derived characteristics, is the fact that in the ancestral group of beetles, there exist fossils in which the forewings are still membranous and are not convex. These fossils lack a shoulder boss so that it can be assumed that these creatures still used the forewings actively in flight.

Beetles of the Mesozoic
All the orders of present day insects were already living in the Palaeozoic era. Starting out from their primitive forms, there occurred in the Mesozoic a vast development among insects, including of course beetles. It is usual to link this process of development with that of the angiosperms (Angiospermae) and even to speak of a co-evolution of insects and angiosperms. It is generally held that this co-evolution provided the foundation-stone for the wide variety of species existing today. Since this development had its origin in the Mesozoic, it is not surprising that we are familiar with large numbers of insect remains from this geological epoch, including many beetles. But the fragmentary remnants of beetles in particular are difficult to interpret. Almost invariably, only the wing cases and the pronotum are preserved, whereas the most essential features for characterizing higher units reside generally in the construction of the thorax, the mouthparts, legs and antennae.

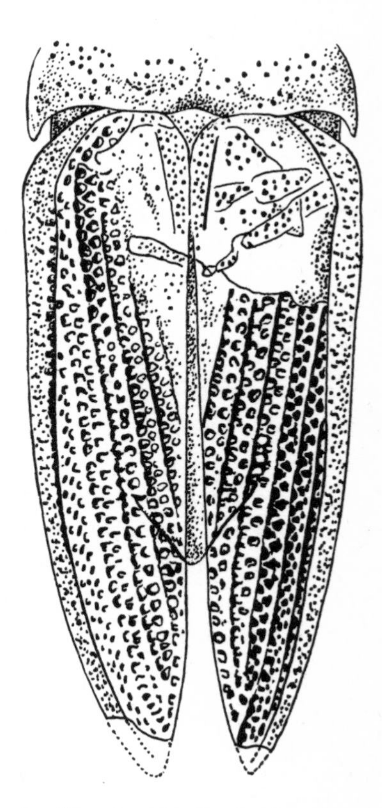

Earliest fossil beetle: *Tshekardocoleus magnus* Rohdendorf from the Lower Permian

In spite of these fundamental difficulties, all fragments found are described, named and classified. Below, we shall look at a small selection of beetles which can fairly reliably be shown to have existed in the Mesozoic.

The Adephaga are certainly known from the Liassic period. Fossils exist in later Jurassic strata that are without doubt very closely related to the Ground Beetles (Carabidae), Water Beetles (Dytiscidae) and Whirligig Beetles (Gyrinidae) of today.

There is a series of fossils which have been included among the Cupedidae (Archostemata). The original wingcase structure is easily recognizable in the fossils. Pieces of fossilized wood from the Triassic have even been found showing traces of damage caused by eating away of the wood which is taken to be the work of Reticulated Beetles (Cupedidae).

There is a good deal of evidence of the existence of the Polyphaga. Some examples are: *Pseudosilphites natalensis* (probably Carrion Beetles) (Silphidae) from the Middle Triassic, *Proteroscarabaeus yeni* (Lamellicorns; Scarabaeidae) from the Upper Jurassic, *Elaterina liassica* and *Tersus crassicornis* (Click Beetles; Elateridae) from the Jurassic. In addition, fossils, of the following families, also belonging to the Cucujiformia, have been found: Flat Beetles (Trogositidae), Blossom Beetles (Nitidulidae), Oedemerid Beetles (Oedemeridae), Longicorns (Cerambycidae), Leaf Beetles (Chrysomelidae) and Weevils (Curculionidae).

Beetles of the Tertiary lignite period

In Tertiary systems containing lignite, very many beetle remains in an excellent state of preservation can be found. Figure 125 shows a beetle found in the Geisel Valley (German Democratic Republic) in lignite, which is some 50 million years old. The coleopteral fauna in Central Europe of the Tertiary must have been extraordinarily abundant. Some 1,500 genera of beetles from the Tertiary are known to have existed, compared with about 1,200 genera today. The comparison is naturally a somewhat unprecise one since there are certainly many genera of that period of which no evidence has yet been found, and on the other hand, opinions held by writers, on the subject of allocation to genera are very divided. But in any case, the tremendous variety existing in the Tertiary fauna is beyond dispute. The underlying causes for this probably lie primarily in the warmer climate and the very luxuriant vegetation of that period. The annual mean temperatures in the Tertiary must have been about 17 to 22°C, compared with today's 8 to 9°C. It is not surprising that of approximately 1,500 genera of beetles, only about 4 per cent are to be found living in Europe today, 50 per cent are found in subtropical and tropical regions and 10 per cent appear to exist no longer.

Amber beetles

Tertiary amber, which is in general some 40 million years old, contains extraordinarily well-preserved fossilized beetles. The collection of amber inclusions has been popular since ancient times, providing us with a comprehensive survey of the amber fauna. The material enclosed with a piece of amber is often so clear that the most minute details of beetle anatomy can be distinguished. Almost all amber beetles can be assigned to recent genera, and there have been several attempts to attribute certain inclusions to recent species —a particular example is the well-known Tiger Beetle *Tetracha carolina* (Cicindelidae)—but a procedure of this kind is a very questionable one, since it is widely accepted that an examination of external form alone is not sufficient to characterize a species. In many groups such as the Marsh Beetles (Helodidae), a much more thorough examination of the amber inclusion can be made, since frequently the genitalia of the beetle have been extruded in the process of inclusion (Figs. 121–124).

Colonization of the earth by beetles in recent times

Number of species

There is a good deal of fascination in following the course of development in man's knowledge of the seemingly endless profusion of beetles. A small table shows the number of species of beetles known to Aristotle and Pliny:

Beetles mentioned by		In Pliny, compared with Aristotle there are		
Aristotle	Pliny	new	present	missing
6	9	5	4	2

Just how gradual was the increase in the number of species known is shown in a quotation which refers to the *Zoologia physica* of Johann Sperling published in 1661: As proof that zoology is one of the most difficult of the sciences, he cites the confusing number of described species, pointing out that so far no fewer than 40 species of beetles, 50 species of caterpillars, 70 species of flies and more than 100 species of butterflies are known. To which Handlirsch retorts curtly "How alarmed the good Sperling would be to see a modern catalogue of insects!" (F. S. Bodenheimer, 1928)

The renowned English systematist John Ray (1628–1705) writes in his *Historia Insectorum* in 1701: "Butterflies and beetles are such numerous groups that I believe we have 150 and more species of each. With larvae and pupae, that makes 900 species. But we exclude larvae and pupae from the concept of species, and class them among the respective insects . . . The number of insect species over the whole earth, on land and water, will be in the region of 10,000, and I believe it will be more rather than fewer." In a note he adds: "Since this time, I have found 200 species of butterflies in my neighbourhood alone and now believe that the total of British insects amounts to 2,000, and that of the whole earth 20,000."

It is very interesting to see the number of species of beetles known to the Swedish naturalist Karl von Linné (1707–1778). In the first edition of *Fauna Suecica*, he lists 294 species, and in the famous 10th edition of *Systema Naturae* 654.

Between 1868 and 1876, a world catalogue of beetles was drawn up by Gemminger and Harold, listing some 77,000 species. Junk and Schenkling's catalogue published between 1910 and 1940 (with supplements added later) contains about 221,480 species. In 1961, within a single year, 3,100 new species of beetles were described. Modern taxonomical works usually recognize 350,000 species of Coleoptera for the entire earth, of which 8,000 belong to Central Europe. Thus beetles have by far the largest number of species of any order in the animal kingdom. In comparison, there are only 8,600 species of birds and 5,000 of mammals.

The largest family of the Coleoptera are the Snout Beetles or Weevils (Curculionidae) in the widest sense, of which 50,000 species are known. Other immense families are the Leaf Beetles (Chrysomelidae) with 35,000 species, Rove Beetles (Staphylinidae) with 30,000, Longhorn Beetles (Cerambycidae) with 26,000, Ground Beetles (Carabidae) with 25,000, Lamellicorn Beetles (Scarabaeidae) with 20,500, Darklings or Nocturnal Ground Beetles (Tenebrionidae) with 20,000 and Metallic Woodborers (Buprestidae) with 13,000 species.

Cosmopolitans

By cosmopolitans we mean those species of beetles that are distributed across the entire earth. In almost every case, they are parasites or pests found in stored food or materials, which have been spread by the action of man.

For the first indication of "incipient" cosmopolitanism, we are indebted to Linné. "At one time, peas were sown by the farmers in North America in sufficient quantities that the seed could be sold at a very high profit in the southern provinces of that continent, as the renowned Professor Kalm of Abo reported when he returned recently from those regions. But he also informed us that this trade came to an abrupt end when a certain pea-beetle was found to have multiplied to such an extent that it was devouring almost all the seed, scarcely leaving enough for sowing. This laudable man brought back with him, among other kinds of seeds, various of the pea genera, among which, after he returned, he found very many live examples of that beetle, some of which he sent not only to the Senator, Count Karl G. Tessin, but also to the Head of the Church Assembly. I greatly fear that colonies of this insect may well be carried with other crops from America to England, and that unless a barrier is set up to their dissemination, they could finally spread across the whole of Europe."

Cosmopolitan beetles are found in particular among the pests living in stored food. In the family of Flat Bark Beetles (Cucujidae) there is the Saw-toothed Grain Beetle *(Oryzaephilus surinamensis)* which, as a result of man's world-wide trading activities, has been carried to every country on earth. Other cereal pests that can be included among the cosmopolitans are the Granary Weevil *(Sitophilus granarius)* and the Rice Beetle *(Sitophilus oryzae)* which is also one of the Weevil family (Curculionidae). Hide Beetles (Dermestidae) have achieved very wide distribution by being carried in ships' holds. Their food, consisting of animal products (hair, dried meat, feathers, furs, textiles and so on) is available everywhere. Usually it is impossible to determine with certainty the original home of cosmopolitans of this kind. Many beetles highly destructive to wood are also distributed worldwide, such as many species of Deathwatch and Furniture Beetles (Anobiidae) and Longhorn Beetles (Cerambycidae). We have already heard, in Linné's account, how a Pulse Beetle (Bruchidae) established itself in a new home. And there are also many other species of Pulse and Seed Beetles (Bruchidae) distributed throughout the world. Also included among the cosmopolitans are the Red-legged Ham Beetles or Copra Beetles *(Necrobia rufipes)* from the family of Checkered Beetles (Cleridae), which travel the world in consignments of dried meat of all kinds. It is interesting that these beetles are even found quite frequently inside Egyptian mummies. There is a particularly high number of cosmopolitans among those beetles that live in flour. These start with the common Meal or Flour Beetle *(Tenebrio molitor)* and go by way of the Rice Flour Beetles of the genus *Tribolium* to the Four-horned Beetle *(Gnathocerus cornutus)*, all of which belong to the family of Darkling Beetles (Tenebrionidae).

The rarest beetles in the world

The concept of rarity is indisputably a relative one. The rarest beetles of all are in fact those of which only one single specimen is known to exist. But mostly these beetles are small and inconspicuous, so that no one is greatly impressed by their rarity. Since they are little sought after, it remains an open question whether they are really rare. People usually start out with the idea that a beetle should be strikingly large or brilliantly coloured or both, and if possible, curiously shaped and very difficult to find. The relative nature of the concept of rarity can also be seen in the fact that many beetles, which for decades have existed only as a single type specimen, have suddenly been found in whole batches. In spite of this reservation, we shall venture below to mention some beetles that can be considered as decided rarities.

A true rarity is the Longhorn Beetle *Titanus giganteus* (Cerambycidae) (Fig. 8). The species was described by Linné in 1771, and to this day, no one knows exactly where he got his model. In the middle of the last century, dead specimens of this species were occasionally washed up on the shores of the Rio

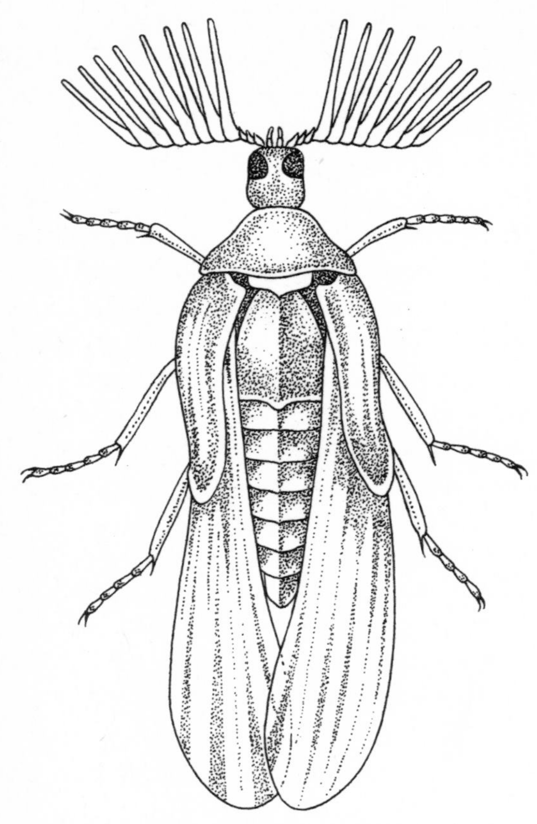

One of the rarest of all beetles, *Rhipidius apicidipennis* Kr. (Rhipiphoridae). Natural size about 5 mm

Negro near Manaos, and indeed many of them were even found when the stomach of some large fish was cut open. For years, these stranded individuals were the only ones to become available for trading. To buy one in 1914 cost 2,000 gold marks. Until 1938, only about 30 such creatures are known to have been found, all of them taken at the same spot by an orchid collector. Incidentally, this man never saw a living *Titanus.* It was not until 1958 that a few live beetles of this species were collected from underneath street lamps in the north-east of South America.

In the fauna of Central Europe, most species of the family of False Click Beetles (Eucnemidae) and Rhipiphorid Beetles (Rhipiphoridae) are considered very rare. One individual of the species *Rhipidius apicidipennis* was caught near Arnstadt in Thuringia in 1867. A second specimen was found in 1929 in Hall in Tyrol. This beetle is probably the rarest of all beetles in Central Europe. Among Langriid Bark Beetles there is a very rare species in *Agnathus decoratus.* And in the family of Metallic Beetles (Buprestidae) there is a particularly large number of rare species. Certain species of the Lamellicorn genus *Plusiotis* (Scarabaeidae), which have the appearance of being made of gold or silver, are also considerable rarities (Fig. 35). These insects are natives of Central America where they live on tall flowering trees; an unusual degree of vivacity makes them particularly difficult to capture. The Goliath Beetles (Scarabaeidae) also include some extremely rare species, as for example the Atlas Beetle *(Goliathus atlas)* or the white-spotted Goliath Beetle *Goliathus albosignatus.* And only a few specimens of the East African *Mecynorrhina oberthueri* have ever been found.

Beetles exterminated by man

Usually it is possible to prove the loss of a species of beetle only within a particular, defined area. When, for example, as a result of the excessive polution of rivers, representatives of the Elmid Beetles (Elmidae) disappeared completely from particular river systems, it was justifiable to speak of regional extinction. The total loss of a species is more difficult to prove. By deforestation living conditions of beetles are increasingly endangered.

Protected beetles

Nature Conservation legislation in many countries places particular species of beetles under protection. It is usually the large and conspicuous species that seem to be particularly threatened. In most of the countries of Central Europe, this includes the Stag Beetle *(Lucanus cervus)* (Lucanidae), the cerambycid *(Cerambyx cerdo)* and the Alpine Sawyer *(Rosalia alpina)* —both Cerambycidae. Since commercial trading is usually restricted or prevented by such laws, the measures of protection taken contribute substantially to the conservation of the species in question. But the real problem in the protection of beetles lies in the maintenance of their characteristic biotopes, a world-wide problem too vast to consider in detail here. The preservation of all species, whether large or small, brightly-coloured or monotone, already rare or still common, known to science or not yet discovered, stands and falls with the conservation of biotopes.

Extremes of habitat

Great heights

Even at a height of 5,500 m where man can scarcely exist without the aid of technical equipment, Ground Beetles (Carabidae) of the genus *Trechus* can still be found. They live on the edges of glaciers and are all wingless. Flying would only bring the danger of being swept away by the winds. Wingless, they are able to survive even on the mountainous, wind-torn Kerguelen Islands.

Beetles in snow and ice

Beetles are to be foûnd even on the islands of Antarctica and on the coast of Greenland. Four species of beetles live on Spitsbergen. Only the snow-clad peaks of the highest mountains and the permanent ice of the Poles (and of course the high seas) have not been conquered by beetles, disregarding the fact that polar stations naturally harbour pests contained in stored food supplies, and other synanthropic species. The extent to which the appearance of insects amongst snow captures the attention of man, especially when they are in large numbers, is illustrated by the following description of a historical event.

Many sources carry reports of a shower of insects that fell from the skies in Hungary on

20 November 1672. Let us first look at one account of the event. "On 20 November 1672 there was a violent snowstorm at Neusohl, Windisch Lipsich and Epericae. Along with the snow, an immense quantity of repulsive yellow and black worms with legs poured down continuously on to the ground, covering it far and wide, to the utter horror of the inhabitants. The size and form of the creatures was approximately as depicted in the enclosed sketch. These insects remained alive for three days, creeping about in groups and attacking one another. In the fighting, the much larger yellow worms were overcome and consumed by the black ones. Examples of both species were sent to Vienna as a most astonishing, momentous and curious object that nobody will be able to observe without dread and amazement."

It is difficult today to find the rational core of this story of a shower of insects. The historical illustrations are of little help. The most credible explanation might be the suggestion that the creatures were the larvae of Soldier Beetles (Cantharidae). The contemporary sketches lend support to this. Moreover, it is well known that the larvae of Soldier Beetles move about on snow even in the very early spring. This has earned them the popular name of "Snow worms." Immediately after a fall of snow, their presence would quickly have attracted the attention of the local inhabitants, whereas beforehand they had failed to notice the dark larvae on the dark ground.

Deep caves

Almost all caves that have been explored by man are inhabited by beetles. Cave beetles are usually without eyes, deficient in pigment, being red to yellow in colour, usually have strikingly long antennae, palpi and legs, the abdomen is often swollen like a balloon and serves as an air reservoir. In many species the stigmata and tracheae are largely regressed, and only cutaneous respiration takes place. They feed on the remains of other cave dwellers, in part of their own kind. Once again the Ground Beetle *Trechus* (Carabidae) can serve as our example, for many of its species occur exclusively in caves. The first cave dweller was described in 1832 as *Leptodirus hohenwarti* (Silphidae) (Fig. 118). As prototype for cave dwelling beetles, one might well take the very long-legged members of the subfamily Bathysciinae of the family of Catopid Beetles (Catopidae). But there are individual cave dwellers in other families as well. The eyeless Diving Beetle *Siettitia balsetensis* (Dytiscidae) lives in subterranean marshy spring pools in France. Almost every cave has its own fauna, and the Bathysciinae are very inclined to speciation in caves. The karstic caves of the Dinaric Alps, Eastern Carpathians and Pyrenees are particularly rich in cave beetles. Since it is possible geologically to determine the age of many caves, the maximum age of particular specialized species of cave beetles can be given very accurately.

Beetles also live in mines. The Long-horned Beetles *Hylotrupes bajulus* has been known to develop within the mine timbers of a gallery 860 m deep.

In arid deserts

In general, deserts possess a surprisingly rich beetle fauna. Particularly large numbers of species belonging to the family of Nocturnal Ground or Darkling Beetles (Tenebrionidae) are found (Figs. 120, 131), but Lamellicorn Beetles (Scarabaeidae) also live here. The extreme conditions of the Namib Desert of South-West Africa, for instance, have produced many endemic species; in the case of Darkling Beetles (Tenebrionidae) alone there are 30 genera with some 200 species, which moreover in many cases are specialists of particular regions of dunes.

Numerous adaptations to desert life have been developed. Most species spend the day buried in sand (fossorial forelegs) and are active only at night. It is remarkable how effective burrowing can be in producing more tolerable environmental conditions for beetles. Towards 2 o'clock in the afternoon, the surface of the desert sand can reach a temperature of 50° to 62°C with a relative air humidity of only 15%. At a depth of no more than 7.5 cm, the temperature has decreased to 27°C and the humidity can be up to 90%. For all the species examined, temperatures in excess of 51°C proved fatal. Many species are particularly well adapted for moving rapidly across sand, even fine quicksand, by lengthening and other morphological modifications of the legs.

The rigid plating, often light in colour, which leaves scarcely any intersegmental or synovial membranes uncovered, provides an effective protection against evaporation. Many species never drink and obtain what water they require

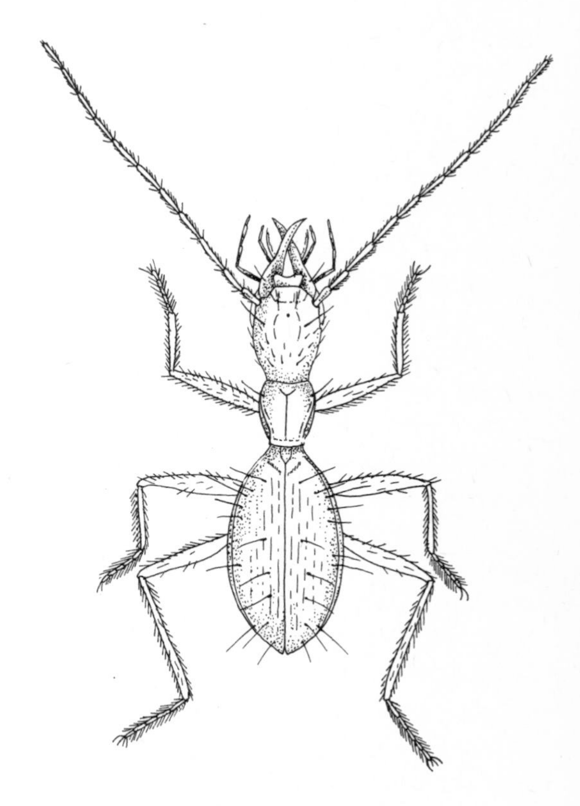

Blind Ground Beetle (genus *Aphaenops*, Carabidae) found in a cave in the Pyrenees. Natural size about 5 mm

from the water of oxidation produced by the combustion of foods. As an illustration, some figures: 100 g carbohydrate produce 55 g of water, 100 g protein 43 g, and 100 g fat 107 g of water. In the extremely arid Namib Desert, species of Darkling Beetles (Tenebrionidae) have developed an interesting method of trapping the moisture in mist. In the early morning, the beetles throw up sand hills along narrow ditches. The mist drifting across horizontally accumulates against them. The walls of the ditches absorb dampness from the mist, and the beetles in turn are able to draw off the moisture. Moisture also condenses on the body of the beetles which they drink.

Even completely desiccated remnants of vegetation provide an adequate basic food supply. In the bare dunes of the Namib Desert where no plants grow, beetle populations, often very large in numbers, live exclusively on detritus blown there by the winds.

In salt

The ocean has not been colonized by beetles. The area of their conquest has extended only to brackish water, coastal regions and marshy splash-water pools, often with a considerably high saline content. A specific saline fauna has developed, with species that occur here primarily because if they lived in salt-free biotopes, they would be unable to compete with other species which, however, cannot tolerate salt. Salt beetles also live inland where salt deposits occur. The family of Ground Beetles (Carabidae) is particularly rich in salt beetles. Very many species of the genera *Clivina*, *Dyschirius* and *Bembidion* are associated with salt (halobiont). In the last-mentioned genus, there is even one species that lives on the North Sea coast below high water mark; when the tide comes in, it burrows into the sand where it remains submerged until the tide has retreated. In the genus *Hydroporus* of the family of Water Beetles (Dytiscidae) and the genus *Ochthebius* belonging to the Hydraenids (Hydraenidae), there are several halophilous species. They are to be found among the Rove Beetles (Staphylinidae) as well, particularly in the genera *Diglotta* and *Bledius*. Many of the Variegated Mud-loving Beetles (Heteroceridae) are also halophilous. The larva of the Wharf-borers *Nacerda melanura* (Oedemeridae) lives in wood that is regularly soaked by sea water, such as the timbers of groynes.

Thermal springs

In Northern Italy there is a Diving Beetle (*Bidessus thermalis*) (Dytiscidae) that lives in thermal springs with a temperature of 45°C. In addition, these springs are colonized by the Water Beetle *Laccobius gracilis* and a representative of the family of Hydroscaphidae (*Hydroscapha gyrinoides*).

Charred wood

Curiously enough, the charred wood left behind after a forest fire, has a quite specific beetle fauna of its own. An area that has been devestated by fire will attract various Longhorn Beetles (Cerambycidae) such as *Criocephalus tristis*, *Acmaeops septentrionis* and *A. marginata*. In the same way, various Narrow-waisted Bark Beetles (Salpingidae) seek out charred wood on which to live. Such places are also the home of the Ground Beetle *Agonum quadripunctatum* (Carabidae). Among the Metallic Wood-borers (Buprestidae) there is one species (*Melanophila acuminata*) which even seeks out the scene of a forest fire while the trunks and branches are still glowing. Many observers have reported seeing these insects sitting and copulating on wood that was too hot to be held in the hand. Obviously fire has a stimulating effect on *Melanophila*, and it is said to be possible to attract certain species by burning wood shavings.

It has been shown that there are sensory organs in the mesothorax which can receive waves of 0.002 to 0.006 μm. It is within this range that the radiation emitted by a forest fire lies. Consequently beetles can perceive forest fires from a distance of 1 km on level ground and from up to 5 km in the mountains.

Nest-dwellers

The nests of mammals, birds and socially evolved insects have various species of beetles as specific guests which feed on the nesting material and remnants of food left by their hosts, or live by predation on other insects that they find there. Particularly among the Rove Beetles (Staphylinidae) there are a great many nest-dwelling (nidicolous) species. They are found in especially large numbers in nests and burrows of the mole, hamster, common souslik, fox and badger, the nests of birds of prey and storks, the holes excavated in sand or gravel by sand martins and the hollows made by woodpeckers. Another family of beetles, the Catopidae or Nest Beetles have even earned their name from their tendency to haunt the nests of other creatures. Most of all they favour those of rodents, insectivores and small predators. Nidicolous species are also found among the Feather-winged Beetles (Ptiliidae), such as *Ptenidium laevigatum* in mole nests, *Acrotrichis atomaria* and *A. fascicularis* in buzzards' nests. There are many nest-dwellers among the Silken Fungus Beetles (Cryptophagidae), Darkling Beetles (Tenebrionidae) and Hister Beetles (Histeridae), for example, *Hister marginatus* which is the guest of the mole. The Trogidae (*Trox*) which belong to the superfamily of Scarabaeoidea liv mainly in the nests of large birds. The Rove Beetle (*Velleius dilatatus*) (Staphylinidae) seems to be found exclusively in the nests of hornets. Nor should we forget the Bees Wolf *Trichodes* of the family of Checkered Beetles (Cleridae), the larvae of which can be destructive to the bee community, and the myrmecophiles that are the guests of ants and termites (p. 135).

Synanthropic beetles
By synanthropic beetles we mean those which occur directly within human habitations and work places, and are no longer found in the wild. In addition to pests they include certain species which are not generally considered as troublesome or undesirable, such as, for instance, the House Beetle *(Opilo domesticus)* (Cleridae) which feeds on beetle larvae that are highly destructive to wood. Our familiar Rhinoceros Beetle *(Oryctes nasicornis)* (Scarabaeidae) can also be numbered among the synanthropes. Originally it inhabited ancient, rotting oak trees. Later, the practice of bark tanning brought the Rhinoceros Beetle into close proximity with man, and it took as its habitat the piles of oak bark. As these became fewer and fewer, it moved over to dung and compost heaps in nursery gardens, where it still completes its developmental cycle today. The species has virtually disappeared from forests.

Some interesting families of beetles

Systematic classification of beetles
For one of the earliest systems of beetle classification, we are indebted to the London physician and zoologist Martin Lister (1638–1711) who divided the order of beetles (he was dealing only with English species) into the following two principal and seven subsidiary groups:

"A. With hairlike antennae and complete elytra.
Chapter 1. On the Cerambycidae. These have the following characteristics: 1. body long and narrow; 2. very long, delicate and knotted antennae; 3. they are found particularly in the vicinity of streams.
Chapter 2. On those beetles with pincer-shaped maxillae (Cicindelidae).
Chapter 3. On jumping beetles. They leap by means of the thorax (Elateridae).
Chapter 4. On slowly creeping beetles, which although they possess elytra, have no wings or only small ones.
Chapter 5. On rapidly crawling beetles with wings.
B. With hairlike antennae and incomplete elytra.
Chapter 1. On earwigs (Dermaptera and Staphylinidae).
Chapter 2. On somewhat mutilated Soldier Beetles without wings (Meloe)."

In the first edition of his famous *Systema Naturae*, the great Linné listed 23 genera. We have already read how the beetle order has more species than any other order of insects. Following Linné, it is usual to combine species into genera, genera into families and families into orders. While it is possible to state the number of known species of beetles with some degree of assurance, little can be said with certainty on the number of genera. This is scarcely surprising since, after all, only the species can be defined exactly and has objective existence. The other categories (genera, families, orders etc.) are artificial concepts created by the systematist in order to cope with the task of bringing order to the system. And it is precisely in the genera that the discretion of the individual worker is given such wide scope, that their totals vary by more than 200 per cent. In the families, this feature is not so marked. There seems, however, to be an increasing tendency to "promote" traditional sub-families to the status of families, but nevertheless the number of families generally in use can be given as about 200. The system of classification featured in the Appendix contains 162 families which are grouped into 21 super-families.

The sub-orders
Beetles (Coleoptera) represent one order within the class of Insects. Orders are usually subdivided into sub-orders. On the one hand this has the object of making manifest important phylogenetic lines of descent, on the other, it is an expression of the urge of every systematist to classify the huge diversity into a hierarchy.

It might seem surprising that even today there exists no universally accepted "subordinal structure". The two sub-orders Adephaga and Polyphaga have been under discussion for some considerable time. Recent years have seen many suggestions put forward for further sub-orders, of which the proposal to establish the sub-orders Myxophaga and Archostemata has some prospect of permanence. Each of the four named groups probably arose from its own single phylogenetic root and thus they reflect broad lines of development. And yet they scarcely fulfil the demand for a clearly organized subdivision. The Myxophaga and Archostemata comprise in each case relatively few species, and the super-order Polyhaga still remains as an intractibly massive block, the broad subdivision of which into super-families is a matter of great difficulty. There has been no shortage of attempts to create a logical hierarchy by the organization of series, and other means, but so far, no one suggestion has gained general acceptance. In the system of classification contained in the Appendix, they are subdivided into five series and 18 super-families.

Reticulated Beetles (Cupedidae)
The Cupedidae are considered to be the most primitive beetle family, principally on account of the construction of their elytra. The family of Cupedidae alone makes up the sub-order Archostemata. Representatives of this sub-order were considerably more widespread in earlier geological epochs than they are today. In modern times they occur only in Eastern Asia, America and Australia, and 20 species in all are known. The larvae develop in timber and show many adaptations to this specialized mode of life.

Tiger Beetles (Cicindelidae)
Although Tiger Beetles show a high degree of uniformity in body form, so that even a non-expert can quickly come to recognize a Tiger Beetle as such, they are among the most brilliantly coloured families of beetles. Perhaps Figures 127, 128, 133, 147 and 148 will give a slight impression of the splendour of their colouring. The typical structure of the Tiger Beetle is varied by alterations in the proportions of its body parts, thus giving an impression of diversity of form. Many species have remarkably long legs, lending them a bizarre appearance, for example, *Cicindela tenuipes* from Eastern Asia and the *Collyris* species which are found in the Philippines, the Sunda Islands, India and Sri Lanka (Ceylon).

The larvae of the Tiger Beetles have a curious manner of capturing their prey. They dig into the ground (and the tropical arboreal Collyrinae dig into branches) vertical burrows which they keep constantly smooth and clean. The larva sits in a burrow and keeps watch for passing prey. Their ocelli are so arranged and constructed that they can look in different directions and scan a wide field of vision as they look out for prey. The structure of the larva is well suited for climbing up its chimney-like burrow, using the stiff spines on the 5th abdominal segment, the end of the abdomen, the legs. In this way, depending upon the size of the approaching prey, it can either retreat with amazing rapidity into the tunnel and grasp the insect as it falls in, or else dart from its lair and seize the creature with its well-developed mandibles.

We are familiar with some 1,600 species of Tiger Beetles, of which the representatives of the African genus *Mantichora* grow to 7 cm in length and are remarkable for their powerful, almost antler-like mandibles (Fig. 127). These great individuals are nocturnal, in contrast to most other species of the family which are markedly active in the hours of daylight, and thrive best in hot sunshine (thermophilic).

Ground Beetles (Carabidae)
The Ground Beetles are among the most popular families of beetles. Almost 25,000 species are known, in an infinite variety of form and richness of colouring which are a delight to the insect-lover (Figs. 9, 126, 132, 134, 160), while at the same time they have been a subject of research for many generations of entomologists, as they will continue to be, even though the problem of their conservation, particularly of the larger species, is a universal one. Many of them are to be found only within quite restricted areas, and changes taking place even within these small areas bring them dangerously close to the limits of their existence.

The degree of ingnorance which prevailed about the habits of even large species of Ground Beetles is effectively illustrated by the words of Schwenckfeld, writing about the Brass or Goldsmith Beetle *(Carabus auratus)*. "It lives on the ground, in those places where toads are also found, and popular belief is that it copulates with the latter. It is also venomous." Most of the species live in the soil, a few beneath bark, on trees or other vegetation. The majority of them are predatory feeders or they may also be scavengers, feeding on carrion (necrophagous), while some only are plant-eaters (phytophagous).

Probably the most curious representatives of the Ground Beetles are the Violin Beetles (genus *Mormolyce*) of which five species occur on the Malayan Archipelago. They are the largest Ground Beetles known to us (Fig. 9). Not including the long antennae, they can be 10 cm in length. They are nocturnal in habit, and the flat shape of their body enables them to hide under loose pieces of bark during the day.

True Water Beetles or Predacious Diving Beetles (Dytiscidae)
The discovery recently of a terrestrial species belonging to the family of Water Beetles (Dytiscidae) caused something of a sensation, for this group is considered the very prototype of aquatic beetles. But leaving aside this highly specialized species, it can be said that all other True Water Beetles (some 3,200 species) live in bodies of water of widely varying kinds: in standing water such as ponds and lakes, running water such as streams and rivers and some even in brackish water.

The Dytiscidae are excellent swimmers, extraordinarily well adapted in terms of bodily structure to life in water. The streamlined body offers little resistance to water. The legs are greatly flattened and fringed with long natatorial hairs which spread out and act as oars in swimming. The frequency of leg stroke is higher in smaller species than in larger ones, for example, for *Hydroporus* it is 16, *Ilybius* 7 and *Dytiscus* 2 strokes per second.

Water Beetles constantly require fresh supplies of air, and it is therefore necessary for them to come to the surface at regular intervals to breathe. The hind end is raised above the water and air taken in through breathing pores, while at the same time a supply of air is retained beneath the elytra for use when submerged (Figs. 141, 142). As an organ of measurement for determining the correct buoyancy force, there is a vesicle or blind sac on the rectum which provides the information by means of the pressure of air contained inside it.

Distribution of the species and the colonization of new bodies of water takes place by air, for virtually all Dytiscidae can fly well and are able to cover considerable distances on the wing.

75 Initial phase of flight of the Cardinal Beetle *(Pyrochroa coccinea)* (Pyrochroidae)
76 Longhorn Beetle *(Agapanthia villosoviridescens)* (Cerambycidae)
77/78 Two-spotted Metallic Beetle *(Agrilus biguttatus)*, bottom right, in free flight.

79/80 Soldier Beetle *(Cantharis fusca)* (Cantharidae) from Europe, in free flight
81–84 Sexton Beetle *(Necrophorus vespilloides)* (Silphidae) from Europe, in flight. In contrast to the Soldier Beetle, the Sexton Beetle twists its wings in flight in such a way that the inner side faces outward. This Sexton Beetle is infested by a large number of mites, all of which sit on its thorax during flight, thus being transported by the beetle. When the mites assemble hastily on the thorax, it is a sign that flight is imminent. Another noteworthy feature is the position in which the mid legs are held: upright at the base of the fore wings.

85 Rose Chafer *(Cetonia aurata)* from Europe, in various phases of flight. Rose Chafers (Cetoniinae, Scarabaeidae) are almost the only beetles that keep the elytra closed in flight. They launch into flight at lightning speed without any previous indication, and are among the most skilful of flying beetles.

86 Longhorn Beetle *(Strangalia bifasciata)* (Cerambycidae) visiting blossom
87 Cardinal Beetle *(Pyrochroa coccinea)* (Pyrochroidae)
88 Cardinal Beetle *(Pyrochroa coccinea)* (Pyrochroidae) launching into flight
89 Nut Weevil *(Curculio nucum)* (Curculionidae) about to fly
90 A specimen of *Stenopterus rufus* mating on a flower, heavily dusted with pollen.
91 A specimen of *Stenocorus meridianus* taking flight; note the light-coloured surface of the abdomen.

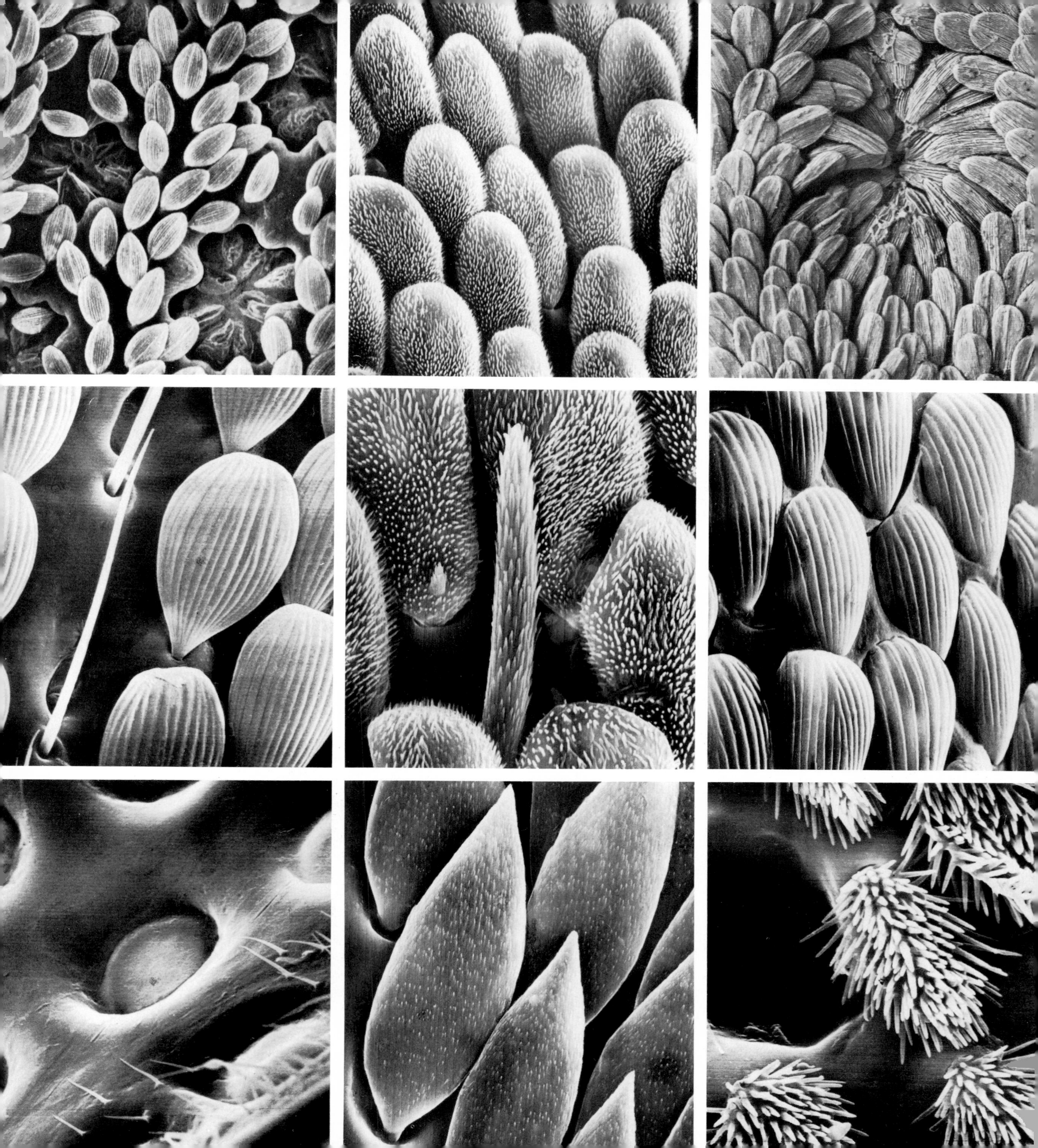

92 Scanning electron micrographs of the surface of elytra
above:
Cupes spec. (Cupedidae), 200×
Hoplia parvula (Lamellicorns, Scarabaeidae), 500×
Cupes clathratus (Cupedidae), 200×
centre:
Phyllobius argentatus (Weevils, Curculionidae), 1000×
Hoplia parvula (Lamellicorns, Scarabaeidae), 1000×
Polydrosus sericeus (Weevils, Curculionidae), 1000×
below:
Oontelus spec., underside of elytron (Soldier Beetles, Cantharidae), 1000×
Polyphylla fullo (Lamellicorns, Scarabaeidae), 500×
Pteleobius vittatus (Bark Beetles, Scolytidae), 2000×

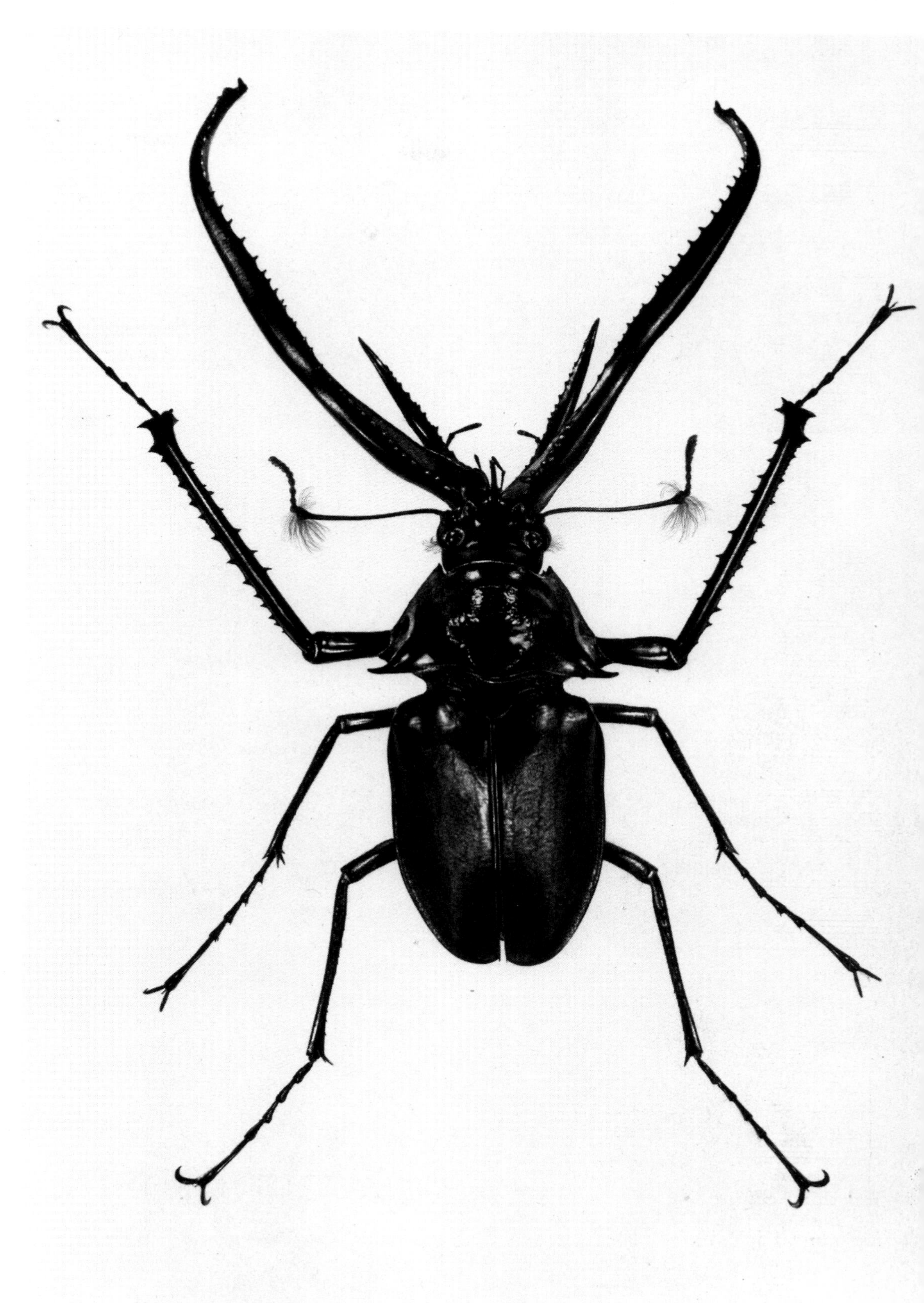

93 Male of the Chilean Stag Beetle *Chiasognathus granti* (Lucanidae)

Following pages:

94 Tropical Longhorn Beetles (Cerambycidae)
left:
Petrognatha gigas from Africa; length of body 6.2 cm;
above male, below female
centre:
Harlequin Beetle *(Acrocinus longimanus)* (Cerambycidae), Mexico to southern Brazil; length of body 7.5 cm
above female, below male
right:
Psalidognathus friendi from Columbia; length of body 7.2 cm,
above male, below female
95 *Phantasis ominosa*, a ground-dwelling Longicorn Beetle from Africa, has something of the appearance of an ibex. Its name means "ominous phantom."

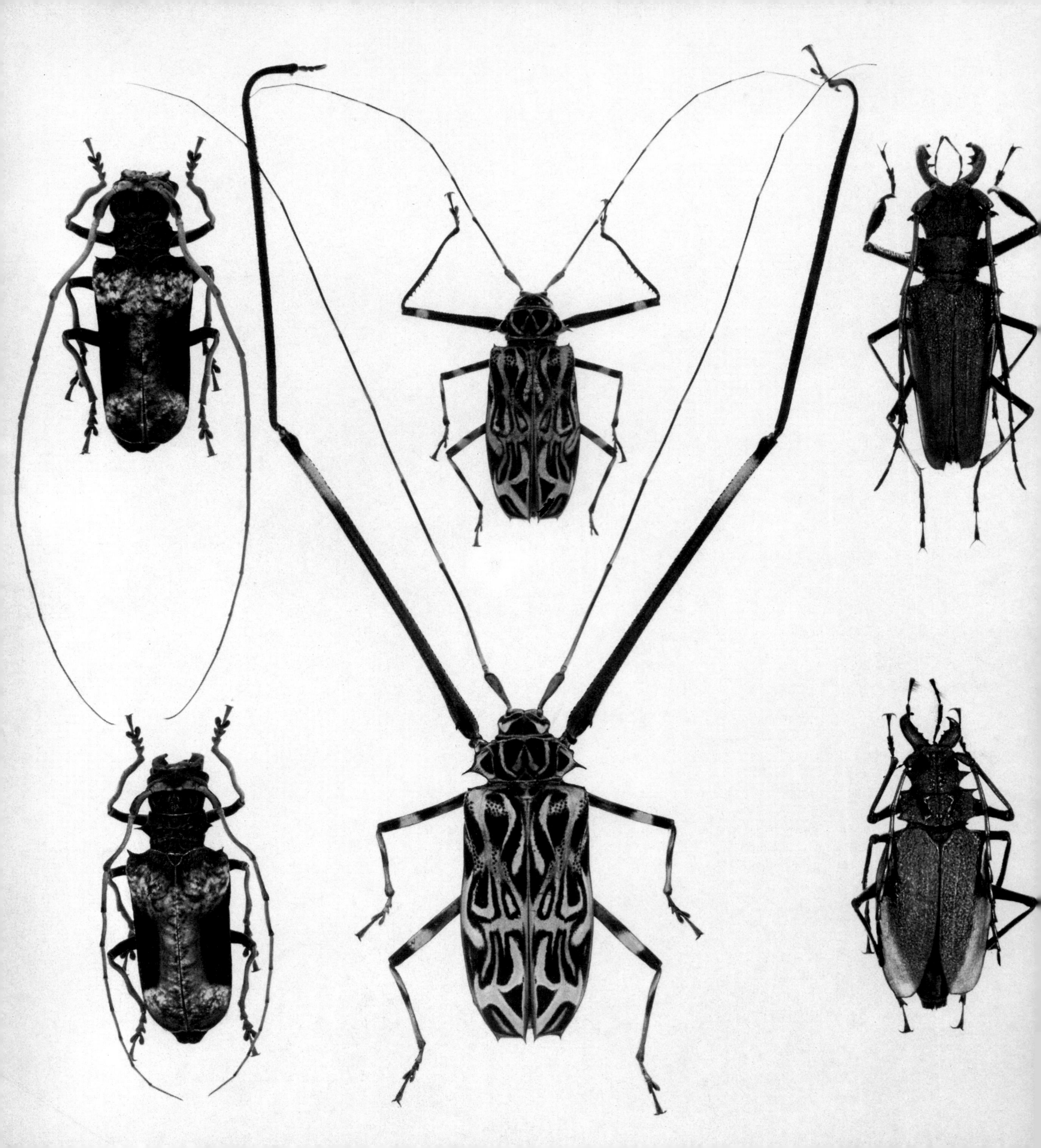

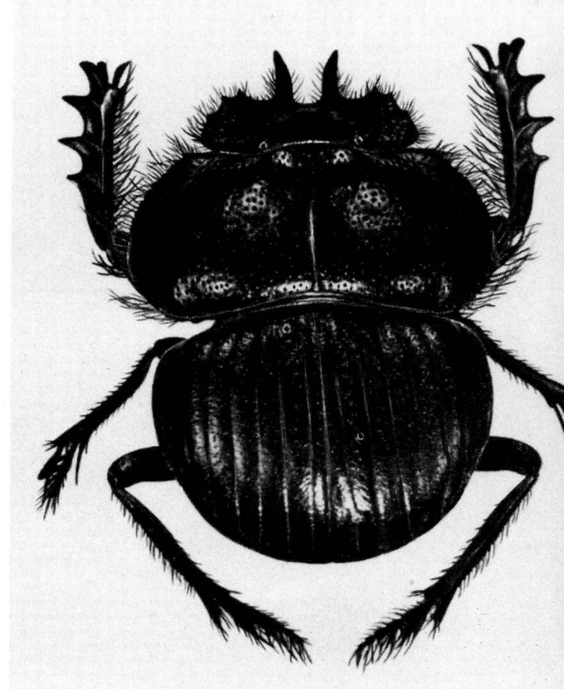

96 Mole Longhorn Beetle *(Hypocephalus armatus)* from Brazil; length of body 5 cm. Its fossorial hind legs show it to be well adapted to life in mould and in the soil.

bottom row:

Pill-rolling Beetles (Scarabaeidae). Note the absence of tarsi on the forelegs and the different shapes of clypeus.
97 *Pachysoma schinzi* from South Africa
98 *Eueranium lepidum* from North Africa
100 *Mnematidium multidentatum* from Lebanon
101 *Anomiopsis luciferum* from North Africa

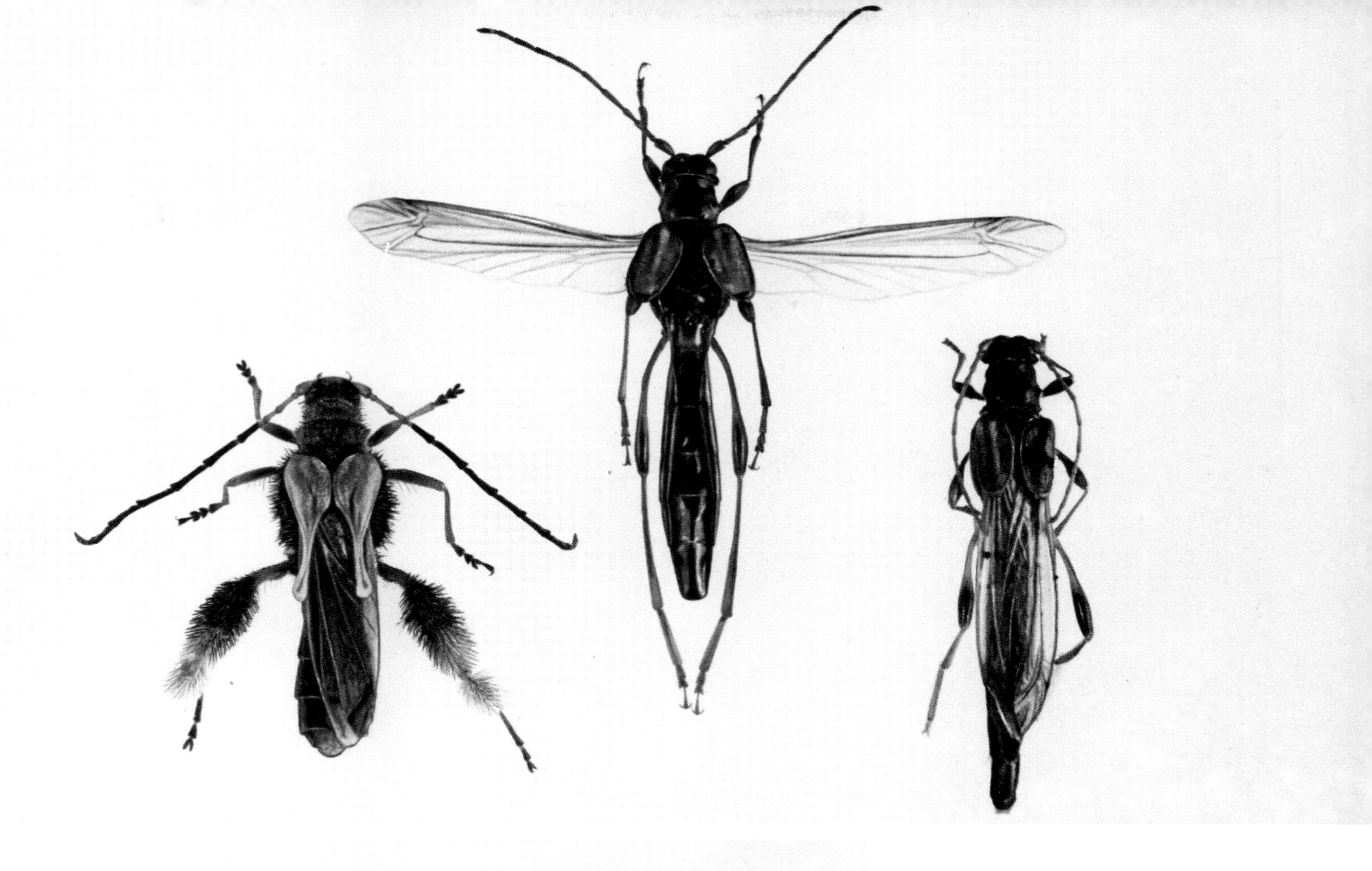

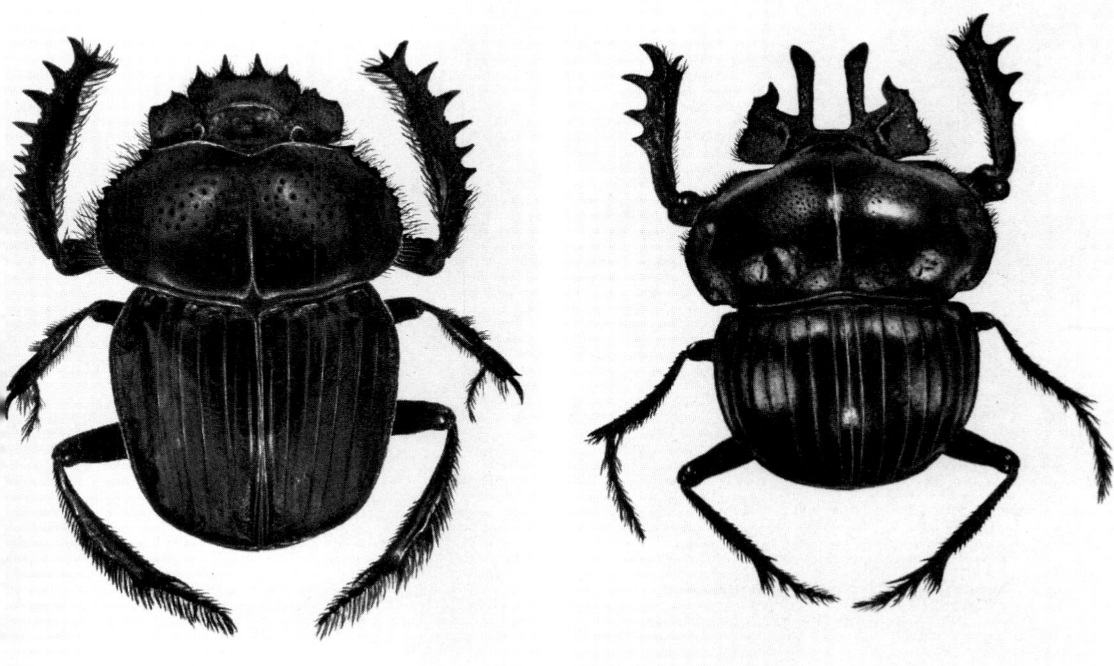

top:
99 Longicorn Beetles (Cerambycidae) with reduced elytra
left:
Callisphyris macropus from Chile; length of body 2 cm
centre and right: Wasp cerambyx *(Necydalis major)* from Europe; length of body 3.5 cm

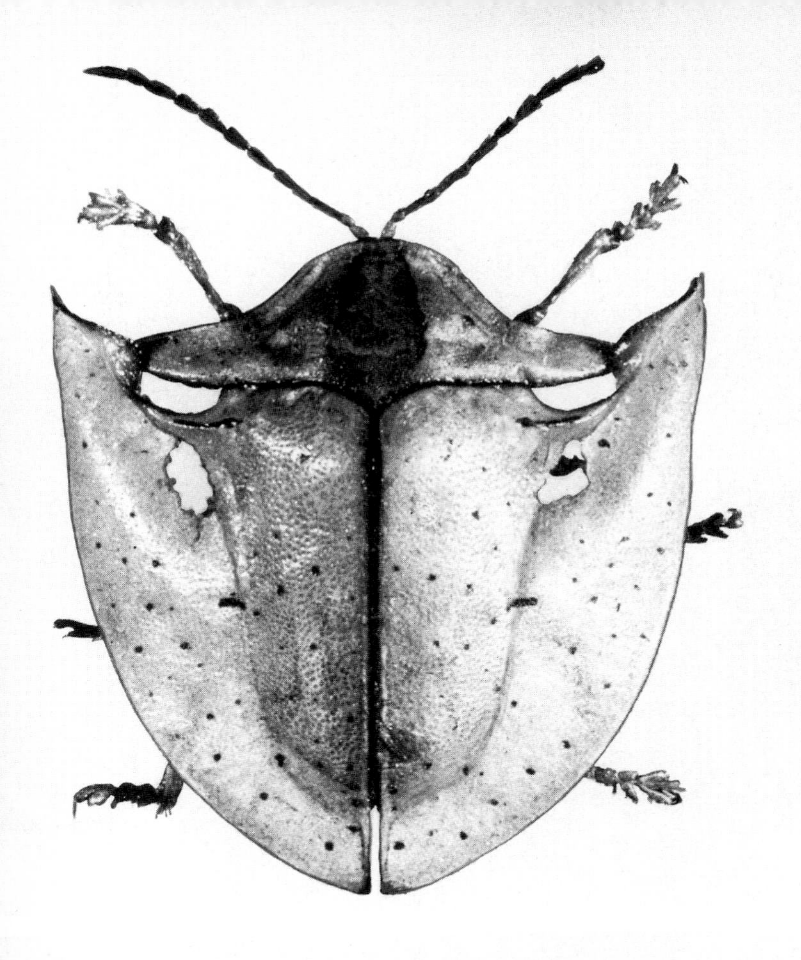

Leaf Beetles (Chrysomelidae)

102 *Selenis sparsa* from Costa Rica, South America
103 *Tauroma casta* from Central America
104 Colorado or Potato Beetle *(Leptinotarsa decemlineata)*
105 Colorado Beetle, death-feigning reflex (thanatosis)

European Leaf Beetles (Chrysomelidae)

106 *Melasoma vigintipunctata*
107 *Dlochrysa fastuosa*
108 *Galeruca tanaceti*
109 *Oulema cyanella*

Larvae of various European beetles

110 Tortoise Beetle (*Cassida* spec.) (Leaf Beetles, Chrysomelidae). Note the accumulation of skin casts.
111 Ladybird (*Scymnus* spec., Coccinellidae). This genus is frequently to be found on parsley fern *(Tanacetum)* and pine trees *(Pinus)*, with white waxy secretions:
112 *Ergates faber* of the Longicorn family (Cerambycidae), in rotting pinewood

113 Willow-leaf Beetles *(Plagiodera versicolora)* (Chrysomelidae). The larvae feed communally.
114 Ladybirds (Coccinellidae)
left: Seven-spot *(Coccinella septempunctata)*;
right: Two-spot *(Adalia bipunctata)*
115 Larvae of the Two-spot Ladybird *(Adalia bipunctata)* just hatching from the egg.

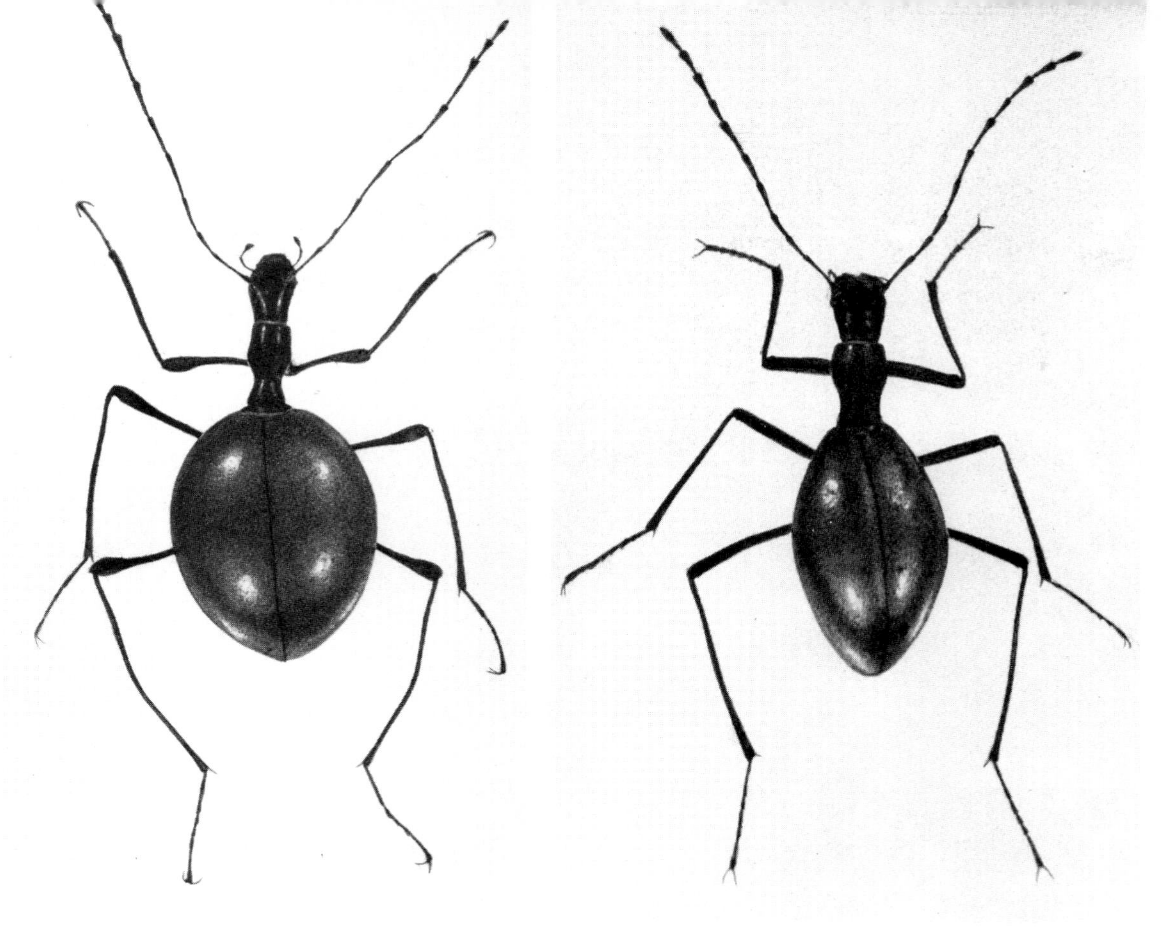

116 Pupa of Metallic Beetle *(Chalcophora mariana)* (Buprestidae) with previously constructed escape gallery filled with wood chips.
117 *Leptura rubra* (Cerambycidae), immediately after eclosion. At first it is white and takes on colour only after some hours.

Cave Beetles

118 *Leptodirus hohenwarti* from Yugoslavia (Carrion Beetles, Silphidae)
119 *Astagobius angustatus* from Yugoslavia (Carrion Beetles, Silphidae)

Desert beetles

120 *Cuphotes immaculipes* from South America (Darkling Beetles, Tenebrionidae)

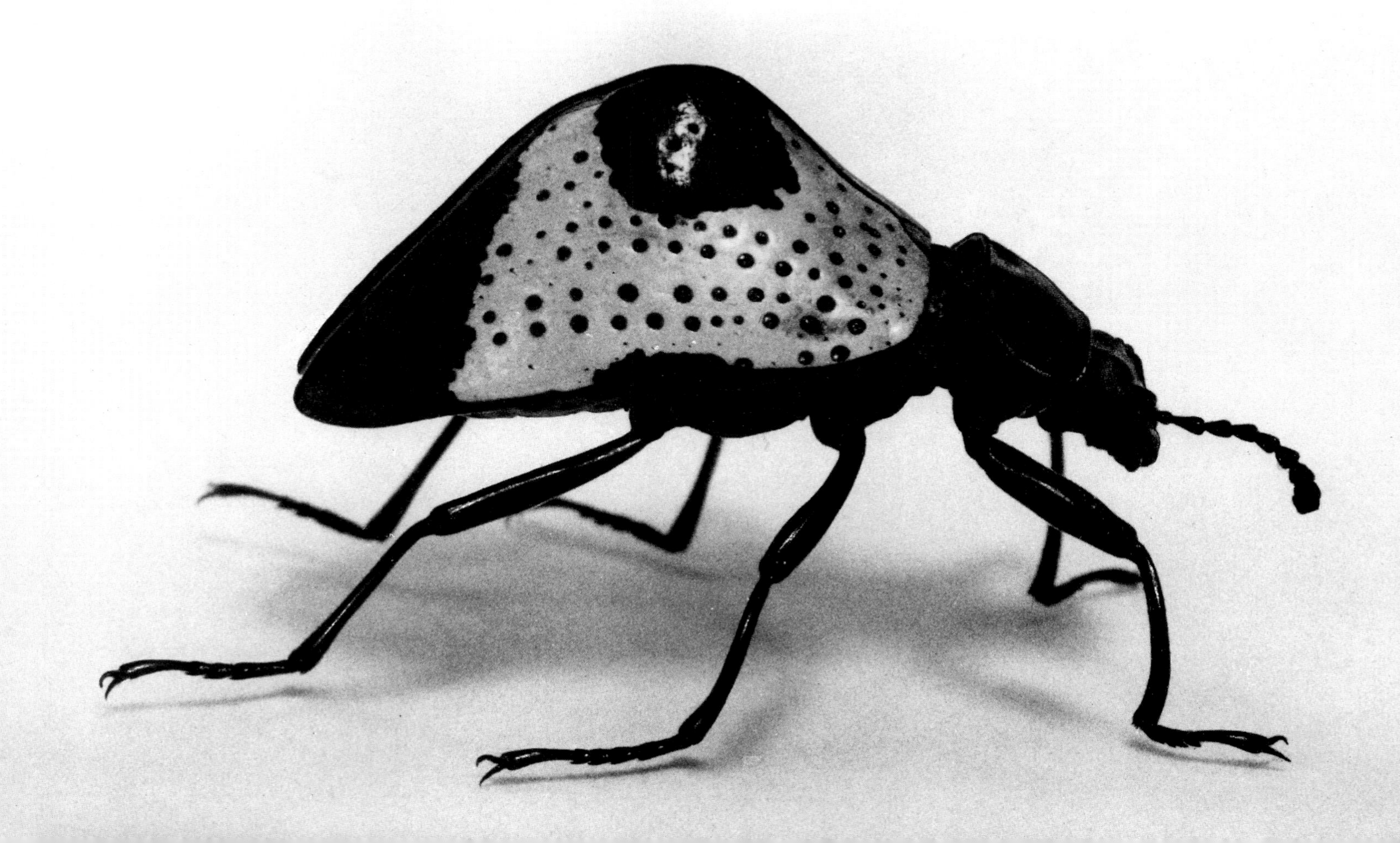

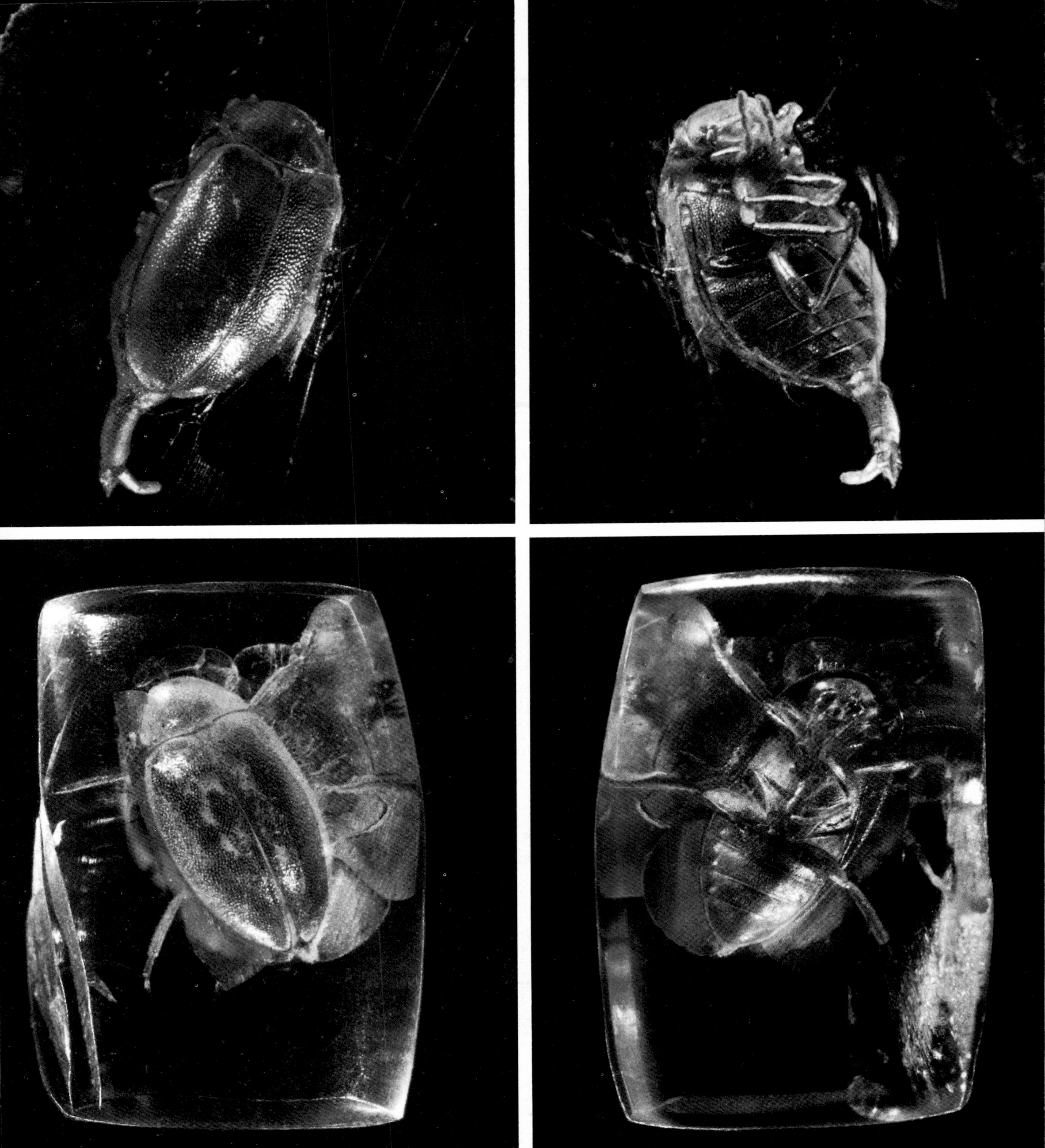

Marsh Beetles (Helodidae) in Baltic amber

121 *Helodes* spec., 0.7 cm
122 Underside
123 *Helodes setosa,* 0.6 cm
124 Underside

125 Underside of *Chlorodema primordinalis* (length about 2.7 cm), found in lignite in the Geisel Valley (German Democratic Republic). The impression glistens in several metallic colours.

126 *Damaster blaptoides* from Japan, Ground Beetles (Carabidae)
127 *Mantichora gruti* from South Africa, the largest of the Tiger Beetles (up to 7 cm)
128 *Tricondyla aptera* from the Philippines, New Guinea, is wingless and resembles a large ant.

Beetles of similar appearance but of quite distinct systematic origin

129 *Trox gigas* from Australia (Lamellicorn Beetles, Scarabaeidae)
130 *Brachycerus ocellatus* from Madagascar (Weevils, Curculionidae)

131 Darkling Beetles *(Blaps gigantoides)* (Tenebrionidae) from Central Asia are interesting, long-lived beetles suitable for keeping in an insectarium.

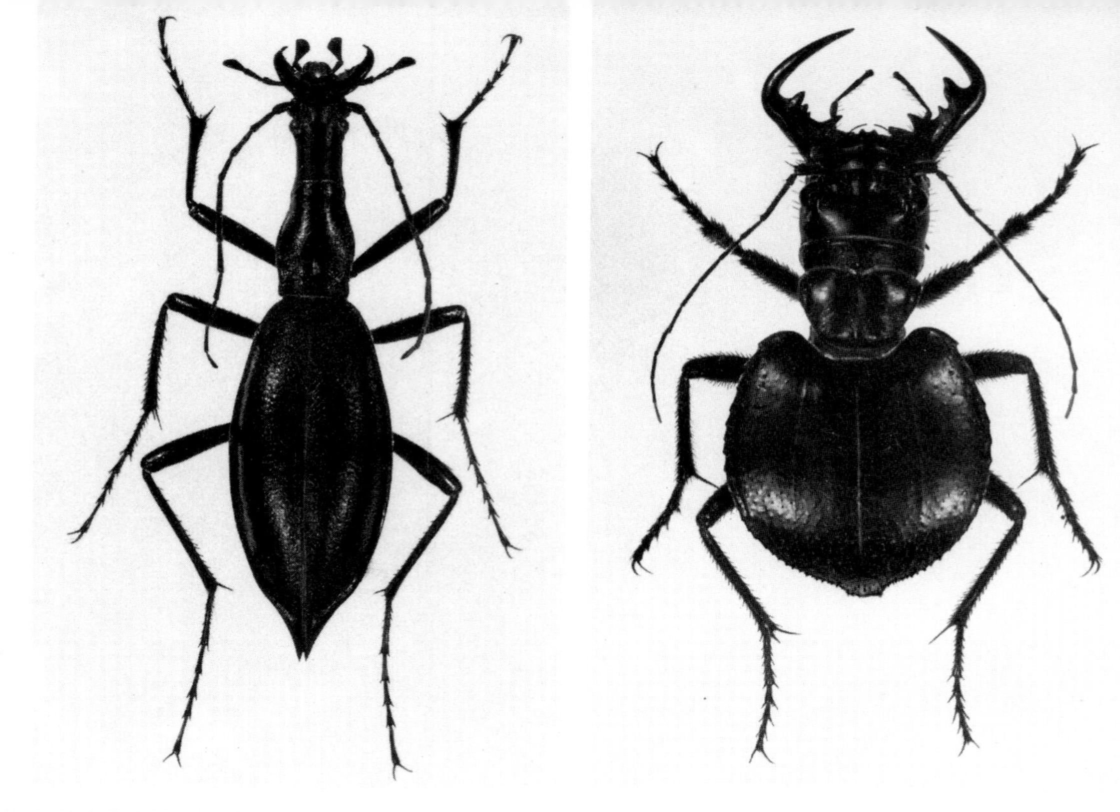

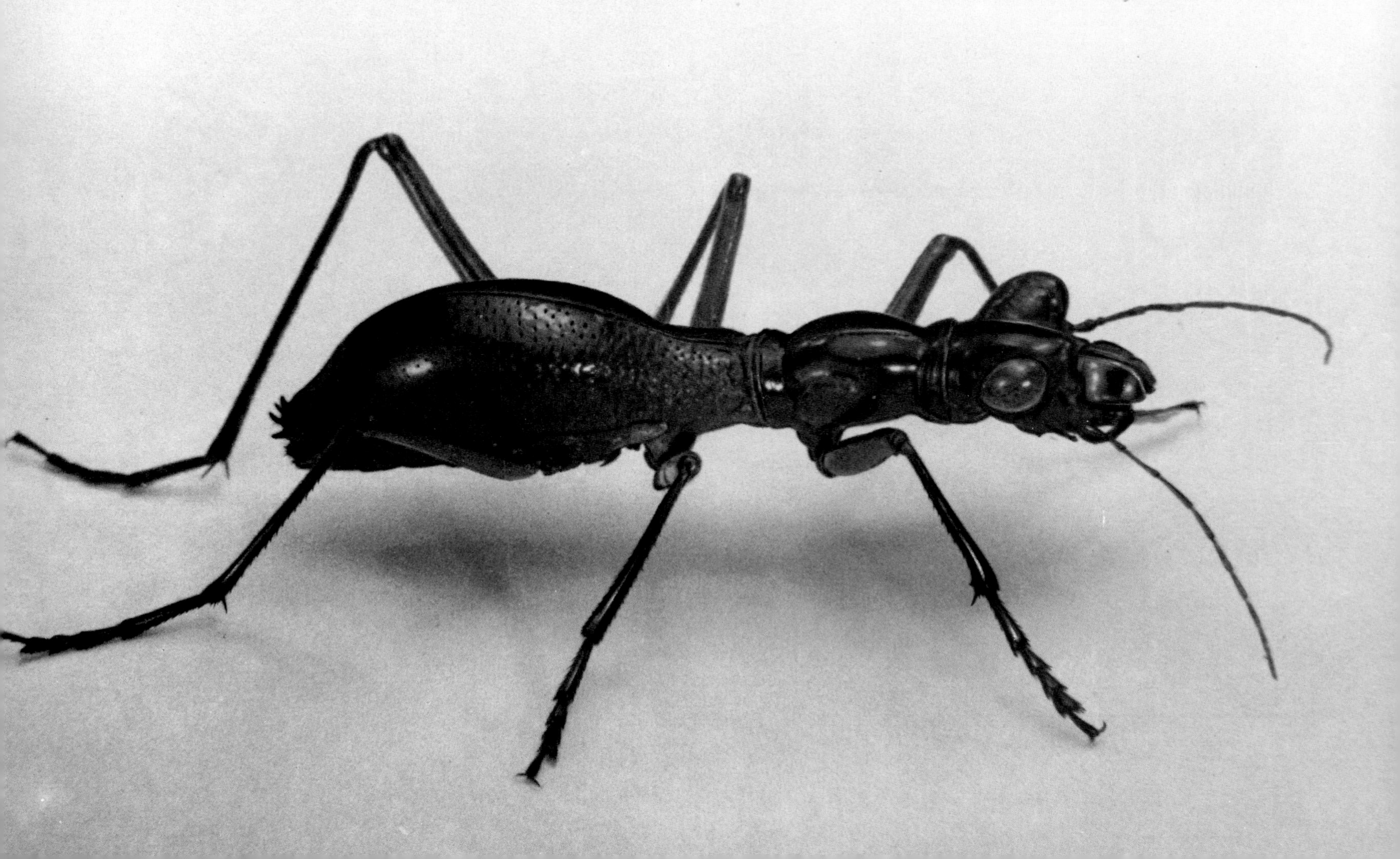

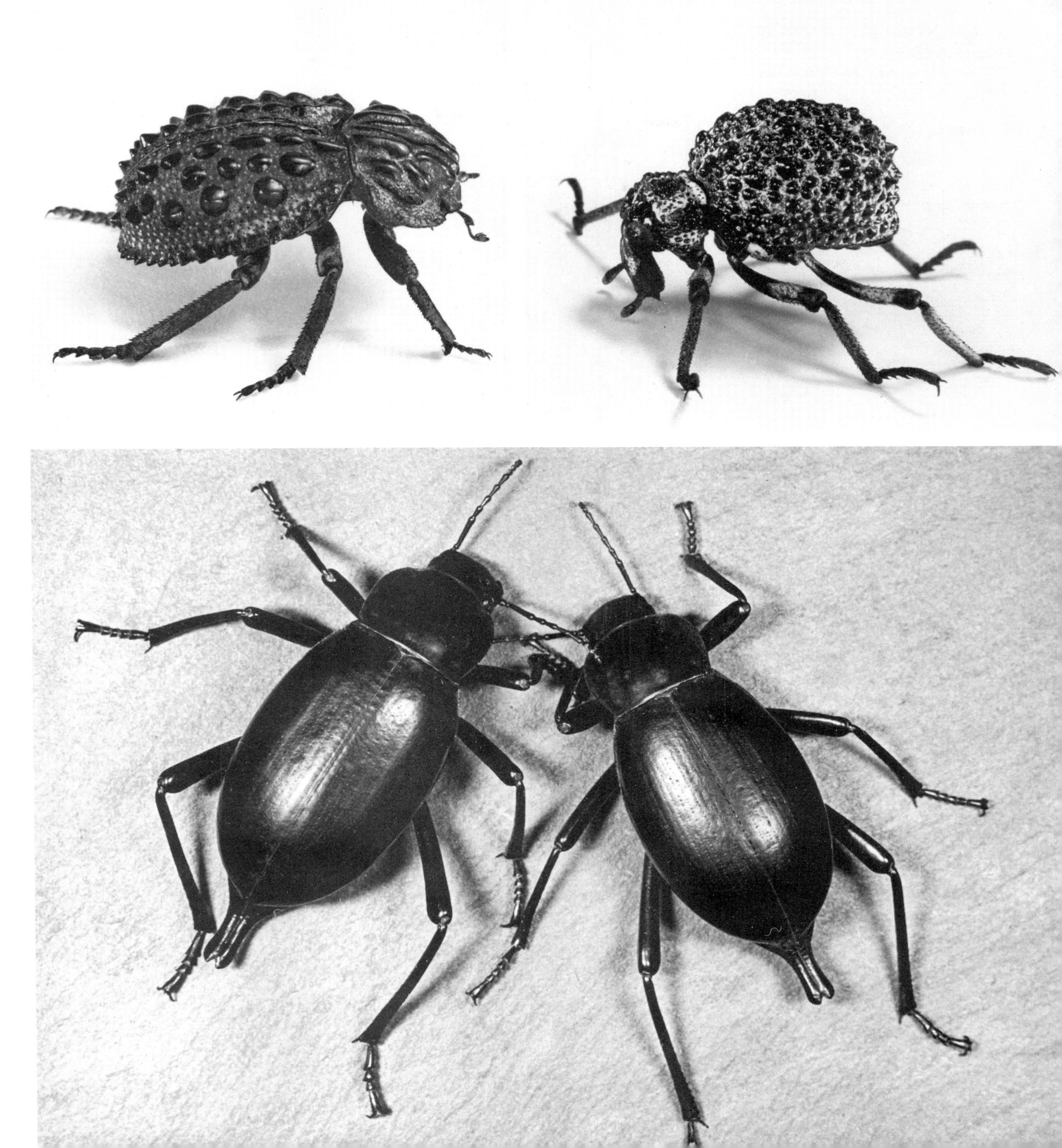

132 European Ground Beetle *(Carabus cancellatus)* (Carabidae) in the process of consuming food.

133 Tiger Beetle *(Cicindela campestris)* (Cicindelidae). These beetles are unrivalled in mobility and mainly catch flies.

134 A European Ground Beetle *Carabus cancellatus* (Carabidae) gets the better of an earthworm.

Paussid Beetles (Paussidae) that live with ants

135 *Platyrhopalopsis picteti* from China
136 *Paussus howa* from Madagascar
137 *Arthropterus melbourni* from Australia
138 *Paussus rusticus* from South West Africa (Namibia)
139/140 European Whirligig Beetle *(Gyrinus paykulli* (Gyrinidae). By making use of surface tension, it can swim on the water; below, it is seen feeding on a butterfly that has fallen into the water.

Copulation takes place under water, and certain of the species have special morphological adaptations for this function. For instance, the elytra of the females are provided with longitudinal striae. In the males, the first three segments of the fore tarsi are modified to form adhesive pads which are provided with sucker hairs, enabling the male to retain a firm hold on the pronotum of the female during copulation. The adhesive force of the pads is increased by the discharge of a glutinous secretion.

Eggs are laid under water, sometimes deposited in parts of plants. The larva also lives in water, but like the imago, depends upon a supply of air which it takes in at the surface of the water (Fig. 179).

For pupation, however, the larva makes its way on to earth near the water. From this pattern of behaviour, it can be concluded that colonization of fresh water by Dytiscidae is firmly established by a series of adaptive changes, but on the other hand, the species remain closely linked to life on land and in the air.

Whirligig Beetles (Gyrinidae)
The performances achieved in swimming by the Whirligig Beetles reach an extraordinarily high standard (Figs. 139, 140). The efficiency of their sculling apparatus is so great that this propulsive mechanism, which works on the resistance principle, is reputed to be the most effective of any to be found in the entire animal kingdom. 84 per cent of the energy applied to the water is converted into propulsive thrust (a turbine wheel achieves only 55 per cent). This extraordinary performance is based on the construction of the oar-shaped mid and hind legs. They are greatly flattened and in addition furnished along the margin with flat, flexibly arranged hair bristles. As the leg strikes back, it presents a broad surface to the water. As it is drawn forward, the margin of bristles falls back into place against the leg, collapsing like a pack of cards. In addition, the leg is turned so that the narrow edge initiates the forward movement (see Diagram p. 62). In this action, the surface area of the hind leg is reduced from 1.625 mm^2 to 0.1 mm^2, that is, by 94 per cent. The stroke frequency of the hind leg in its rowing action also achieves record figures of 50 to 60 strokes per second. The highly effective streamlining of the body and the resistance to moisture of its surface contribute to this unusual degree of mobility in water.

The Whirligig Beetles are the only beetles that live on the surface of the water. The latter represents a specific ecological segment of a body of water and is known as the neuston. The Whirligig Beetles show a number of interesting adaptations to life in this biotope. First of all, let us consider the eyes. They are divided into an upper and lower organ (Fig. 70). The fine structure of the eye is optimally adapted for vision in its appropriate medium (water, air). Four-eyed beetles are comparatively common, but in no other case does the division of the eye serve such a clearly functional purpose. Curiously enough, the Whirligigs are not able to see their insect prey as they fall upon the water, since the surface of the water lies precisely at the insect's shielded angle of vision. However, the potential prey creates short waves and these are perceived by the antennae of the Whirligigs. The antennae have a specially enlarged second segment in which a sensory organ known as Johnston's organ is located. By means of this organ, the direction of disturbance in the water surface can be perceived. And it is capable of more besides. When a beetle is swimming about on the water it creates waves. If these strike an obstacle, they are bounced back in the manner of an echo, and can be perceived by Johnston's organ, even at a speed of up to 24 cm/s. For an insect 4 to 8 mm in length, this represents a very considerable speed. In experiments, Whirligig Beetles were able to swim between wires placed so that their distance apart corresponded exactly to the width of the insect's body, without coming into contact with them. We might also mention here that not only are Whirligig Beetles the most agile of swimmers but they can also fly extremely well.

Paussid Beetles (Paussidae)
Paussid Beetles are remarkable for the curious form of their huge antennae. These consist of a basal segment topped by a large club hollowed out like a spoon (Figs. 135–138). A large number of glands opening into this cavity diffuse an aromatic secretion which is highly attractive to ants (for example *Pheidole*) and termites. The ants attempt to increase the flow of the secretions by tapping the antennae of the beetles. All Paussid Beetles inhabit the nest of the two groups of insects mentioned above and feed on the eggs and young of their hosts. A single Paussid Beetle has been observed to suck out the bodies of ten ant larvae in five minutes. Because of the ants' enjoyment of the sweet secretions, there is much jostling to get to the "drug trafficker," even resulting in battles in which the creature is dragged through the nest, and in the course of which the reflexes and instincts which provide for the protection of the brood seem temporarily to be lost.

In all there are about 1,000 species in this family, most of which grow to a length of one or at most two centimetres; they occur for the most part in tropical regions.

Telephone-pole Beetles (Micromalthidae)
In their manner of reproduction, the Micromalthidae are probably the most remarkable beetles in the world. As far as is known, there is only one species, *Micromalthus debilis*, which originally came from North America, and has been carried from there in timber exports to various parts of the earth, to Africa, for example. *Micromalthus debilis* lives in fungus-infested hard and soft-wood timber, which also provides its food.

The first larval stage has legs and provides for the distribution of the species. But first of all the female larvae of the first stage devour their mothers, then move about for some days on the breeding substratum, and after that they begin to chew their way into damp, fungus-infested wood. There, after a while, they cast their skin, developing into a second type of larva without legs. (An alternation of larval type of this kind is called hypermetamorphosis.)

This larva bores passages into the wood and moults at least three times. Finally a third larval type develops which has a relatively small head and takes in no nourishment. (The intestinal tract and mouthparts are reduced or vestigial.) This larval stage is capable of reproduction without the participation of males, that is, parthogenetically. This kind of parthogenetic reproduction by an immature organism is known as paedogenesis. Propagation can occur in three different ways:

1. Female larvae are born.
2. An egg is laid, from which a larva develops which finally develops into a male beetle.
3. First of all an egg of this kind is laid, and subsequently female larvae can be born.

The first case has been described above. In case 2, a single egg only is laid from which a legless larva hatches, which then proceeds to feed exclusively on its parent. When the mother has been devoured, the larva moults to produce a pre-pupal stage furnished with leg stumps, followed by a pupa from which emerges a male beetle which has a haploid (simple) chromosome complement. A proportion of the female larvae do not reproduce paedogenetically, but progress through a prepupal stage without leg stumps directly from the second larval type to a pupa, from which a female beetle develops. As far as is known, these beetles are not fertile. Any eggs laid are abnormally large and do not develop further. In this species, the imago is clearly a relict and has no longer any significance whatever for the preservation of the species. This mode of reproduction is unique within the insect kingdom.

Micromalthus debilis Lec. (Micromalthidae), diagram of developmental cycle

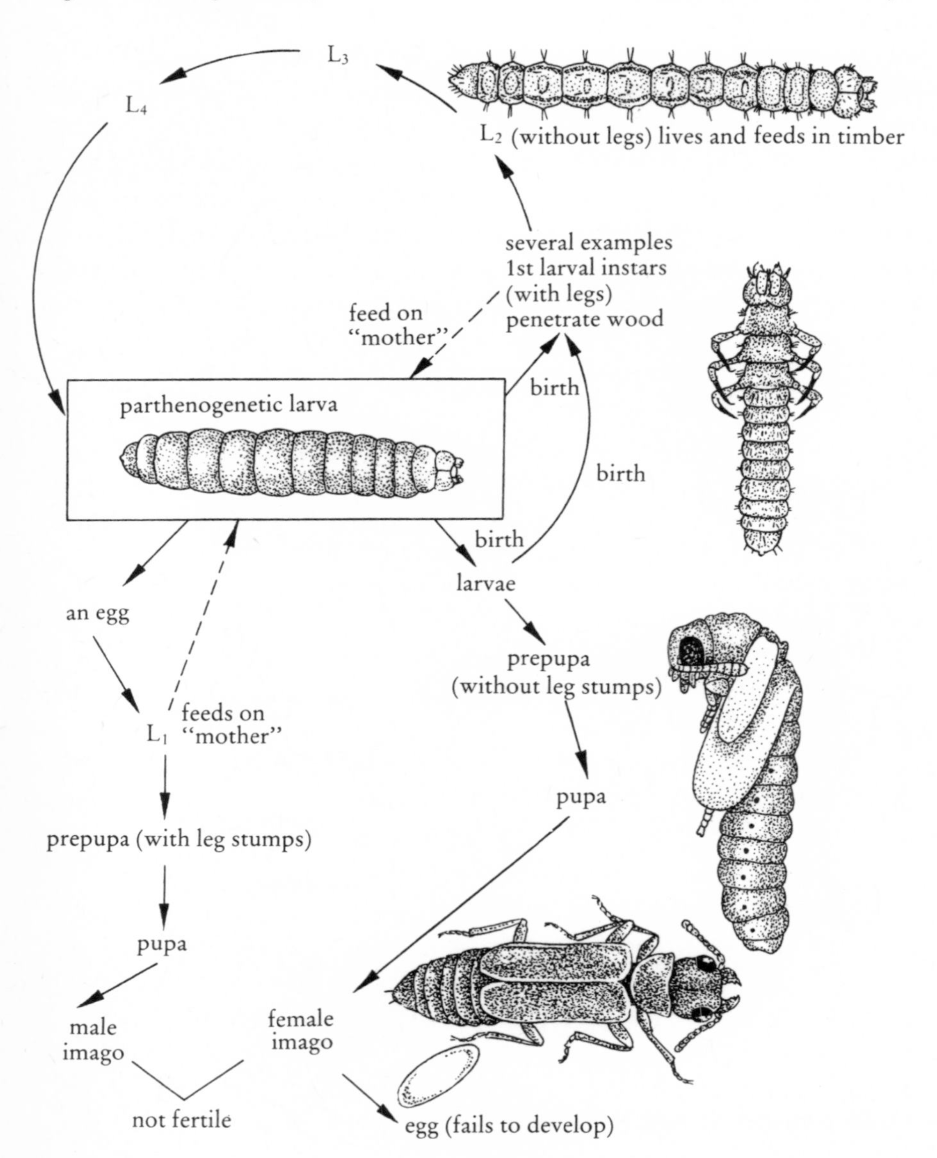

Mammal-nest Beetles (Leptinidae)

All ten species of Mammal-nest Beetles known to man live in some way in the company of rodents, usually mice. One species known as the Beaver Louse *(Platypsyllus castoris)* lives in the fur of the beaver and, with the latter, is distributed across the entire Holarctic region. This species of beetle is highly adapted to life in the fur of its host. The body is flattened dorso-ventrally (in contrast to fleas which to some extent also live in the coats of mammals but in which the body is compressed laterally), the provision of spines and the construction of the tarsi make it possible to maintain a firm hold in the fur, eyes are absent. Even when the beaver enters the water, the beetles are in little danger of drowning. A quantity of air always remains trapped in the beaver's fur which is adequate for the respiratory requirements of a beetle only 2 to 3 mm in length. The larvae also live on the host, although eggs are laid and pupation takes place in the earth of the beaver's lodge. Occasionally, forty or more Beaver Lice have been found on a single dead beaver. The beetles probably feed on a species of ectoparasitic mite living mainly in the corners of the mouth, ears and genital region of the beaver. When this beetle was discovered in 1869, the aberrant structure of its body caused it to be placed in a quite different order of insects, namely that of Bird Lice (Mallophaga).

Feather-winged Beetles (Ptiliidae)
The Feather-winged Beetles constitute one of the most curious families of beetles (see p. 19). One of their most striking characteristics is their size, or rather their minuteness. The largest species reaches the "gigantic" dimensions of 1.2 mm. Because of their extreme smallness, little is known about their biology. They probably feed on fungus spores. For this reason, they usually colonize habitats in which there is a rich fungoid flora, such as among decaying vegetable matter, compost, rotting timber. Many interesting phenomena in the life of the Feather-winged Beetles still remain to be explained, such as the reason for the simultaneous occurrence of winged and wingless, eyed and eyeless forms within the same species.

Glow-worms and Fireflies (Lampyridae)
The most outstanding feature of this family of beetles, which with more than 2,000 species is distributed across the entire earth, is its capacity to emit light (Figs. 61, 143). But in addition, the Lampyridae are of particular interest because the females of almost every species have more or less reduced wings. In many cases, no wings at all remain and the creatures resemble beetle larvae. It is also noteworthy that the larvae are carnivorous, usually being keen hunters of snails and slugs. If as they move about, they come upon a track of slime secreted by a slug, they follow it until they find their prey, which is seized, injected with a poisonous secretion and devoured. In dealing with snails, the larvae exhibit extraordinary perseverance. If, after the first bite, the snail withdraws into its shell, the larva will sit waiting on the rim for many hours until the snail reappears, when the attack is renewed. The imago takes no food, so the larva has the task of being "sole provider."

Drilid Beetles (Drilidae)
Like glow-worms and fireflies, Drilid Beetles specialize in preying on snails (in their case exclusively snails and not slugs). The larvae usually discover their prey by means of the slime track which they follow. Once the snail has been found, the larva climbs upon the shell, gaining a firm hold by means of a

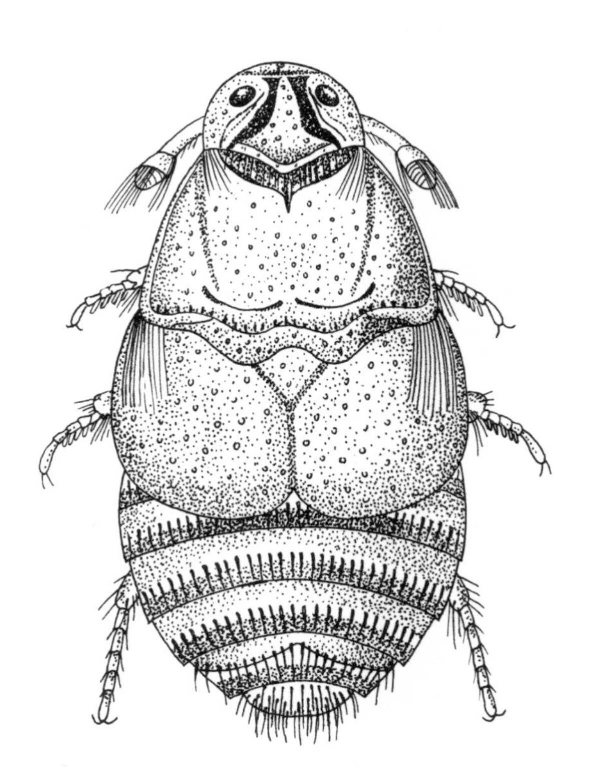

Beaver Louse *Platypsyllus castoris* Rits. (Leptinidae)

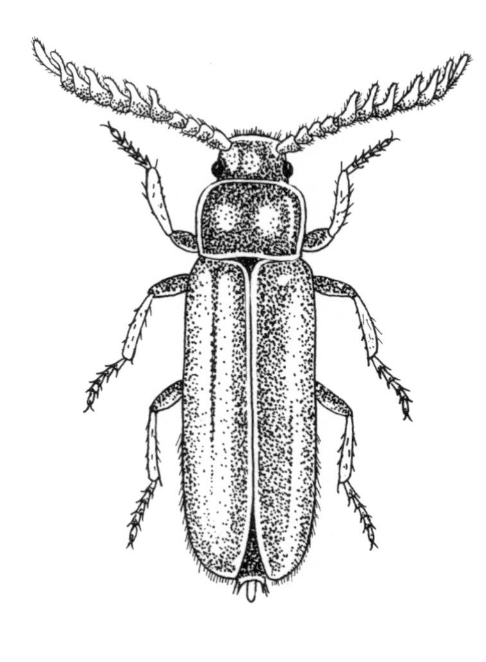

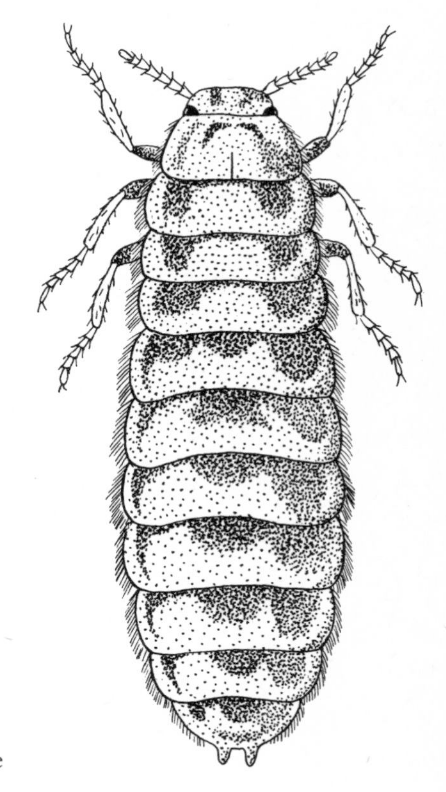

Drilus flavescens Geoffr. (Drilidae), left male, right female

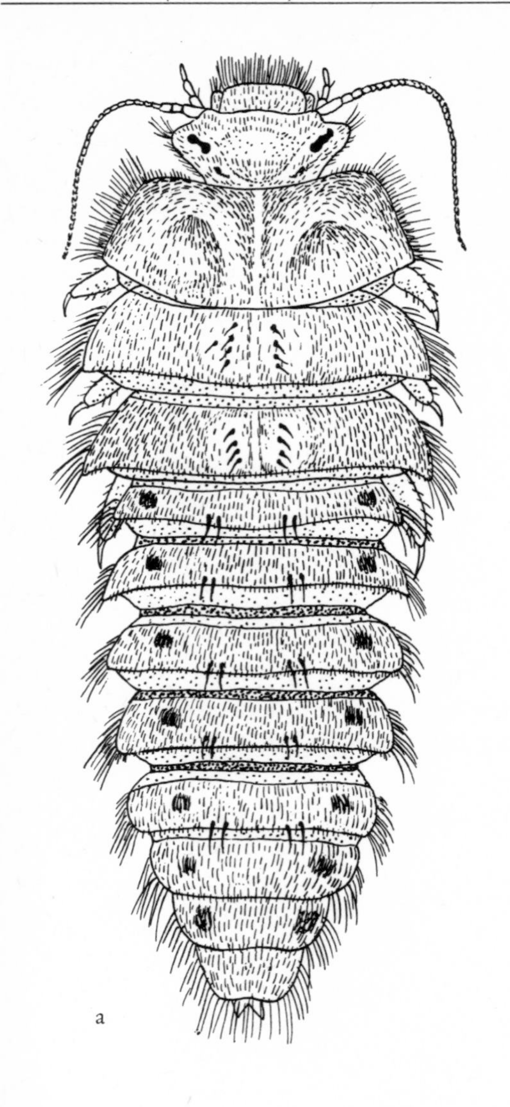

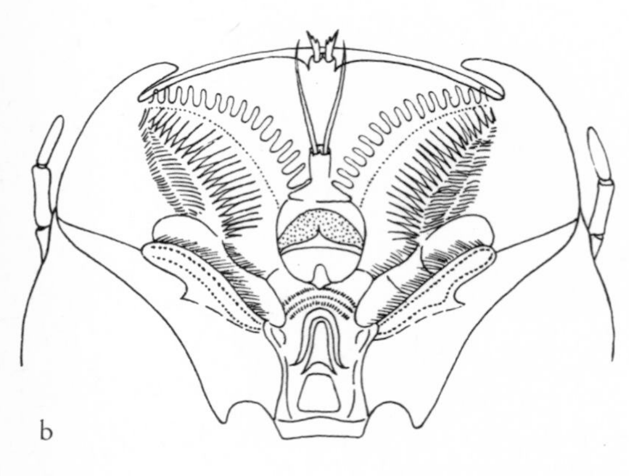

Marsh Beetles (Helodidae)
a) Larva of *Helodes hausmanni* Gredler
b) Hypopharynx of *Hydrocyphon deflexicollis* Müller

special organ, the pygopodium situated at the end of the body, and bites the snail, usually attacking its feelers. The secretion injected with the bite soon brings about the death of the snail. Apparently the dead snail is now carried off, the larva once more making use of its pygopodium. Finally it begins to devour the snail. For this purpose, it creeps into the shell. A dense covering of bristly hairs protects the larva, preventing its respiratory spiracles from being obstructed by the snail's slime. The hair covering and special posterior processes also enable the larva to carry out a thorough cleaning of the interior of the shell. Snail shells are used by larvae both as a retreat for short lengths of time during their periods of activity and as winter quarters. When the larva spends the winter there it seals the opening of the shell with the skin from the previous larval moult. In the course of development, the Drilid larvae show considerable differences in form. The mobile summer forms which set out actively in search of food are followed by the inactive, dormant forms of the winter hibernation. Both morphs alter several times, since a male larva requires two and a female three years for complete metamorphosis. And of course, as the larvae increase in size, they seek out progressively larger prey. Other noteworthy features are that, like the majority of the female Lampyrid Beetles, the female Drilid Beetles are devoid of wings, and that they attract the males by emitting a specific scent.

Marsh Beetles (Helodidae)

The Marsh Beetles are an utterly inconspicuous, little-known family of beetles, and yet they have many features of exceptional interest. They are probably the only beetles in the world to have their obligate habitat in very small bodies of water that collect in hollows in vegetation (phytothelms). Pools of this kind may form in the hollows of trees or in the leaf sheaths of bromeliaceous plants. Both types of pool may be inhabited by a varied assortment of different species of Helodids, and the wide variety within the family, particularly in the tropics, is the result of the large numbers of phytothelms occurring in forests. In Europe, the species *Prionocyphon serricornis* specializes exclusively in living in phytothelms. The larvae of this species do not exist in any other body of water. The forests of the Amber era were probably also very rich in habitats of this kind. This can still be seen today from the comparative frequency with which these beetles occur in amber. Marsh Beetles that lived in phytothelms are found enclosed in amber more frequently than any other species.

The feeding habits of the larvae of the Helodid Beetle are also interesting. Their food consists of matter which sinks to the bottom of the water or else settles on underwater vegetation. The larvae of other beetles ignore these sediments, but the Helodid larvae take them up using a special organ of their mouthparts, the hypopharynx (a structure which, in its position, can perhaps best be compared to a tongue). In adaptation to its particular use, the hypopharynx has a very curious construction. There is a series of small denticles and rows of bristles to sift through the sedimental matter, and in the different species, they differ in form, depending upon the grain size of the material to be processed. It might be interesting to look more closely at the process of ingestion. It consists of four phases which follow one another almost automatically, of which the first and third, and the second and fourth coincide, so that food is taken in in a two-stroke rhythm.

1st phase: food is drawn in with a wide, sweeping action of the maxillae;
2nd phase: the food particles are taken over by the collecting apparatus of the hypopharynx;
3rd phase: the food is passed back to the grinding area;
4th phase: the food is prepared in the grinding area.

The amount of food taken in by the larvae is very large, since the sedimental materials contain a great deal of indigestible ballast and only a small portion of valuable organic matter. On the other hand, the considerable mobility and size of the larvae demands an adequate supply of energy. Therefore the intake of food must proceed at great speed. Food is drawn in 70 to 80 times per minute. The upper part of the intestinal canal works like a suction pump, sucking the processed and concentrated food from the mouth cavity through the oesophagus into the central intestine, in which digestion takes place. The presence of large amounts of ballast material makes rapid passage essential, so that the larvae produce considerable quantities of excrement.

Minute Mud Beetles (Georyssidae)
In their manner of feeding, the Minute Mud Beetles also show themselves to be exceptions to the normally familiar pattern of beetle behaviour. The larva and the imago of this family live in wet, sandy mud on the edge of water. They eat this mud and, like the Marsh Beetles, have to ingest great quantities in order to obtain adequate nourishment from the meagre amount of organic material contained in it. It is in just such a way that earthworms feed, and like them, the Minute Mud Beetles excrete comparatively large quantities of faecal matter.

Nosodendrid Beetles (Nosodendridae)
Only 30 species of Nosodendrid Beetles are known to exist in the whole world, but there is something very special about them. The larvae are specially adapted to live in the sap which flows from trees, even in resin, and to feed on this sap. This particular food substratum attracts large numbers of beetles, but none is so well adapted to living in it as the Nosodendrid Beetle. At the end of the abdomen it has special respiratory orifices which can be held clear of the substratum for the purpose of gaseous interchange. The juices of plants make for a very one-sided diet, but symbiotic microorganisms help to extend the dietary range of the Nosodendrid Beetle.

Furniture Beetles
including Deathwatch Beetles (Anobiidae)
Most people are familiar with "wood worms." Costly pieces of furniture and valuable wood carvings by great masters have not infrequently fallen victim to them. The larvae have bored their way into the solid wood, creating a network of channels. The beetles reveal their presence by small heaps of sawdust that fall from the round exit holes they make. How is it possible for a beetle larva to live at all on a substratum such as wood, which is poor in nutrients and sometimes hundreds of years old? The secret lies in the fact that they have assistants to help in the preparation of food and also to provide additional substance to it. They are yeast-like microorganisms which live within the larvae and imagines of the Furniture Beetles in cells situated in protrusions of the central intestine. It is important for the preservation of the species that these symbionts should be transferred to the progeny. Close to their egg-laying organ (ovipositor) the females have long tubes into which they introduce symbionts immediately after emergence from the pupa. There they are stored until the beetle is sexually mature. When the eggs are laid, the surface of the egg is smeared with symbionts from the "store room." The hatching larva eats part of the egg covering, thus infesting itself in a process which is vitally important for the young larva. If infestation by symbionts is prevented experimentally, the larva dies.

There is another characteristic of the Deathwatch Beetle which is of great interest, and that is the production of sound. It is this feature which has provided the beetle with its popular name of Deathwatch Beetle. The tapping noise came to be associated with the approach of death, and it even obtained official recognition as a sign of death, in a plague ordinance drawn up in 1594 in Lucerne. The tapping is heard most frequently in the reproductive season, and is presumably part of a courtship ritual. The beetles (both sexes) draw in their antennae and strike the lower part of the front of the head against the ground of the boring tunnel. In this way they are capable of producing quite a loud noise. Many species tap five times in a second. The sound of one beetle tapping stimulates others, and they can be heard to answer one another. It is even possible to induce beetles to reply to artificially created sounds. It is scarcely surprising that the tapping of the beetle has attracted the attention of observers from the earliest times, and that they have attempted to explain and interpret it. There is, for instance, the legend of the seer, Melampus, a character from Greek mythology. He understood the language of

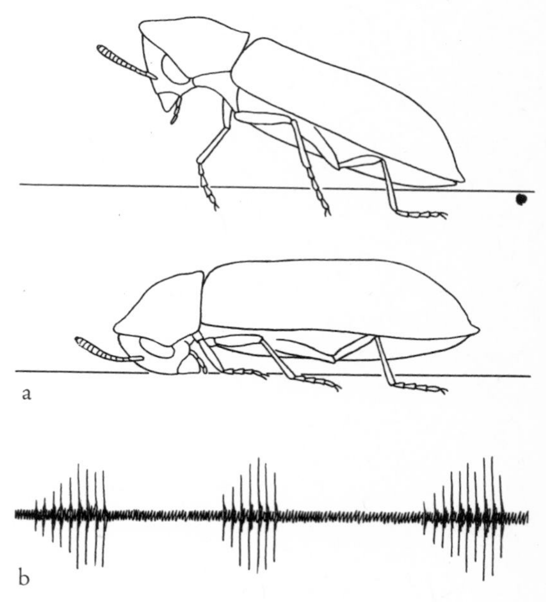

Deathwatch Beetles (Anobiidae)
a) *Xestobium* sp., female, natural size about 5 mm, taps with head every 7 to 8 seconds
b) Oscillogram of three series of taps made by the Deathwatch Beetle *Xestobium rufovillosum* Deg. (Speed of film 10 m/s)

many animals, even that of the larvae of the Deathwatch Beetle. Once, as he sat in prison, he heard the "wood-worms" talking together in the ceiling timbers of his cell and telling how the roof would very soon collapse. Melampus demanded to be moved to a different place of imprisonment, and this was done. And as he had foreseen, the roof did indeed fall in soon afterwards. An example of how these creatures have occupied the mind of man in a different context can be seen in the writings of the Wittenberg Professor of Theology Wolfgang Franz, who, in his *Animalium Historia Sacra* (1612) wrote: "Teredines or Scolices are those small creatures which come into being in wooden beams, which they gnaw, and with much noise, bore through the hard timbers. Within the beams, they originate from other small worms, as certain writers clearly show, although others are of the opinion that they originate from dirt. Although they bore through the beams incessantly, yet as soon as they come to the end of the beam, they perish. And these insects are symbols of those men who direct all their thoughts and energies to the increase of their fortunes.

1. As the wood-worms bore into beams with great zeal, in just such a way do they hasten through mountains, through great heat, across oceans and continents.
2. As the wood-worms, when they have made their way right through the beam, surely perish, in just such a way do those men perish who have gathered together great treasures, often dying suddenly without having tasted a single fruit of their endeavours. One such wood-worm was Alexander the Great, who endured unprecedented hardships to bring the whole world into subjection. But what did it profit him? After those hardships and many valiant deeds, he met a sudden death in Babylon. Another such wood-worm was Julius Caesar, who wanted to rule over all the earth, but who met an early death from 23 wounds. Quoting from the Holy Scriptures (Proverbs 17), Nazianzenus compares the wood-worm with care. Just as wood-worms hollow out trees causing their destruction, so too care and anxiety breaks the spirit and 'drieth the bones' of man."

Rhipiphorid Beetles (Rhipiphoridae)

The Rhipiphorid Beetles are some of the most curious beetles that exist. Their German name *Fächerkäfer* (Fan Beetles) refers to the large fan-shaped or flabellate antennae of the male. The elytra of most of the species are more or less reduced and gape widely; in many species, the females are devoid of wings. These and other peculiarities of structure have led many writers to consider them to be closely related to the Stylopids (Strepsiptera). There is much in favour of the view that the Strepsiptera should be treated as a separate order (as are beetles). But if they are to be considered as belonging to the Coleoptera, then they are probably best placed near the Rhipiphoridae. This view is frequently supported by reference to similarities in their biology. Both groups are parasitic on other insects. The Rhipiphorid Beetles have developed very complicated and specialized habits (see p. 124).

Stag Beetles (Lucanidae)

This family of beetles is probably one of the best known of all, not least because it includes the largest of the Central European beetles, the European Stag Beetle *(Lucanus cervus)* (Fig. 149). Throughout the whole family, it is possible to observe a tendency towards the enlargement and special development of the mandibles in the males, and moreover, the males are almost always larger than the females (sexual dimorphism) (Figs. 93, 150, 151). The beetles are fond of licking the sap oozing from tree scars. The larvae of most species inhabit the rotting wood of trees and often require several years to complete their larval development. As do many other timber dwelling beetles, Stag Beetles exhibit great variation in size among individuals of the same species (Fig. 24).

Stag Beetles have always aroused a good deal of interest among nature lovers, as can be seen from the many references made to them even in very early literature. Schwenckfeld, for example, writes: "The Stag Beetle develops out of dry wood, particularly the wood of the oak tree, and in part also breeds by impregnation. It lives in oak forests in May and during the summer." *Ortus sanitatis* (1480) contains the following on the subject of Stag Beetles: "Towards evening they fly about in large numbers with much noise. They have large horns that can be used for medicinal purposes and which are furrowed and toothed and also have a lustrous sheen, and which they use like pincers. Their legs are long and bent back, and shine in the night like rotten wood. Their sides and hind parts often gleam in the colours of bird's plumage and are sometimes dark."

Both of these texts bear witness to a considerable gift for the observation of natural life. And yet each account also contains a very curious statement. They both write (as does Brückmann also): "If the head is separated from the body, both parts remain alive, the head for a longer time than the body."

An extraordinarily detailed account of the biology of the Stag Beetle is given by Franz Ernst Brückmann, a physician from Wolfenbüttel (1696–1753). "Like all animals, they multiply by copulation. In the process, the male and female are turned away from one another . . . Some time after pairing, the females lay eggs which are hatched by the warmth of the sun. No exact figure can be given for the number of eggs laid . . . The males enjoy fighting and often engage in combat, like stags at rutting time. In the autumn, with the approach of the winter cold, they are no longer to be seen, for at this time, a natural instinct drives them to prepare winter quarters. These are round or oval cells which they construct ingeniously out of damp and soft clayey soil not very far down beneath oak trees. The inside of the cell is smooth, and the beetle lies in it on its back, its legs on top, firmly pressed to its abdomen, spending the whole winter asleep without food and without any sign of life."

Brückmann's writing shows us that a new age has dawned for biology, which seeks to liberate natural phenomena, and thus the Stag Beetle as well, from all mystical elements. The time in which a magic talisman was made bearing a representation of a stag beetle trying to seize a tortoise in its mandibles; when in Turkey stag beetle horn mixed with dried desert lizard was sold as a specific against witchcraft or when stag beetles flying at night were held to be witches, is now finally at an end. In spite of this, or perhaps precisely because of it, these creatures have retained the interest and attention of men right up to the present day.

Lamellicorn Beetles (Scarabaeidae)

The Lamellicorns represent a family of beetles with a wide variation of forms and a very large number of species (20,500 species). They include such well-known creatures as Cockchafers, June Beetles, Rose Chafers, Dung Beetles, Scarabs, Goliath Beetles, Hercules Beetles and Rhinoceros Beetles (Figs. 10–22, 25–30, 35, 40–43, 85, 97, 98, 100, 101, 129, 145, 152–156). It is not only in their external form that the representatives of the Lamellicorns differ considerably, but also and perhaps to an even greater extent, in their way of life. There have been numerous attempts to dissociate this very varied family into a large number of smaller families. Let us consider the Cockchafer or May Bug in rather greater detail.

Already today, Cockchafers are something of a rarity. There are many children who have never seen one, and perhaps only know them as chocolate novelties wrapped in silver paper, or else from pictures. The reason for this drastic decline in their numbers almost certainly lies in the widespread use of plant-protective pesticides, which, although they are probably not employed primarily against Cockchafers, nevertheless also affect them together with other insects. Text books used by the crop protection services to agriculture and forestry cite common and woodland Cockchafers as highly destructive pests, and at one time they certainly were. Even a few decades ago, they could be gathered up by the hundredweight without difficulty, and were used as animal feed. But in earlier centuries, cockchafers were much more of a problem. And the farmers had no means whatever of dealing with them. So it is not surprising that ecclesiastical courts should have turned their attention to the plagues of cockchafers. Let us hear what an old report has to say on the subject. The first lawsuit against cockchafers for which documentary evidence exists took place in 1320 before the ecclesiastical court in Avignon.

"Two arch-priests, ceremonially robed, made their way to the stricken estate, and in the name of the Ecclesiastical Court, summoned all cockchafers still in their minority to appear before the Bishop, threatening them with excommunication should they not appear. At the same time, copies of the summons were posted up on boards facing the four cardinal points, informing them that a legal adviser and defending counsel, in the person of the procurator, had been duly appointed. The latter then stated in the name of his clients who had failed to appear for the legal proceedings within the allotted time, that they, like every other creature created by God must lay claim to their right to seek their food where it was to be found, and excused their non-appearance on the grounds that nobody had thought to provide them with a guarantee of safe conduct to and from the place of judgement, as was the custom. The sentence was that the cockchafers were to withdraw within three days to a particular field marked out by boards, at which place there was an adequate supply of food for them, and that those who contravened this decision, were to be treated as outlaws and exterminated."

Later on, other lawsuits were brought against cockchafers, one, for instance, in 1497 before the Ecclesiastical Court in Lausanne, and again in the same place in 1579. Occasionally there are reports in old documents of the multiplication of cockchafer populations on a massive scale. For example, Thomas Mouffet, an English physician (1550–1599 or 1604) wrote: "According to an English chronicle, on 24 February 1574, cockchafers fell into the River Sabrina in such vast numbers that the wheels of the water mills were blocked and brought to a halt, and had not hens, ducks, goatsuckers, falcons, bats and other birds of prey come to man's aid, the mill wheels would doubtless still be motionless today." The date given for the event seems rather surprising,not only in view of the presence of cockchhafers, but also that of goatsuckers and bats.

Longicornia (Longhorn, Longicorn or Capricorn Beetles) (Cerambycidae)

With 26,000 species, the Longicorn Beetles are among those families of beetles with the largest number of species (Figs. 8, 44–49, 67, 68, 76, 86, 90, 91, 94–96, 99, 157–159, 162, 184, 188, 204). They are extremely popular with collectors and photographers. Mention of them is made in writings dating from very early times. On the subject of their biology, Aristotle says: "In the same way, longhorn beetles develop from the worms in dry wood; their worm also lies motionless at first for some time, then breaks open its integument and becomes a beetle." In the writings of Thomas Mouffet we find a detailed description of the Musk Beetle (*Aromia moschata*), which has something of the quality of fable. "The Platyceros or Wood Tick has a broad head and great ox-eyes. It is almost three fingers wide. The mouth is forked and dreadful to behold when the two powerful teeth stand open. By means of these, so the experts tell us, it produces a pig-like grunting as it bores into wood. It is also said that when fastened on to trees, they will keep pests at bay by this same action. The ivory-smooth, handle like shoulders with their fine sculpting are very noticeable. They have six legs, each with three joints. The legs, however, are too weak and too limp to carry the great weight of the body. As an aid to them, two horns project from above the eyes, which are longer than the body and consist of 9 to 10 flexible segments. They are not completely smooth but somewhat roughened like goat-horn. In flight, they serve as a rudder, on the ground as legs. As if conscious of its weakness, this beetle hangs itself by its horns to the branch of a tree and remains resting that way, as Bruerus has observed near Heidelberg."

Early classical authors give accounts of large longicorn beetles (they probably refer to *Cerambyx*) being tied on to fruit trees by country people, where their loud stridulation was believed to ward off injurious beetles. A cruel measure which will certainly have proved to be of no avail. One of the most detailed accounts from earlier times of the biology of the longicorn beetle is that written by August Johann Roesel von Rosenhof (1705–1759). His *Insekten-Belustigungen* (Insect Entertainments) brought him world renown, both on account of his masterly representations of the creatures and also the extraordinary precision of his text. Over several pages he describes the biology of the Hazel-nut Beetle (*Saperda linearis*). The following is a small sample of his writing. "Another distinguished patron and amateur of my work, who last May honoured me with his custom, brought me at the same time a few dry twigs from a hazel-nut bush, in which there was an orange-yellow worm, which we can see in Plate III, Fig.1, and which had bored a hole through the core of the twig and now lay with its head directed downwards, but did not yet appear to be full-grown. The other, stouter branch was likewise deeply holed, but instead of the worm, contained a yellow pupa which lay with its head upwards. Both twigs had been split and opened with the greatest care in order that the worm and pupa could be seen and the aperture made in them could be closed up again with the portion that had been removed, so that the two insects could be preserved safely and carefully until the time of their metamorphosis."

Leaf Beetles (Chrysomelidae)

Like the Longicorns, Leaf Beetles also feed exclusively on plants. There is indeed no species of higher plant that may not be attacked by Leaf Beetles. In contrast to Longicorns, most of the Leaf Beetles are small to minute. With some 35,000 species they are the second largest family of beetles and have representatives in every part of the world (Fig. 52, 102–109, 146, 161, 186).

Weevils or Snout Beetles (Curculionidae) *in the wider sense*

The popular name of Snout Beetle illustrates the most immediately striking feature of this family; all species have a pronounced rostrum. With 50,000 species they are the largest family of beetles. This means that there are more species of weevils than there are of vertebrate animals. It is inevitable that a group made up of such a wealth of species will include many bizarre and colourful forms, of which a selection can be seen in Figs. 23, 53–60, 65, 66, 89, 130, 163, 164, 166–173, 187, 203). For a weevil, the normal pattern of behaviour is to feed on living plants. There is virtually no part of a plant that does not serve as the feeding or breeding substratum for some particular species of weevil. Whether it be seed, fruit, blossom, bud, leaf, twig, branch, stem, outer bark, inner bark or root, whether it be dead wood or living plant tissue, the weevil has conquered every part that a flowering plant and even a water plant can offer. In some instances they exhibit particularly interesting adaptations which enable them to prepare a specific larval food. Weevils are generally accepted to be a classic example of an exclusively phytophagous group of beetles.

But there are a few species which show aberrant behaviour patterns. In Australia, there is a species of weevil *(Tentegia)* which eats dung. The discovery of the habits of *Tentegia* caused something of a sensation among coleopterists throughout the world. The two species so far known collect the dung of marsupials, which they store in small cavities in the ground, within each of which a larva develops. This habit is very similar to that of many Dung Beetles. A number of American weevil species are known to inhabit the burrows and holes of various rodents. But so far little has been learned of their biology.There are certain weevils that live in association with ants and are furnished with tufts of hair which diffuse secretions. Other weevils have developed the practice of living as guests in the abode of another insect (they are inquilinous). These species deposit their eggs in plant galls produced by quite different species of insects (e.g. gall wasps, sawflies). The weevil larvae, as inquilines, feed off the plant tissue which is intended as food for the larvae of the gall-maker. They do not attack the larvae directly, but nevertheless cause their destruction in the competitive struggle for food and space. The practice of inquilinity has developed in a particular way in the case of shoot-piercing weevils and leaf rollers. There are several species of weevils which lay their eggs in the prepared breeding substrata of other weevils, and in this way are truly "Cuckoo-weevils." *Lasiorhynchites sericeus,* for instance, deposits its eggs in the intricate leaf rolls made by the weevil *Attelabus nitens.* Subsequently the *Lasiorhynchites* larvae develop alongside the *Attelabus* larvae. But other Cuckoo-weevils do not display this degree of amity. In these cases, the females destroy the egg of their host with their rostrum and the larva of the Cuckoo-weevil has sole possession of the "nest."

In the Amazon region, there is one species of weevil (*Ludovix fasciatus*) which feeds exclusively on insect eggs, that is, it is purely entomophagous (insectivorous). This weevil lives on the eggs of a grasshopper *(Cornops longicorne)* which the latter lays in the stems of the Water Hyacinth (*Eichhornia crassipes*) in groups of about twenty at a time. Even as an imago, *Ludovix* lives on these eggs, which it cuts into from outside with its long rostrum and devours in the course of about an hour (the eggs are relatively large), as it had also done in the larval stage. The female lays a single egg in the nest of eggs belonging to *Cornops*, then within a few days the larva has consumed the entire clutch and pupates in the hollow prepared by *Cornops* inside the water hyacinth. The process has to be a rapid one, since otherwise the grasshopper's eggs would hatch and the weevil larva would starve; egg-laying to pupation in fact takes no more than 11 to 13 days.

In the misty mountain forests of New Guinea there are 25 species of weevils some 30 mm long, the upper surface of which is covered by a growth of fungi, algae, lichen, moss and liverwort. Within it, protozoa, rotifers, threadworms and moss-mites live. These beetles reach an age of 3 to 5 years, and within that time can accumulate a considerable concentration of different organisms on their body.

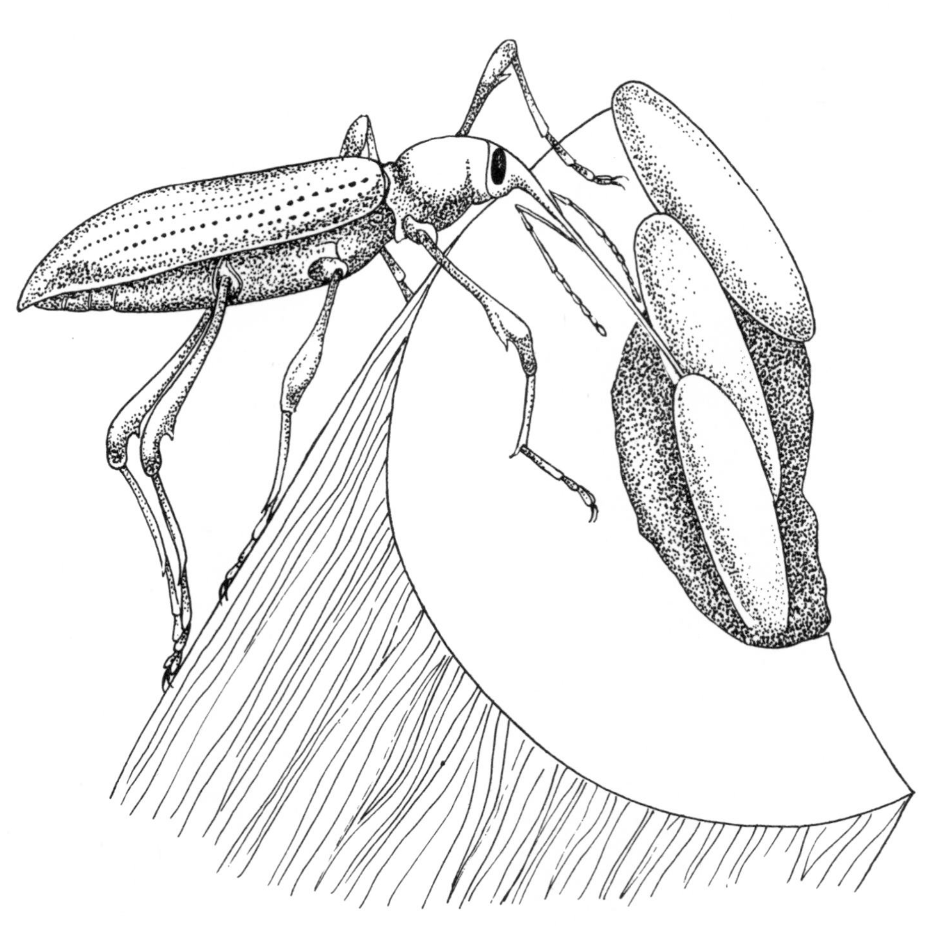

Ludovix fasciatus Gyll. (Weevils, Curculionidae) sucking up grasshopper eggs (artificially exposed).

In early entomological literature, a good deal of attention was paid to weevils, mainly on account of harmful infestations that have sometimes occurred. For example, Johann Leonhard Frisch (1666–1743) gives a detailed description of the habits and the damage caused by the Apple-blossom Weevil *(Anthonomus pomorum)*. About the same time (1724), a report appeared in a local Silesian newspaper on the subject of this pest. Maria Sibylla Merian (1647–1717) who was renowned for her wonderful watercolours, writes in detail about the Palm Weevil, and of their larvae, has this to say: "In the centre of the plate, a whitish worm is creeping across a green leaf. The Dutch call it a Palmyt-Worm, that is a Palm Worm, since it feeds on this tree. I have drawn it here on a leaf, since a palm frond is too large for this sketch. It is short and soft . . . The natives maintain that it takes 50 years to complete its growth. They cut it from the base of the leaf sheath or from the stem of the palm at head-height, and cook it as we cook cauliflower. Its taste is superior to that of the heart of an artichoke. It lives in the trunk of the palm tree feeding on its pith. To begin with, it is not larger than a cheese mite, but later grows to the size depicted here. This worm develops into the black beetle that I have drawn here, the parent of the Palm Worm."

In his *Household Book* published in 1590, the preacher Johann Colerus (died 1639) shows us that weevils were also of socio-economic significance. "Worms in acorns signify an unfruitful year and a rise in prices." The acorn worms of which he speaks were most probably the larvae of the Acorn Weevil (*Curculio glandium*).

Feeding Habits, Beetles Beneficial and Harmful to Man

Feeding organs and sources of food

Mouthparts and some of their special forms
It is typical of all beetles that they have mouthparts adapted for biting and chewing. There are only very few exceptions to this normal pattern. For example, members of the South American genus of Honey Beetles *(Nemognatha)* belonging to the family of Blister Beetles (Meloidae) have a special sucking apparatus. The sucker is formed by the extension of the maxillae and enables the beetle to obtain nectar and pollen from the innermost parts of the blossom. Another genus, *Leptopalpus* (Meloidae), has also developed a suction snout, although in this case, different structural elements have been used.

All the organs of the mouthparts are more or less highly modified in the different families of beetles but the maxillae the most markedly of all. They are sometimes strikingly large and in certain cases this has led to a change of function. Particularly large mandibles occur in the genera *Chiasognathus, Neolamprima* and *Lamprima* belonging to the family of Stag Beetles (Lucanidae) (Figs. 24, 93, 150, 151). But there are also other families with massively enlarged maxillae. For instance, among the Hister Beetles (Histeridae), there are some African species with maxillae almost as long as their body. Among the Scarabaeidae, the males of the genus *Lethrus* have particularly large mandibles each of which is in addition furnished with a thorny process pointing downward. Great pincer-like mandibles also occur in the Straight-snouted Weevils (Brenthidae) (Fig. 23). Among the Longicorns (Cerambycidae), members of the genera *Macrodontia* and *Callipogonius* are conspicuous on account of their particularly long mandibles (Fig. 67).

The digestive system and symbiosis
The digestive system of the beetle shows only a few peculiarities when compared with that of other insects, one example being the feature of extraintestinal digestion (see p. 179) which occurs in Ground Beetles (Carabidae), Diving Beetles (Dytiscidae), Fireflies (Lampyridae), Drilid Beetles (Drilidae), Burying Beetles (Silphidae) and others. Another peculiarity is the presence of a gizzard, in, for example, Bark or Engraver Beetles (Scolytidae), situated at the end of the fore intestine and which is able to grind the food to a fine consistency. It is provided internally with chitinous ridges and prominent denticles.

Many beetles live on sound and decayed wood, so their food consists largely of cellulose, which most species are unable to digest. Only a few Longhorn Beetles (Cerambycidae) and Wood-boring Beetles (Anobiidae) are capable of producing their own cellulase (an enzyme which breaks down cellulose). As a result, symbiosis with celluloclastic micro-organisms, for example, bacteria and yeast-like organisms, is common. Symbiotic bacteria produce cellulase in the larvae of Lamellicorns (Scarabaeidae) and Stag Beetles (Lucanidae). In the case of the Scarabaeids, the symbionts are cultivated in a saccular outgrowth of the hind

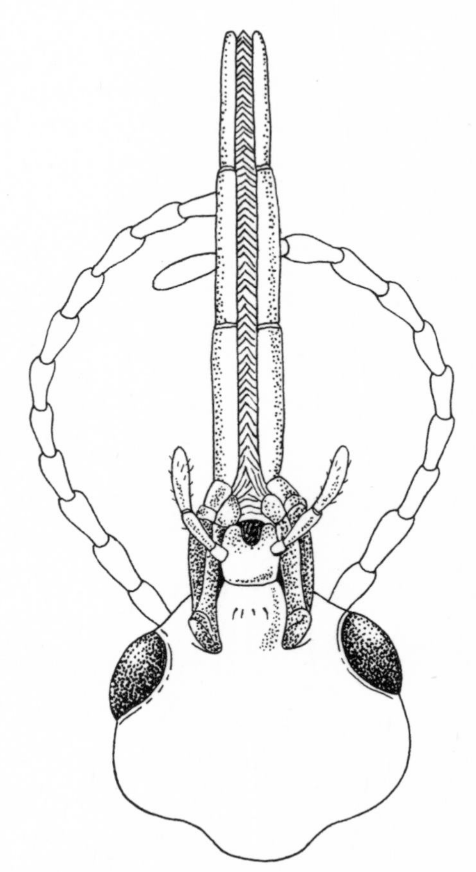

Aberrant mouthparts
left: Mouthparts of the nectar-sipping *Leptopalpus rostratus* F. (Blister Beetles, Meloidae)
right: *Nemognatha bicolor* Lec. with suction snout as an extension of the galeae (Blister Beetles, Meloidae)

intestine, which acts as a fermentation chamber in which the food is broken down. Afterwards it is returned to the mid intestine where it and the large numbers of bacteria attached to it are digested. Wood-boring beetles (Anobiidae) are richly provided with symbionts; yeasts occur, for example, in the Biscuit or Drugstore Beetle *(Stegobium paniceum)* in special organs called mycetomes. Apart from those families already mentioned, other groups such as the Longicorns (Cerambycidae) and Weevils or Snout Beetles (Curculionidae) also rely on the presence of symbionts. Beetles of the sub-family Donaciinae (Reed Beetles) which belong to the Leaf Beetles (Chrysomelidae) have symbiotic bacteria in their excretory organs (Malpighian tubules).

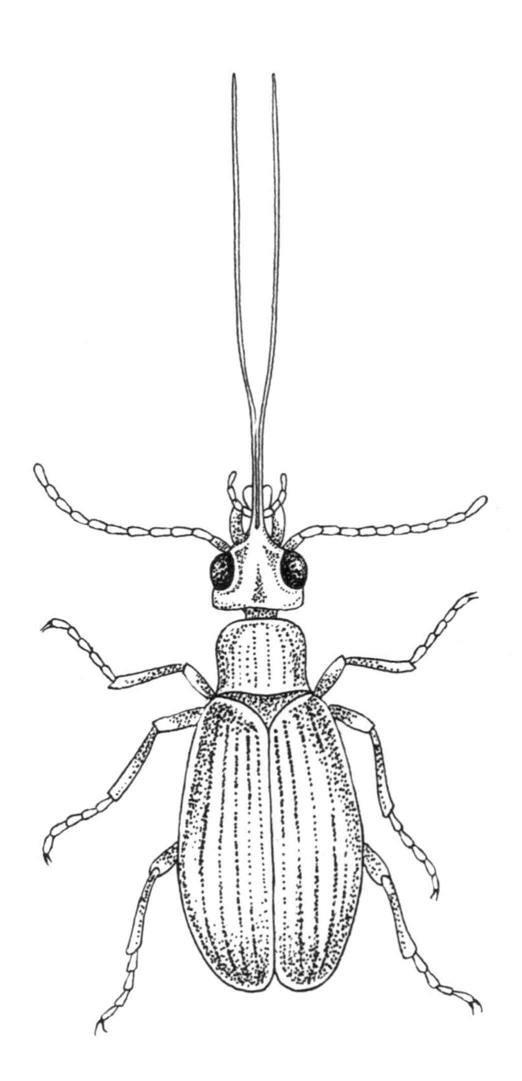

The value of symbiosis lies on the one hand in the breaking down of cellulose, while on the other hand the symbiotic micro-organisms themselves supply essential nutrients and vitamins which would otherwise be lacking. The symbiotic yeast cells which are stored intracellularly in large intestinal blind sacs provide the Drugstore Beetle *(Stegobium paniceum,* Anobiidae) with the following "vitamins": riboflavin, niacin, pyridoxin, pantothenic acid, folic acid and biotin. Many beetles *(Tenebrio molitor, Tribolium confusum)* (Tenebrionidae) specifically require the vitamin carnitin. However, beetles of the genus *Gnathocerus* (Horned Flour Beetles; Tenebrionidae) which also belong to the family of Darklings (Tenebrionidae) are little affected by the omission of carnitin from their diet.

Symbiosis in beetles is always obligatory. Loss of the symbionts causes the death of the beetle. Therefore transmission from parent to progeny must be assured. The symbionts emerge by way of the intestine and the eggs are smeared with them. The larvae always consume part of the egg covering. In many Weevils (Curculionidae), Shot-holt Borers or Powder-post Beetles (Lyctidae) and Flat Bark Beetles (Cucujidae) for example, in *Oryzaephilus* (Silvanidae), the symbionts penetrate the mature eggs while they are still in the ovary of the parent beetle. The females of the Reed Beetles (Donaciinae) which belong to the Leaf Beetle family (Chrysomelidae) surround their eggs with a secretion that contains the symbionts, part of which is consumed by the larvae, at any rate that part with the greatest concentration of symbionts.

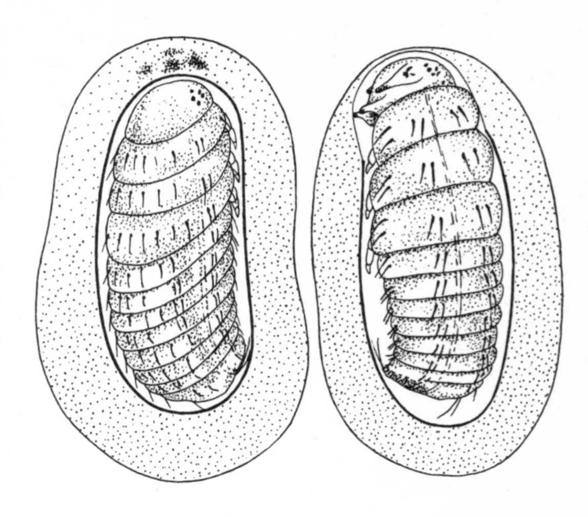

Bacterial symbiosis in *Donacia semicuprea* Panz. (Chrysomelidae)
left: The fully developed larva within the egg, the mound of symbionts lies above the larva's head.
right: The larva in the process of eating through the egg case, the mound of symbionts has already been consumed.

Omnivores

Almost every imaginable source of food has been exploited by beetles. In addition to extreme specialists, we also find species which have a very wide dietary range. A good example of the latter is the Golden Spider Beetle *(Niptus hololeucus)* (Ptinidae). It can maintain itself of starchy foods of all kinds, particularly grain, grain products and refuse. But it also attacks the most varied range of textile goods as well as hair and feathers, furs, leather goods, tobacco products, tea and even poisonous drugs of vegetable origin. The species was introduced to Europe from Asia Minor. In the 1920s, they several times appeared in massive numbers reaching epidemic proportion. A newspaper of the time reports: "Where the Golden Spider Beetle has once gained a foothold, there is nothing that can be done. Left to get on with its work undisturbed, it will destroy the house down to its foundations. Now it has carried into Europe its work of destruction, which in Asia made it the terror of natives and Europeans alike. It consumes entire houses." Here, of course, imagination has been spurred on by ignorance. But omnivorous pests in houses have always been a source of concern.

A second example of a beetle with an extraordinarily wide-ranging diet is the Meal Beetle (*Stegobium paniceum*) (Anobiidae). It eats virtually anything. Only stone, glass, china, plastics, cast iron and other very hard metals are safe from its attack. It is able to bore through or eat its way into lead and tinfoil.

Plant specialists

Almost every species of plant is attacked by the larva or imago of some beetle or other. And certain of these beetles are extremely specialized feeders. The Metallic Beetle *Agrilus integerrimus* (Buprestidae) lives exclusively on the shrub mezereon (common daphne). The Blue Alder Leaf Beetle *(Agelastica alni)* (Chrysomelidae) occurs only on alders, and it would be possible to list a whole series of such specialists. Usually specialization is further accentuated in that the species of beetle in question does not attack the whole plant, but restricts its attention to a particular region of it. This is the case, for example, with two species of Bark Beetles (Scolytidae) which are specialist feeders on Clematis *(Clematis vitalba)* and Almond-leaved Spurge *(Euphorbia amygdaloides)* respectively, but which are found exclusively in the pith of the stem of the host plant. Beetles living in wood include False Powder-post Beetles (Bostrychidae), Deathwatch Beetles (Anobiidae), Longicorn Beetles (Cerambycidae), Weevils (Curculionidae), Ambrosia Beetles (Platypodidae) and Bark Beetles (Scolytidae). Many monophagous weevils (Curculionidae)—feeding on only one kind of food—are dependent entirely upon the seeds of their host plant. This is true of many species of the genus *Apion* (Clover Weevils; Apionidae) and also of those beetles belonging to the genus *Curculio* (Curculionidae) which attack hazel nuts or acorns. A high degree of specialization in respect of the species of plant selected or of the organ of that plant is exhibited by the mine-boring beetles. The externally visible galleries excavated in plant tissue by burrowing beetle larvae and other insect larvae are called mines. They are most frequently found between the upper and lower epidermis of leaves. The form and arrangement of the mines so constantly exhibit features characteristic of each species that it is possible to identify the insect responsible without even seeing it. Leaf miners include Weevils (Curculionidae), Metallic Beetles (Buprestidae) and Leaf Beetles (Chrysomelidae). Some familiar examples are members of the genera *Rhynchaenus* and *Rhamphus* (Curculionidae), various species of which may attack beeches, oaks, birches, willows, poplars and other deciduous trees. The larvae of the Duckweed Weevil *Tanysphyrus lemnae*, which are only 2 mm in length, mine in the very small leaves of the Water Flax-seed or Duckweed. Among Metallic Beetles (Buprestidae), the genus *Trachys* is particularly well known for its mining habits, producing blotch mines in various plants, with, in part, a high degree of specialization. Another species of Metallic Beetle *(Habroloma nana)* mines exclusively in the leaves of the Bloodred Cranesbill *(Geranium sanguineum)*. Among the Leaf Beetles (Chrysomelidae), species of the genus *Zeugophora* are leaf miners, as are various Flea Beetles (Chrysomelidae, Alticinae). And in its larval form, the Hedgehog Beetle *Hispella atra* mines in the leaves of various grasses.

Abnormal growths of plant tissue caused by the stimulus of foreign organisms are known as galls. The formation of a gall is always the result of interaction between stimulating agent and host plant. They are so characteristic in form that it is possible to identify the causa-

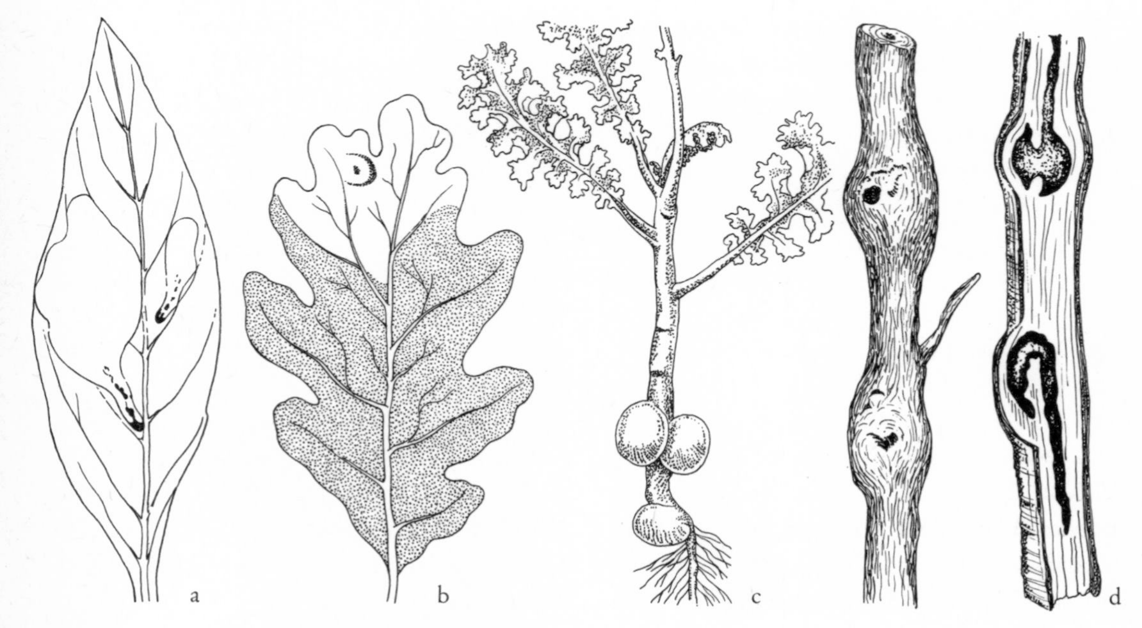

Phytophagous beetles
a) Leaf of blue scabious of "devil's bit" *(Succisa pratensis)*, with two mines made by the Metallic Beetle *Trachys troglodytes* Gyll. (Buprestidae).
b) Oak leaf with bladder mines excavated by the larva of the Oak Weevil *Rhynchaenus quercus* L. (Weevils, Curculionidae).
c) The Cabbage Gall Weevil *Ceutorhynchus pleurostigma* Marsh. (Curculionidae) with galls produced by the larvae.
d) Galls of the Lesser Poplar Longhorn *Saperda populnea* L. (Longhorns, Cerambycidae), cut open on the left.

tive organism from the appearance of the gall itself. The larva of the beetle is contained inside the gall. Among beetles, the principal gall-causers are Weevils (Curculionidae). Many species of the genera *Apion* (Fig. 174), *Ceutorhynchus* and *Gymnetron* can serve as examples. They induce the formation of galls at the point of growth of shoots, on roots and flowers. Species of *Smicronyx,* 1.5 to 2.5 mm in length, cause galls 12 mm by 6 mm on the stems of species of *Cuscuta.* Apart from Weevils, Leaf Beetles also cause galls; for instance, the Flea Beetle *Psylliodes napi* causes growths in the axis of shoots of cardamine. Also responsible for galls are the curious *Sagra* species of the family Chrysomelidae. Many species of Seed Weevils (Bruchidae) also cause the formation of galls, for example, the species *Bruchus pisorum* is responsible for growths on the fruit of Laburnum. Bark Beetles (Scolytidae) such as *Tamnurgus kaltenbachi* can cause swellings in the axis of shoots of the Dead Nettle, Marjoram, Woundwort and Germander. A particularly interesting gall is produced by the Lesser Poplar Longhorn *Saperda populnea.*

It is not only higher plants that are attacked by beetles: there are certain specialists which infest exclusively the so-called "lower" plants. The larvae of the Crawling Water Beetles (Haliplidae) feed only on green algae. The Feather-winged Beetles are specialist feeders on fungus spores. Indeed, fungi provide a source of food for very many different beetles. Whole books have been written dealing exclusively with the subject of fungus beetles. As an example, we might mention *Liodes cinnamomea* of the family of Round Carrion Beetles (Liodidae) which eats only truffles growing underground, and in particular the Black Truffle. Species of *Lycoperdina*, which belong to the family of Handsome Fungus Beetles (Endomychidae) live only in blindballs (fungi of the family Lycoperdaceae). It should be noted that the *Lycoperdina* species are instrumental in the distribution of fungus spores.

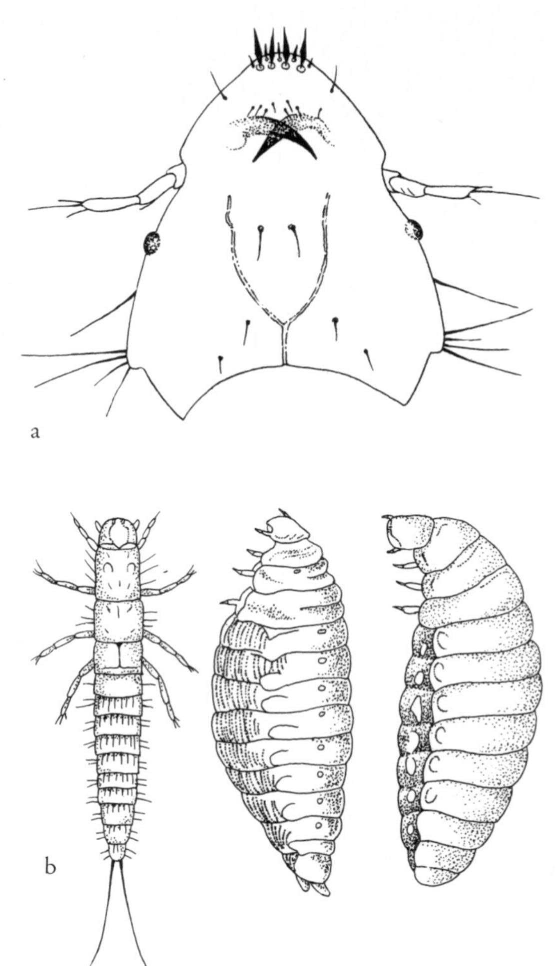

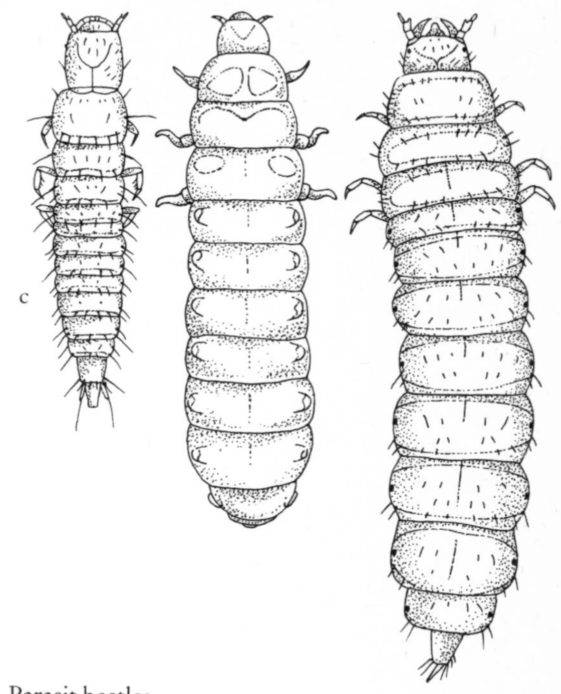

Parasit beetles
a) Head of the triungulin larva of *Meloe cavensis* Pet. (Blister Beetles, Meloidae) with rows of barbs at front edge.
b) The three larval forms of an Oil Beetle (*Meloe* spec.): left triungulinus, centre 2nd larval stage, right 3rd larval stage.
c) The three larval stages of the Rove Beetle *Aleochara curtula* Grav. (Staphylinidae).

Dead plants, processed plant products and stored plant materials are also attacked by beetles many of which rank as major pests. A good example is the Tobacco Beetle *Lasioderma serricorne* (Anobiidae), the larvae of which live in tobacco bales but also in processed tobacco, especially cigars. On this subject, Horion (1949) writes: "It is no pleasure at all to smoke a fine cigar in which there is a roasting *Lasioderma* larva; the effect is very much like that of one's first attempt at smoking." The dust produced by decay in wood is a *dorado* for a wide variety of species of beetles such as Longicorns (Cerambycidae), Click Beetles (Elateridae), Cardinal Beetles (Pyrochroidae), Stag Beetles (Lucanidae), Metallic Beetles (Buprestidae) and other families.

Beetles as parasites

Within the insect orders of Hymenoptera and Diptera, there are many parasitoids. By this term we mean those insects which live parasitically in or on other insects and, in contrast to true parasites, ultimately cause the destruction of their hosts.

This is a phenomenon which is rare in beetles. A borderline case of parasitoid behaviour is that of various Fungus Weevils (Anthribidae). The larvae of some species eat the eggs lying beneath the egg scale laid by the female Scale Insects. Indeed, many Fungus Weevils seem to specialize in particular coccids. *Brachytarsus nebulosus* for example, seems to occur only with coccids (mealy bugs) found in the whorls of spruce trees.

Other parasitoids are Rove Beetles of the genus *Aleochara* (Staphylinidae). The first larval stage of this genus of beetle is very mobile, with well-developed eyes. It seeks out the puparia of flies. In this process, the larva is clearly attracted by an odiferous substance emitted by the pupa, and enters the hind body of the host pupa. There it moults to produce the second larval stage which is grub-like and devoid of eyes. It consumes the rest of the fly pupa and moults, producing the third larval stage which once again has well-developed legs and eyes. It leaves the puparium and buries itself in the earth to pupate.

The members of the family of Blister Beetles (Meloidae) all seem to live parasitically. The larvae which hatch from the egg are known as triungulins or three-clawed larvae, since the last segment of each tarsus bears two claw-like bristles in addition to the claw. These larvae climb on to flowers, where they take no food, but remain waiting for bees to arrive. Then they attach themselves to the hairy body of the bees with their curious claws, at the same time boring rows of spines at the front edge of the head into the intersegmental skin of the "porter bees." The triangulins allow themselves to be carried to the nests of their hosts. There they moult into a maggot-like second stage which feeds off the larvae of the host. Then they generally pass into a dormant stage, which is known as a pseudo-pupal or coarctate (pre-pupal or pharate) condition. This is followed by the genuine pupal stage, in which the pupa often remains encased in the skin of the last larval instar. The details of this development process may show modifications in different species of Blister Beetles. Let us look first of all at the beetles of the genus *Meloe* (Oil Beetles). Their hosts are solitary bees of the genera *Anthophora* and *Andrena*. The triungulins can develop only if they succeed in making their way into the nests of these species. Consequently losses are high, although they are to some extent counterbalanced by the extraordinarily large number of eggs laid by the female beetle (4,000 to 10,000) (Figs. 182, 183). The triungulin has to find its way on to the egg which floats on a supply of nectar in the cell in the ground. If, as it slips from the bee's body, the larva fails to alight on the egg but falls into the nectar, there is no hope for it. If however it reaches the host egg, the triungulin consumes the contents and moults into a blind, maggot-like larva with vestigial legs. It feeds upon the stored nectar and pollen and later makes its way out of the nest into the soil. There it moults into a pseudo-pupa and presumably winters in this condition. In spring, a maggot-like larva emerges, which takes no food and soon changes into a pupa. In Central Europe, the beetle emerges in May. In many *Meloe* species, the pseudo-pupal stage may be omitted while in others it may be assumed a second time. The triungulins of some species make their way actively into the nest of the host. The members of the genus *Sitaris* deposit their eggs close to the entrance of the nests of the Potter Flower Bee *(Anthophora)*. The triungulins attach themselves to the body of the male bees which hatch out first. In the course of the bee's pairing, they transfer themselves to the female bees and so get carried to their nests. The triungulins of the Spanish Fly *(Lytta vesicatoria)* actively penetrate the nests of their host bees *(Colletes, Megachile, Halictus)*. The larvae of *Cerocoma* allow themselves to be carried by Thread-waisted Wasps *(Tachytes, Tachysphex)* into the nest of the latter. These Thread-waisted Wasps have already brought to their nest a supply of grasshoppers or praying-mantises which they have killed by means of a poison sting, and on which the larvae of the wasps feed. The *Cerocoma* larva first kills the wasp larva and then feeds upon the remaining food supplies. And finally the species *Epicauta* and *Mylabris* live as larvae on the egg pods which are deposited in the ground by the grasshoppers.

Rhipiphorid Beetles (Rhipiphoridae) also live parasitically on other species of insects. The females of the Wasp Beetle *(Metoecus paradoxus)* lay their eggs in the soil. Out of these, triungulin larvae hatch, similar to those we have already met in the case of the Blister Beetle (Meloidae). It is probable that these larvae actively penetrate the nests of ground wasps. There, each one bores its way into a wasp larva, on which it feeds, though without causing its death. Moulting of the triungulin larva produces a maggot-like second stage which feeds externally on the larva (as an ectoparasite) and in doing so, finally kills it. When the wasp larva is consumed, the *Metoecus* larva pupates in the now empty wasp cell, from which the beetle emerges after some time. Occasionally more than 100 beetles have been found in a wasp nest. Another genus of Rhipiphorid, *Macrosiagon*, parasitizes Yellow Jackets of the genus *Odynerus*. The triungulin is carried by the host into the nest and lives there, much as the *Metoecus* larva in the wasp larva. The development of Cockroach Beetles *(Rhipidius)* (see p. 116) follows a quite different course. The female deposits more than 2000 eggs from which triungulins hatch and make their way to young Cockroach larvae *(Blattella, Ectobius)*. They attach themselves firmly to an articular membrane, with at first the head only and later the whole body inside the body of the host. They moult to produce

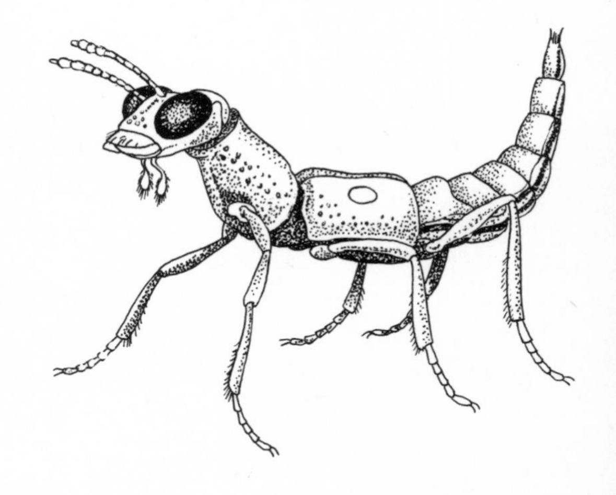

a maggot-like second stage which survives the whole winter within the living host. In spring, the parasite larva moults again twice and grows very considerably in size. The final stage has regained legs, and emerges from the end of the host's abdomen to pupate in the ground and finally to emerge in beetle form.

Other interesting special forms of parasitism occur in beetles. For instance, among Bark Beetles (Scolytidae) there are some very small species (1.1 to 1.8 mm) in the genus *Crypturgus.* On their own, they are incapable of penetrating bark. Certain species such as *Crypturgus pusillus* make their way through the bore holes and into the brood galleries of larger species of Bark Beetles, such as *Blastophagus minor*, and starting out from a parent tunnel belonging to the host, they excavate their own system of tunnels (brood-space parasitism). Brood parasites of another kind are many of the Dung Beetles of the genus *Aphodius* (Scarabaeidae). They do not collect dung themselves but lay their eggs in the egg balls of larger Dung Beetles.

Some of the few parasitic beetle species do not parasitize insects but vertebrates, in particular mammals. The Beaver Louse *(Platypsyllus castoris)* is a beetle which lives on the beaver *(Castor fiber)* (see p. 112). Another member of the family of Mammal-nest Beetles (Leptinidae) is the Mouse Flea *(Leptinus testaceus)*, which various writers consider to be parasitic. It is found in the nests of mice, moles, hamsters and rabbits. Considerable doubts exist as to its parasitic habits which have not been demonstrated conclusively.

Sometimes parasitism by beetles is not obligate. The Bacon Beetle *(Dermestes lardarius)* (Dermestidae) is said to attach itself in rare cases to newly hatched hen, duck and pigeon chicks. Both larva and imago will bore tunnels in the skin or the flesh of the chick and even penetrate an egg which has been cracked by the chick before it emerges. A Dor Beetle *Macropocopris symbioticus* (Scarabaeidae) lives in the intestine of certain kangaroos, where it feeds on the faeces. This species attaches itself to the fur around the anus and drops off on to the dung when the animal defecates. It has been reported that in Sri Lanka (Ceylon), larvae of a small Dung Beetle *(Onthophagus bifasciatus)* have been found in the intestines of children. There is some doubt about the reliability of the reports.

Beetles as predators

Many families of beetles are predators, living by seeking out and devouring other insects, as do Ground Beetles (Carabidae) (Figs. 126, 132, 134), many Rove Beetles (Staphylinidae) (for example, those *Stenus* species with a protrusible labium rather like the stickey-tipped tongue of the chameleon), Predacious Diving Beetles (Dytiscidae) (Figs. 141, 142), Whirligig Beetles (Gyrinidae), Ladybirds (Coccinellidae) (Fig. 144) and others. Here we would like to examine rather more closely another source of nourishment, namely the eating of snails and slugs. Various beetles, such as Ground Beetles (Carabidae) of the genus *Cychrus* specialize in feeding on snails. The head and pronotum are narrow and elongate, allowing penetration of the snail's shell. The head is very mobile, the mouthparts show specialized structural modification, as a result of which even the narrow, inner spirals of a snail's shell are accessible to them. A further adaptation is the ability of these beetles to carry with them a supply of air beneath the elytra, which can be vitally important to their survival when they are among the large quantities of slime secreted by snails. Specialists in a diet of snails are to be found among Carrion or Burying Beetles (Silphidae), particularly in the genera *Ablattaria* and *Phosphuga*, which show similar structural adaptations to the mouth parts of *Cychrus.* The larvae of these species also feed on snails. The larvae of some Water Scavenger Beetles (Hydrophilidae), such as *Hydrophilus* prey on various species of water snails. The larvae make their way far into the shell as they consume the snail within. In the Drilid Beetles (Drilidae), as in many other predacious beetles, the habit is linked with extra-intestinal digestion. This occurs in many beetles, for example, the larvae of Predacious Diving Bee-

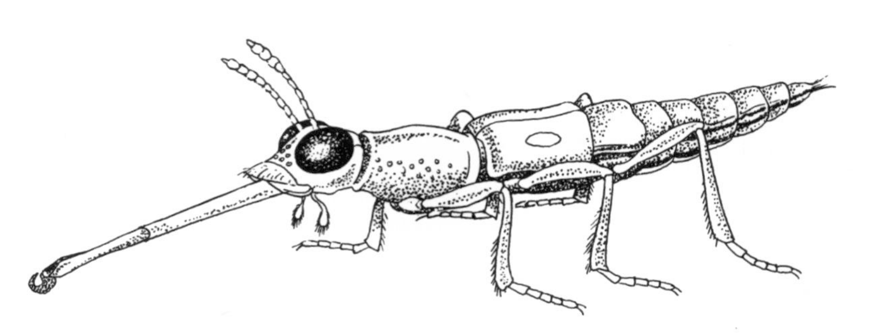

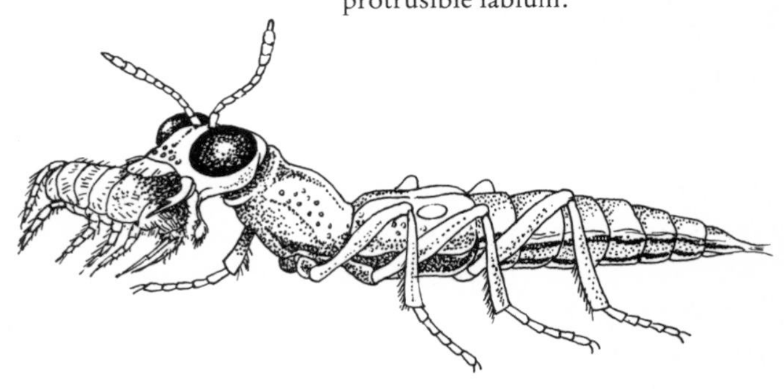

Predacious beetles
Stenus bipunctatus Er. (Rove Beetles, Staphylinidae) taking its prey ; note the adhesive protrusible labium.

tles (Dytiscidae), Glow-worms and Fireflies (Lampyridae), Ground Beetles (Carabidae) and Tiger Beetles (Cicindelidae). A digestive secretion is injected into the prey from mandibles that in most cases are channelled or grooved. The mixture of enzymes comes from the mid gut and has the effect of liquefying the food almost completely. The larva of the Great Water Beetle sucks up the resulting pulpy mass which once again passes through the mandibular canals (Fig. 179), while in other species, the prepared food is taken in through the mouth.

Dead animals as a source of food

Dead animal matter also represents an important source of food for a number of beetles. For example, various species of the family of Hide or Skin Beetles (Dermestidae) make use of dead insects as food. Almost every insect collector knows this from his own experience, for infestation by Museum Beetles (*Anthrenus*) is one of the worst things that can happen to an entomological collection. Insect remains or fragments of dead insects occurring in nature are also consumed by Hide or Skin Beetles. Certain species (*Trinodes hirtus* among others) have the specialized habit of feeding on the chitinous parts of insects which are food remnants left by spiders in their webs. Other species concentrate in places where mass breeding of butterflies takes place, and eat the cast skins of caterpillars. The Silken Fungus Beetle *Micrambe abietis* (Cryptophagidae) feeds on the larval moults of the Processionary Moth.

Other species of beetles specialize in feeding on carrion (dead vertebrates). Burying Beetles, also called Gravediggers or Sexton Beetles (*Necrophorus* species) (Silphidae), are well-known for this practice. Most of the other species of Carrion Beetles (Silphidae) also live on dead vertebrates (Fig. 185). Added to these are several species of Rove Beetles (Staphylinidae) and Hister Beetles (Histeridae). Once the carrion is dry, Checkered Beetles (Cleridae) and Hide or Skin Beetles (Dermestidae) will join them, the latter being the only beetles capable of breaking down keratin in their digestive processes. They possess an enzyme which causes the disintegration of the disulphide linkages of the keratin and so makes the protein chains susceptible to attack by other enzymes. Common to all carrion-eating (necrophagous) beetles is great rapidity of development, representing an adaptation to the short period of existence of their specific food substratum. In addition, it is noteworthy that individual species are restricted to food which is in a particular state of development, so that a distinct succession in their appearance can usually be observed. The mentioned Rove Beetles (Staphylinidae), Histerids (Histeridae) and Checkered Beetles (Cleridae) almost all prey on the larvae of other necrophagous insects. Moreover, there are certain specialist feeders which settle only on dead fish, for example, or other highly specific substrata. And certain species seem to accept only carrion of a particular size as the substratum in which to develop; for example, the largest European species of Sexton Beetle (*Necrophorus germanicus*) (Silphidae) is most frequently found on the carcases of roe deer.

Dung Beetles

The excrement of mammals is the specific feeding substratum of many species of beetles. They include various sub-families of the Scarabaeoids: Dung Chafers (Aphodiinae), Dor Beetles (Geotrupinae) und Tumblebugs or Pill-rollers (Coprinae) (see p. 116). Various Water Scavenger Beetles (Hydrophilidae) (genera *Sphaeridium* and *Cercyon*) live in dung. Many Histerid Beetles (Histeridae) and Rove Beetles (Staphylinidae) prey on the larvae of true dung-eating insects.

The dung-eating habit (coprophagous) is probably derived from that of plant-eating (phytophagous). The material consumed is almost exclusively the excrement, rich in cellulose, produced by phytophagous species of mammals. The step from feeding on decaying plant matter to consuming dung was, after all, not a particularly long one. Interestingly enough, all these forms of feeding occur within the family of Scarabaeoids.

The dung-eating beetles are of great significance to man. They bring about the rapid conversion of the excrement of grazing livestock into humus, and in addition, improve the fertility of the soil by their burrowing activities.

In the same way as Carrion Beetles, (Silphidae), Dung Chafers (Aphodiinae, Scarabaeidae), are also obliged to make rapid use of their nutritional substratum. A number of adaptations make this possible. Perhaps the most important feature is the instinct of brood care, which almost all the species possess to a greater or lesser degree. The individual species of Dung Beetles (Scarabaeidae) take up residence in their chosen substratum in a particular sequence. Cow-dung which is quite fresh, for instance, is inhabited first of all by Water Scavenger Beetles (Hydrophilidae) of the two genera mentioned above. While it is still semi-liquid, they swim in it rather than crawl. As it becomes increasingly dry, they are joined by various other species of dung beetles in a particular succession. Among the dung-dwelling beetles there are numbers of specialists: certain *Aphodius* species (Scarabaeidae), for example, live particularly in the excreta of roe deer and red deer.

141/142 European Great Water Beetle *(Dytiscus marginalis)* (Dytiscidae), female, can be recognized by the grooved elytra and the absence of suction pads on the forelegs. The beetle is taking in air at the surface of the water.

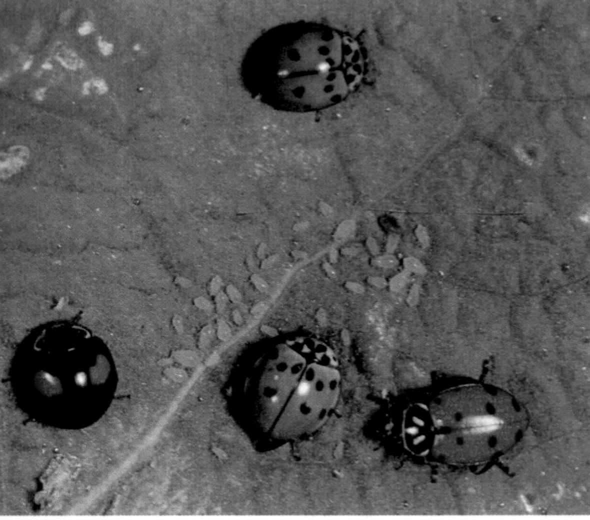

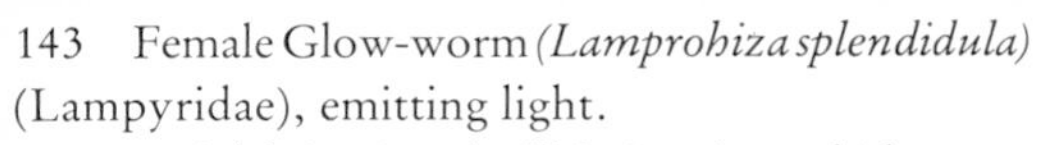

143 Female Glow-worm *(Lamprohiza splendidula)* (Lampyridae), emitting light.
144 Ladybirds (Coccinellidae) eating aphids right: *Adonia variegata*, the other three are all *Adalia decempunctata*.
145 Rose Chafer *(Stephanorrhina guttata)* (Scarabaeidae) from Africa

146 Cucumber Leaf Beetle *(Diabrotica duodecimpunctata)* (Chrysomelidae)
147 Copulating Tiger Beetles (Cicindelidae)
148 Arboreal Tiger Beetle (Cicindelidae) seen from front

149 European Stag Beetles fighting *(Lucanus cervus)* (Lucanidae)

150 Stag Beetles (Lucanidae); *Prosopocoelus giraffa* from Nepal, Assam, Java. Male (12 cm) with large mandibles and female (4.2 cm) and also *Aegus platyodon* (male, 4.3 cm) from Indonesia.

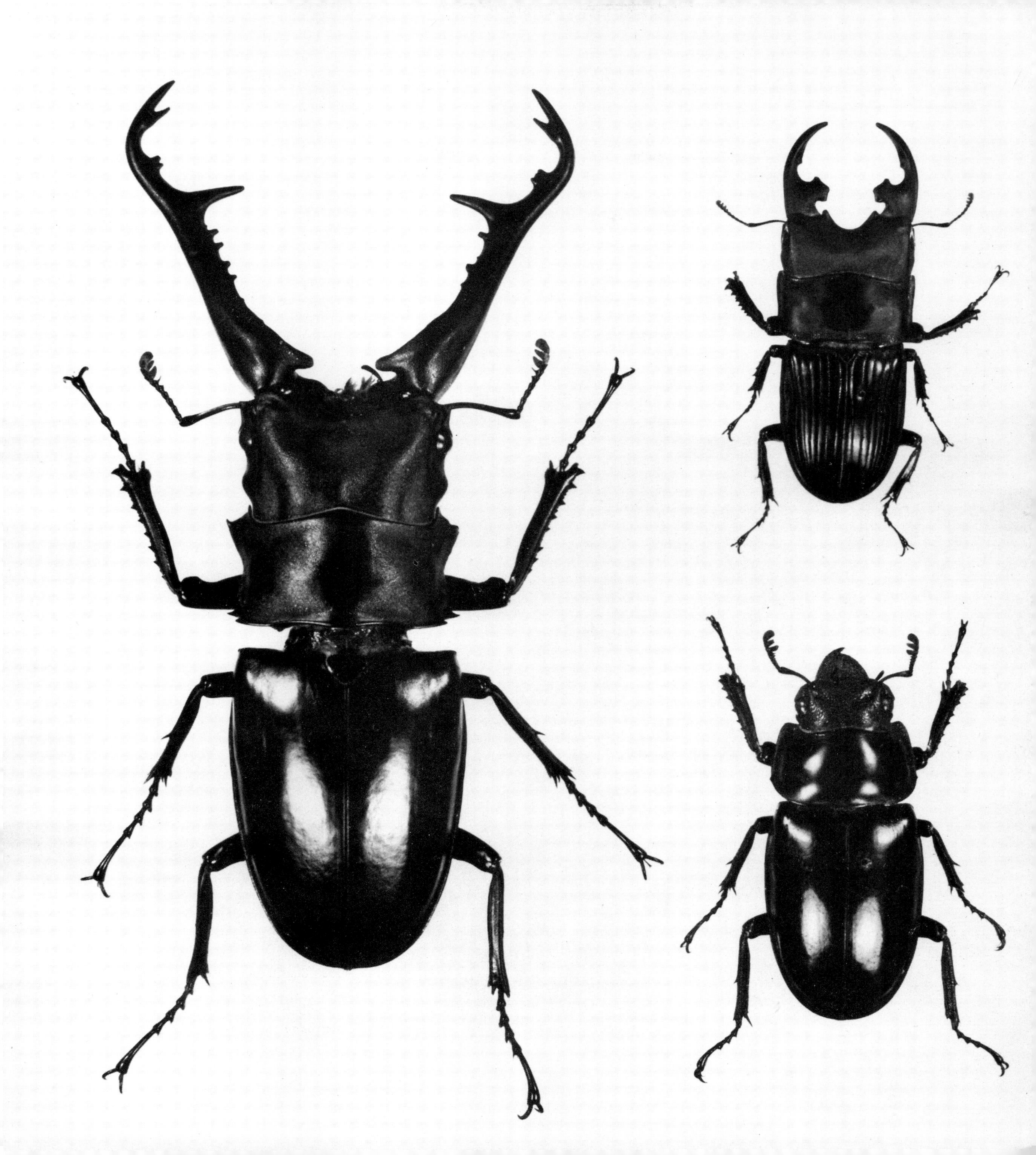

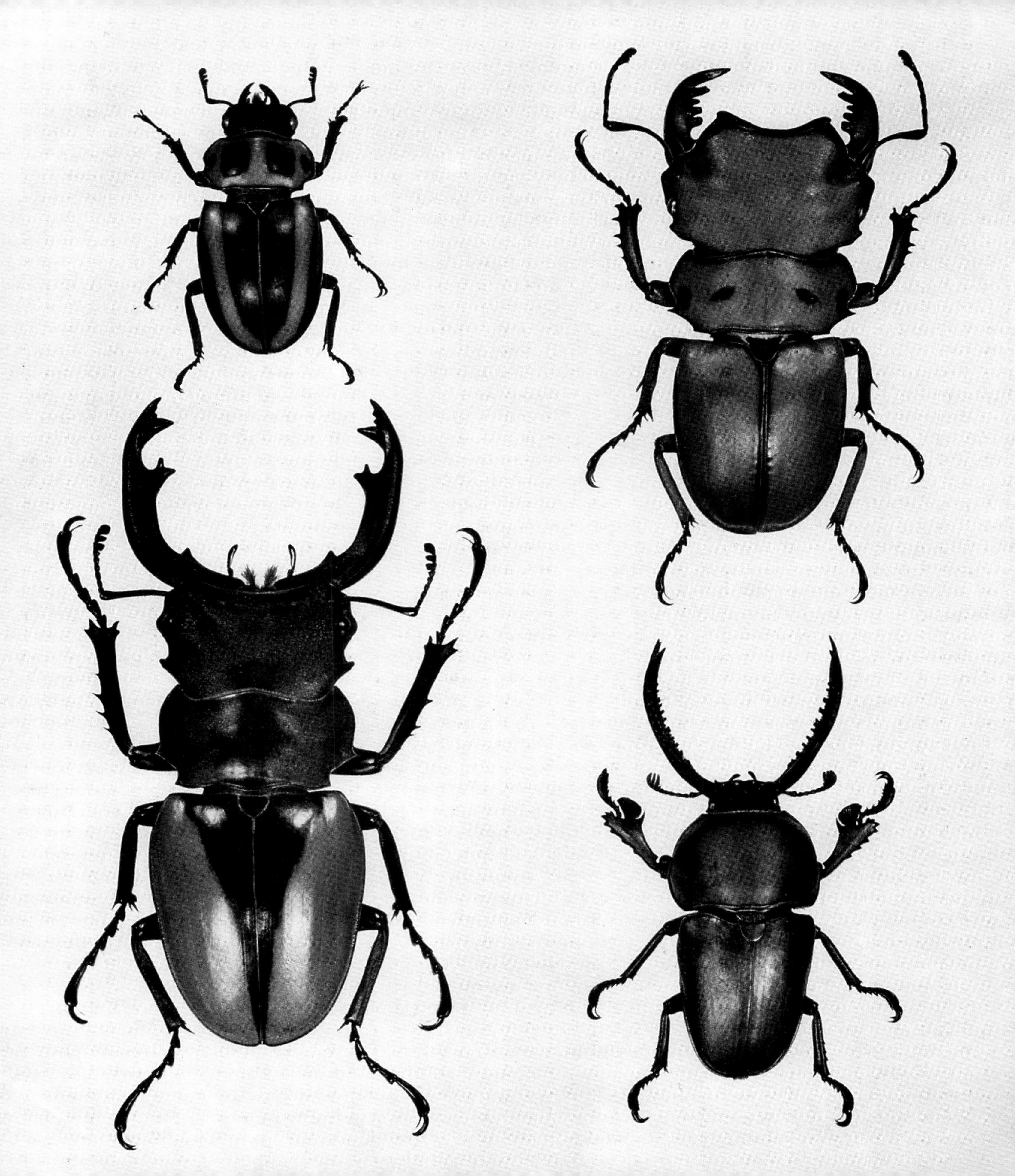

151 Stag Beetles (Lucanidae)
above: Female and male of *Homoderus mellyi* from Cameroon, light ochre with black markings
below: *Odontolabis cuvera* from Northern India, the Himalayas, black with ochre-coloured elytra, male
Lamprima adolphinae from New Guinea, greenish-gold with flame-red head and black "antlers," male

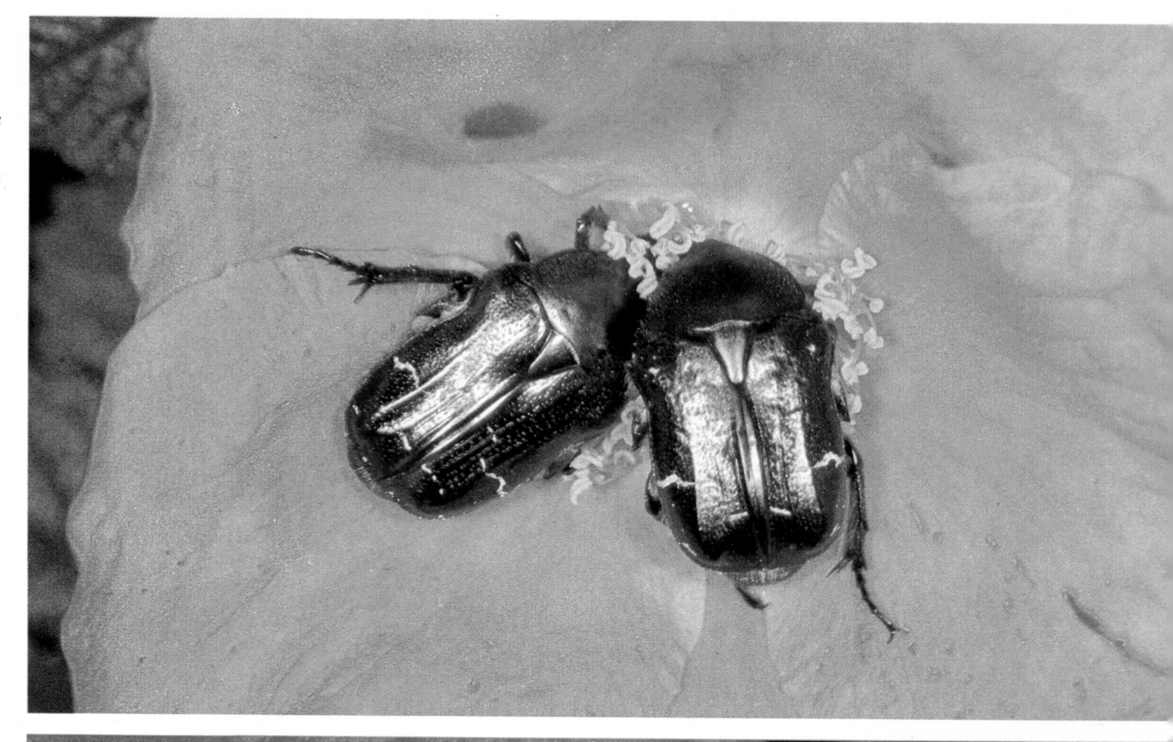

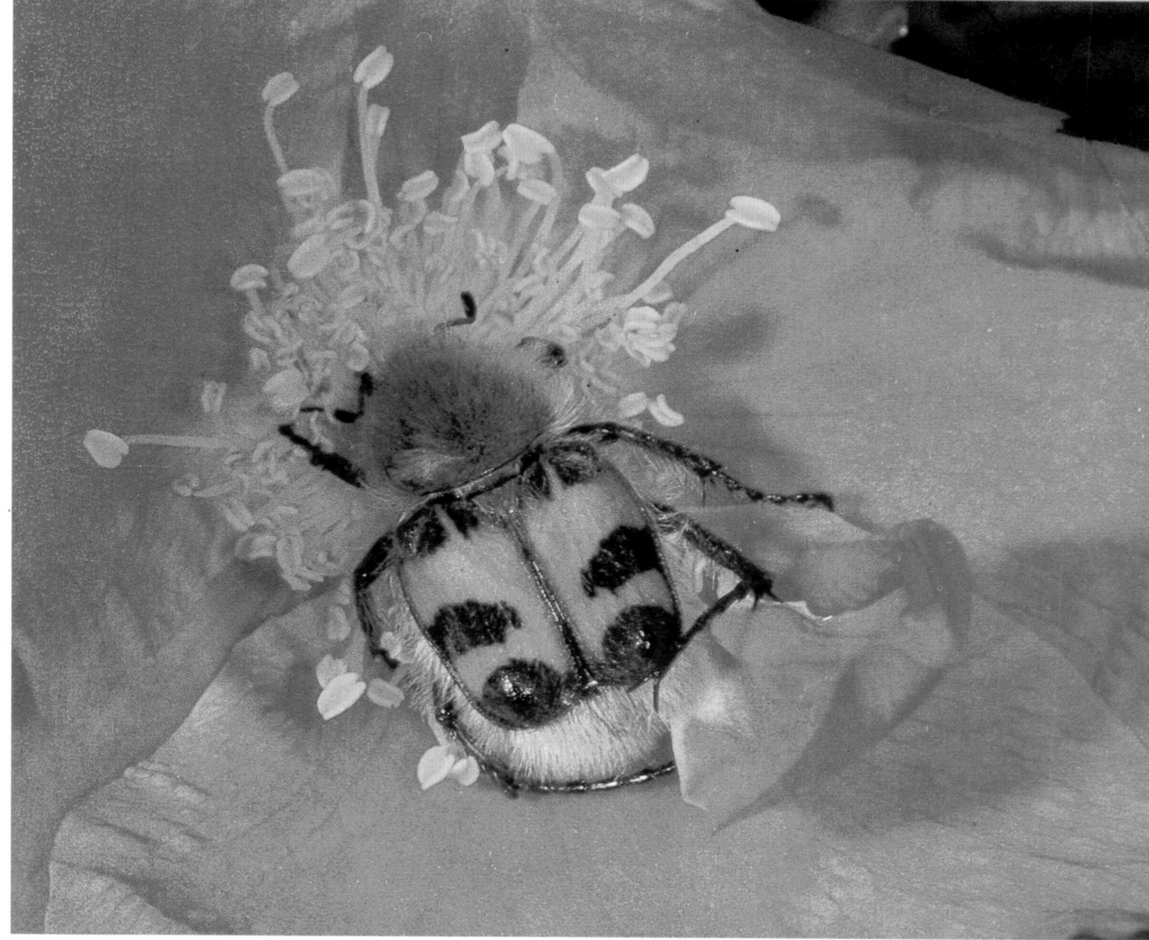

152 European Rose Chafer *(Cetonia aurata)* (Scarabaeidae) on a rose
153 Brushed Flower Beetle *(Trichius fasciatus)* (Scarabaeidae) on a rose

Myrmecophiles—guests of ants and termites

There are some species of beetles which, in their feeding habits and indeed their whole life cycle, are specially adapted for living in the nests of socially evolved insects. The guests of ants and termites, or myrmecophiles, have developed a particularly close relationship with hosts. Among these insects there always exists the primary instinct to kill intruders or to remove them from the nest. For this reason, the guests of ants and termites have evolved various procedures which enable them to escape this fate.

There are some 3,000 species of myrmecophiles, and they can be divided into three ecological groups, representing various stages in the relationship between ants and beetles, although the division between the groups is not sharply delineated.

1. The synechthrans

The guest lives by predation on the hosts. It is clearly recognized as an enemy and treated with hostility. As an example, we might mention the *Myrmedonia* genus of Rove Beetles (Staphylinidae). The beetles spray the ants with a secretion from their anal glands which has a narcotic effect. After this, the ants are consumed entirely except for the head. Within two days, a large *Myrmedonia* can kill 25 ants.

2. The synoeketes

In general, these guests are not recognized as foreign bodies and consequently do not arouse animosity. Many species cause the ants no harm, since they eat up refuse of various kinds. Others represent a slight encroachment since they consume food collected by the ants. The synoeketes are mostly quite diminutive species and it is precisely their small size that protects them from the ants. One example is that of the Rove Beetle *Dinarda dentata* (Staphylinidae), which in addition has a hard, chitinous integument and can run very swiftly. It lives on mites which are the parasites of ants. Other synoeketes are those beetles which exhibit a very close resemblance to ants and so are clearly not always recognized as extraneous elements. For example, species of the genus *Mimanomma* (Staphylinidae) look very like their hosts, the African Foraging or Migratory Ants of the genus *Dorylus* (Driver Ants). The American Foraging Ants of the genus *Eciton* (Legionary Ants) have Rove Beetle guests (*Myrmeciton*) which are deceptively similar in appearance. These Rove Beetles (Staphylinidae) have even evolved mimetic knots in the central region of the body which are a typical feature of the ants. The Foraging Ants carry out long hunting expeditions, in the course of which they are sometimes accompanied by Rove Beetles which, as symphiles (see below) secrete special exudations, and which sit on the head or back of the ants, "Horsemen" of this kind of the genera *Doryloxenos*, *Dorylomimus* and *Dorylogaster* have even evolved a special gripping apparatus on the tarsi with which they avoid falling off. Included among the synoeketes are the larvae of Rose Chafers (*Cetoninae* spec.; Scarabaeidae) which live on the outer edges of the nests of ants, particularly of Red Forest Ants, feeding on refuse produced by the colony, and also the larvae of Leaf Beetles of the genus *Clytra* (Chrysomelidae).

3. Symphiles

These guests are clearly recognized as foreign elements by the ants. But they ingratiate themselves by providing glandular secretions for their hosts which bring about an attitude of caring behaviour towards the symphiles. So the ants protect and care for these species and will even feed them. On the other hand, the symphiles are able to move freely within the nest and sometimes devour the eggs and young of their host. The *Lomechusa*, *Atemeles* (Europe) and *Xenodusa* (North America) genera of the Staphylinidae live in particularly close association with their hosts. On the integument at the side of the front segments of the abdomen they bear tufts of yellowish hairs, beneath which glands are situated. These glands exude an aromatic secretion which is avidly taken up by the ants. The beetles are fed and reared by the ants from whom they actively solicit food. But they also consume eggs and larvae of their ant hosts. In addition, *Atemeles* exhibit an interesting exchange of host. At first, the females live in the nests of Forest Ants of the genus *Formica*. There they produce larvae (viviparously) or lay eggs which hatch immediately (ovoviviparously). Viviparity and ovoviviparity are common among myrmecophiles, because the dangers threatening a clutch of eggs would be great. When reproduction is concluded, the beetle leaves the nest and seeks out a nest of the *Myrmica* species of ants, to which it is led by its sense of smell. The beetle remains for some time sitting at the entrance to the nest. The ants examine the beetle and, in doing so, discover the secretions from the "adoptive glands" which also emit special exudations into tufts of hair on the abdomen, which, however, prove attractive only to *Myrmica*. In addition, the beetle has pygidial glands at its disposal which have a generally placatory effect on ants. If, in spite of everything, the beetle is attacked, it is able to protect itself by means of defensive glands also situated in the abdomen. But usually *Atemeles* is adopted by the ants and carried to their nest. In contrast to the ants of the *Formica* species, those of the genus *Myrmica* spend the winter with their progeny. In this way, the beetle obtains the best possible conditions for feeding right up to the start of hibernation. But for the development of the larvae, the nest of *Formica* is more suitable.

154 A hornet-like Lamellicorn Beetle *(Ancistrostoma vittigerum)* (Scarabaeidae) from Peru (note the abdominal barb).

155 Lamellicorn Beetle (*Chrysophora* species) with adherent (clasping) legs from South America. It is light green with steel-blue tarsi.

And so *Atemeles* leaves the *Myrmica* colony in the spring, and seeks out the nest of a Forest Ant, once again guided by its sense of smell. The beetle actively penetrates the nest and there brings its larvae into the world. The *Atemeles* larvae are assiduously tended and fed by the ants, even to the extent of neglecting their own. The ants are stimulated by an intensive, imitative begging activity, and in addition, the *Atemeles* larvae exude a pheromone which triggers off brood care behaviour. There is another possible explanation for the change of host by *Atemeles* species. The *Formica* worker ants are extremely avid in their attempts to obtain the secretion, whereas the beetle young, which emerge in autumn, are at first still very soft-bodied and would be incapable of withstanding the importunate harassment of the ants. Therefore they leave their hosts and spend the winter among the "more peaceful" *Myrmica*. In each case, when the change of residence is made, an interval of a few days must be interposed, so that the smell of the old nest is lost.

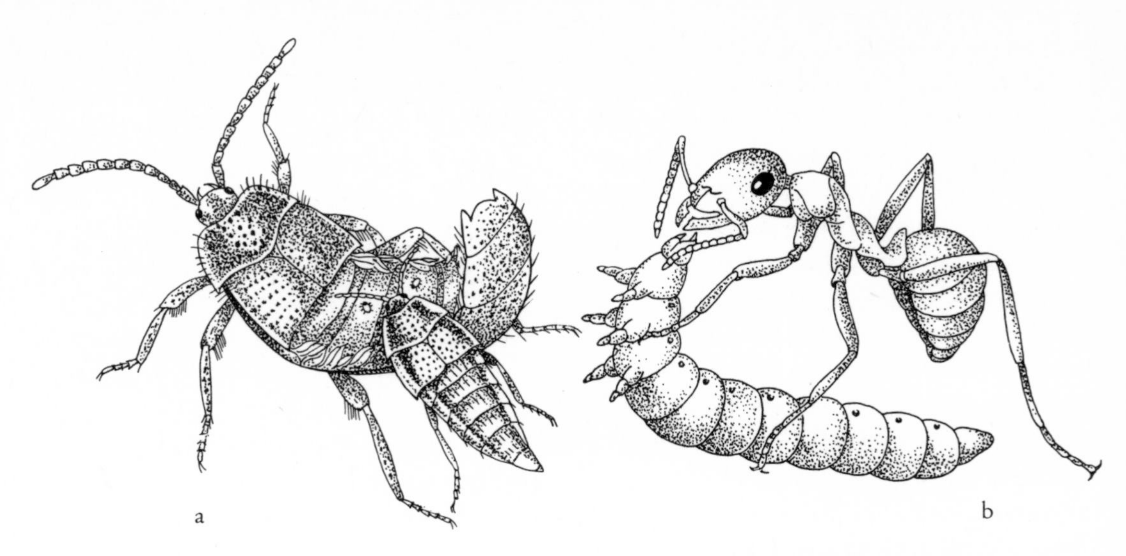

a b

Particularly highly adapted are the Claviger Beetles (*Claviger* species) of the family of Short-winged Mould Beetles (Pselaphidae) which are unable to survive without ants. Their way of life was first described by P. W. J. Müller in 1818 in his monograph on the "Ant Cow." The Clavigerids have greatly reduced mouthparts and are almost entirely incapable of independent feeding. They are fed from mouth to mouth by the ants with drops of regurgitated food, which they solicit from their hosts by tapping with their specialized antennae. When danger threatens an ants' nest, it is the Claviger Beetles that are saved first of all, and only after that do the ants attend to their own progeny. At the front of the abdomen, the beetles have glands which open beneath a tuft of golden-yellow hairs on either side. The glandular secretion collects in a hollow at the base of the abdomen and is greedily imbibed by the host ants (genus *Lasius*). Without doubt, these secretions are in the nature of stimulants or even narcotics. Excessive ingestion is said to cause symptoms of degeneration in the hosts.

Other well known symphiles are the Paussid Beetles (Paussidae) (see p. 111).

Catopid Beetles (Catopidae), Fringed Ant Beetles (Ptiliidae) and Histerid Beetles (Histeridae) also include a number of myrmecophiles. Particularly notable among the last-mentioned family is the species *Hetaerius fer-*

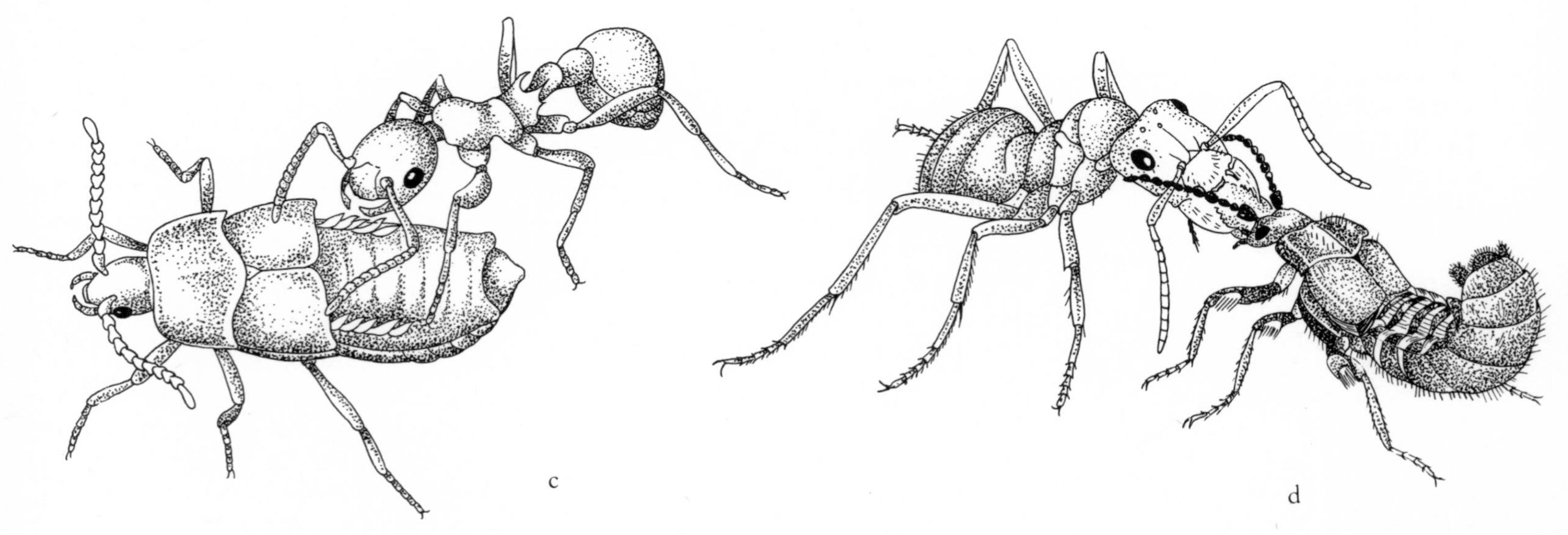

c d

rugineus which also accepts the secretions of the Rove Beetle *Lomechusa* (Staphylinidae). Tropical species of Histerid Beetles have also developed exudative hair tufts. Some Silken Fungus Beetles (Cryptophagidae) also live in ants nests, as do some Ant-like Flower Beetles (Anthicidae), a family which includes many representatives very ant-like in appearance. We can also find myrmecophilous species among the Darkling Beetles (Tenebrionidae). Rose Chafers, which belong to the family of Scarabaeidae, have already been mentioned as myrmecophiles. But in this family there are other examples of close adaptation to ants. The Dung Chafer *Choeridium granigerum*, for example, lives in the nests of Brazilian Leaf-cutting Ants. Another guest of ants is one of the Sap-feeding Beetles (Nitidulidae), namely *Amphotis marginata* which solicits food from ants even outside the nest. The Thorictidae of the genus *Thorictus* attach themselves to the antennae of ants and allow themselves to be carried about. They are fed by the ants.

Termites also have a wide and varied guest fauna—Ground Beetles (Carabidae), Rove Beetles (Staphylinidae), Hister Beetles (Histeridae), Brown Scavenger Beetles (Lathridiidae), Darkling Beetles (Tenebrionidae), Lamellicorn Beetles (Scarabaeidae). The guests of ants and those of termites resemble one another closely in many features, for example, in the nature of and varying degrees of adaptation. Among the termites' guests there are, for instance, also many species which exude attractant secretions from special glands ("narcotics"). As an example we might take the South American Rove Beetle *Thyreoxenus antuorii* (Staphylinidae). Among termitophiles there are various species which show a considerable distension of the abdomen (physogastry). Many workers are of the opinion that this physogastry may well be connected with the food fed to the beetles by the termites, since the same foodstuffs also bring about physogastry in the queen termites. Many of the species extend their balloon-like abdomen forward across the back. A second parallel to the myrmecophiles is shown by the termitophiles *Doryloxenus* (India) and *Pygostenus* (Africa) belonging to the family of Rove Beetles (Staphylinidae). They have tarsi adapted for climbing (scansorial), but make no use of them whatever. Other Rove Beetles *(Discoxenus, Termitodiscus)* have a disc-shaped fore body, beneath which all remaining parts of the body can be concealed.

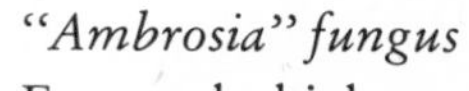

"Ambrosia" fungus

Extremely high specialization in feeding has been achieved by those beetles which prepare a fungus-bed (this fungus food is known as "ambrosia") which provides a source of nourishment for their larvae. Species belonging to several families of beetles cultivate fungus of this kind. We shall take as an example the Ship Timber Beetles (Lymexylidae), of which the Wood-boring Beetle *Hylecoetus dermestoides* cultivates a supply of ambrosia fungus. The larvae bore horizontal burrows into wood, on the surface of which, if the water content is adequate, a bed of fungus *(Endomyces hylecoeti)* develops which is very rich in glycogen. Infection of the passages with the reproductive bodies of the fungus is carried out by the female. Close to the ovipositor, the latter has two sacs containing fungus spores. When the eggs are laid, the surface of the eggs is covered with fungus spores and then in addition with a layer of slime. The newly-hatched larvae cover themselves thoroughly with this spore-transporting slime and then penetrate the wood. The fungus is now able to grow on the walls of the galleries. Later on the larvae ensure that spores are also distributed in the feeding galleries. Finally spores pass via

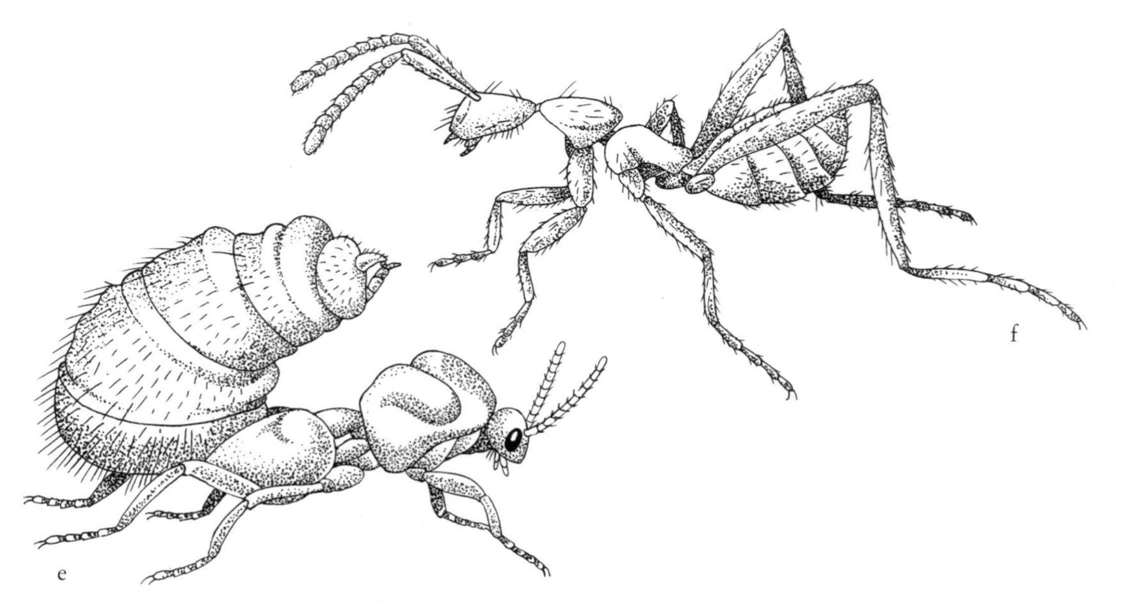

Myrmecophiles
a) The Rove Beetle *Dinarda dentata* Grav. eating parasitic mites from the Rove Beetle *Lomechusa strumosa* F. (both Staphylinidae).
b) Forest worker ant feeding on an *Atemeles* larva (Rove Beetles, Staphylinidae).
c) Scene showing the adoption of *Atemeles pubicollis* Bris. in a *Myrmica* colony. A *Myrmica* worker ant is licking the hair-tufts of the beetle which are associated with the so-called "adoptive glands" (Rove Beetles, Staphylinidae).
d) An *Atemeles* solicits food from a *Myrmica*.
e) Highly specialized Rove Beetles (*Thyreoxenus antuorii*, Staphylinidae) that live with termites, show extreme enlargement of the abdomen.
f) *Myrmeciton antennarum* (Rove Beetles, Staphylinidae) lives with foraging ants, and is notable for its ant-like form.

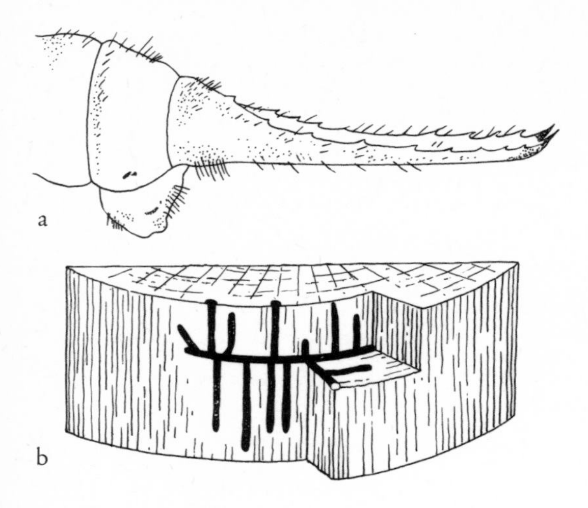

Beetles that cultivate Ambrosia fungus
a) 9th abdominal segment of larva of Ship Timber Beetle *Hylecoetus dermestoides* L. (Lymexylidae)
b) Diagram showing the tunnellings of a Bark Borer (Scolytidae) which breeds in timber.

the larva into the pupa, and then into the infestation sacs of the female. The presence of the fungus can easily be detected since it stains the walls of the galleries dark brown or black. With their specially constructed abdomen tip, the larvae remove the boring dust from their galleries. The whitish fungus develops and spreads very rapidly and the larvae keep the culture under control by constantly feeding off the conidia (fungus spores). The micro-climate within the galleries, in particular the degree of humidity, can be regulated by the larvae, by means of temporarily blocking up certain galleries with boring dust. The length of the galleries varies from about 18 to 26 cm.

The Ambrosia Beetles (Platypodidae) are also fungus cultivators. In the case of these beetles, the female constructs boring tunnels from which, with the help of the male, it carefully removes the boring dust. The larvae live in these brood galleries, feeding on the fungus-bed which grows on the wall of the tunnel. The infestation is spread by the female. Certain tropical species have depressions on the head in which the conidia are carried. It is probable that each fungus-cultivating species (among the Platypodidae there are 800 species) has a specific fungus.

Some of the Bark Borers or Engraver Beetles (Scolytidae) also cultivate ambrosia fungi. They are those few species that breed in wood, including, for example, the Conifer Ambrosia Beetle *(Xyloterus lineatus)*. The female of this Engraver Beetle first constructs an entrance tunnel, from the inner end of which a breeding chamber is constructed to the right and left. Egg niches are constructed along the walls of the egg tunnels. The larvae excavate mines or larval burrows at right angles, upward or downward, producing an overall ladder arrangement of galleries. Within this tunnel system, an ambrosia fungus is cultivated. The female parent spreads the infestation by means of spores which are stored within the gizzard and which are not digested even during a long period of starvation. It may be that it is precisely this period spent in the digestive tract of the beetle that gives the spores their germinative capacity. The female "weeds" the cultures, and removes foreign fungoid growths, yeasts and bacteria. In addition, it clears the galleries of boring dust and larval excrement, and regulates the air supply and humidity by temporarily closing off the burrows. The importance of this maternal activity is clearly illustrated if, for some reason or other, the female is lost. The culture of ambrosia fungus rapidly collapses and the larvae starve. In only a few species does the male participate in brood care by clearing the burrows.

Cannibalism

Especially among those species of beetles that live by predation, there are many which eat other members of their own species. This is a particularly striking feature among Ladybirds (Coccinellidae). Occasionally the females even eat eggs that they have just laid. The larvae are quite likely to attack one another and frequently the pupae are devoured by larvae of the same species.

How much food do beetles eat?

Detailed information on the quantities of food consumed is available for only a few beetles. Ladybirds of the species *Coccinella septempunctata* (Seven-spotted) require 420 aphids per larva in the course of their development. The descendants of a single female are said to consume 230,000 aphids within a single season. At a temperature of 30°C, the larvae of the Rose Chafer *(Potosia cuprea)* (Scarabaeidae) increase their body weight by 178.4 per cent in a period of 15 days. The fifth (final) larval stage of the Stag Beetle (Lucanidae) eats about 250 cm^3 of rotting roots of trees per month.

There are beetles which do not feed: many of the Scarabaeidae and one of the Fireflies, *Lampyris noctiluca* (Lampyridae). The Bread, Biscuit or Drugstore Beetle *(Stegobium paniceum)* (Anobiidae) is able to go long periods without food. In these species, the larva has accumulated such a stock of nutrients that the beetle is still able to live on them and even to produce eggs, a phenomenon which is also found in other insect orders.

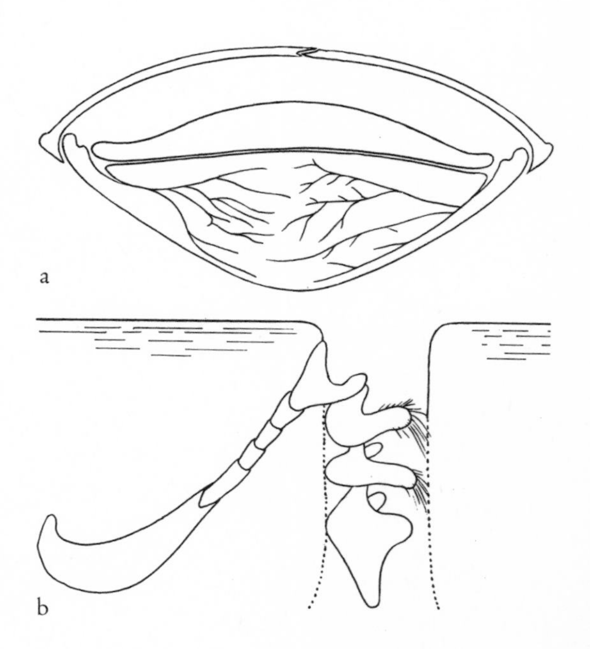

Respiration under water

In terms of the history of their evolution, the beetle's conquest of water as a viable environment was a secondary process. All of today's water beetles are descended from terrestrial ancestors. A great many adaptations were necessary to allow for respiratory exchange under water. The imagines of all aquatic beetles breathe air from the atmosphere and carry a supply of air with them under water.

Certain of the aquatic beetles have adopted "plastron respiration." The plastron is a thin film of air over the general body surface communicating with the spiracles. It is usually trapped in place by a felt-like system of hairs. The hair covering is extraordinarily compact with 800,000 to 250 million hairs per square centimetre. The plastron is highly resistant to water pressure and can withstand an excess pressure of 1 to 2 atm. It acts as a physical gill, that is, oxygen is obtained from the surrounding water and the insect does not need to retain a connection with the surface of the

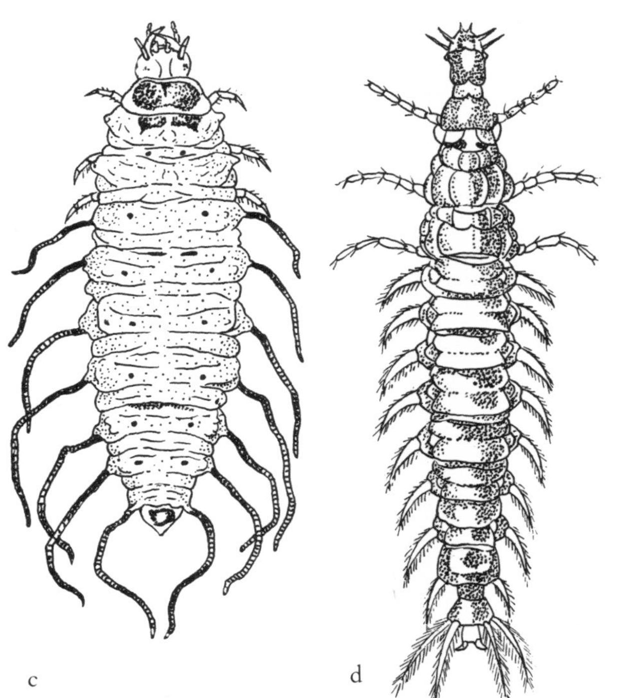

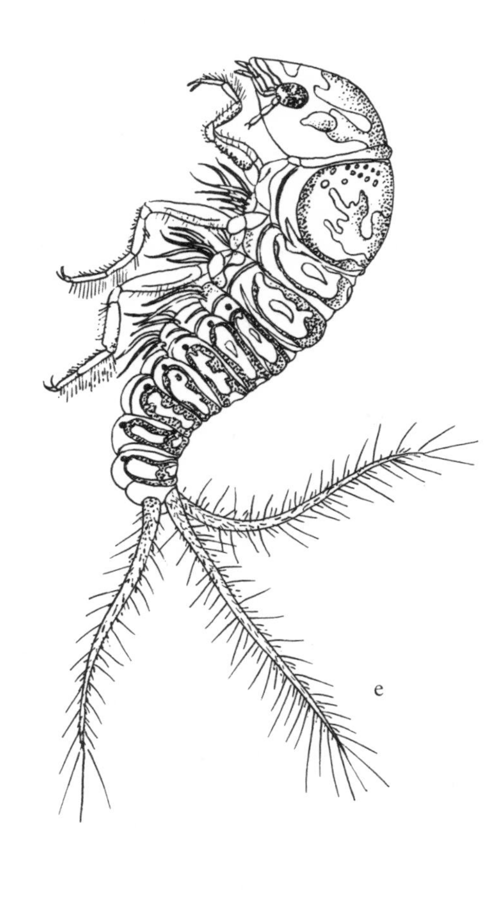

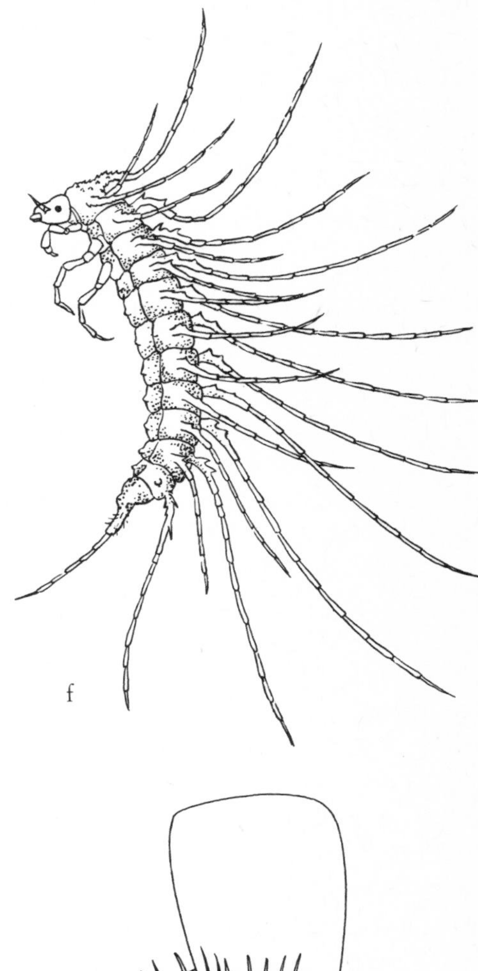

Respiration under water
a) Great Water Beetle *Dytiscus marginalis* L. (Predacious Diving Beetles, Dytiscidae), diagram of section through the abdomen; only the spiracles and the air space beneath the elytra marked.
b) Great Silver Beetle *Hydrous piceus* L. (Hydrophilidae) taking in air with the left antenna.
c) Larva of *Berosus spinosus* Steph. (Water Scavenger Beetles, Hydrophilidae)
d) Larva of *Gyrinus* spec. (Whirligig Beetles, Gyrinidae)
e) Larva of *Hygrobia tarda* Hbst. (Screech Beetles, Hygrobiidae)
f) Larva of *Peltodytes* spec. (Crawling Water Beetles, Haliplidae)
g) Branchial organ of *Helodes hausmanni* Gredl. (Marsh Beetles, Helodidae)
h) Abdominal gills of *Potamophilus acuminatus* F. (Elmid Beetles, Elmidae)

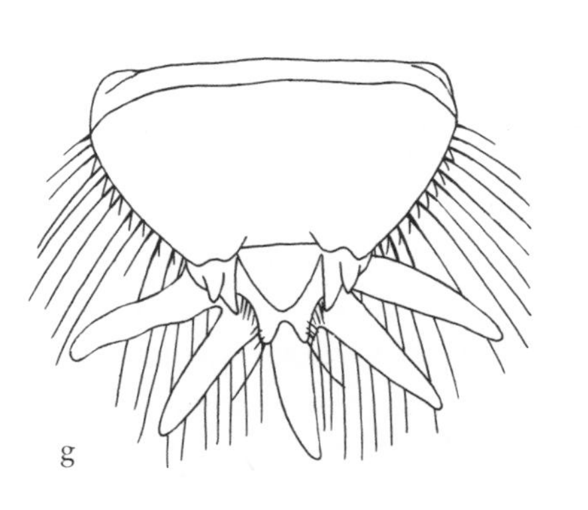

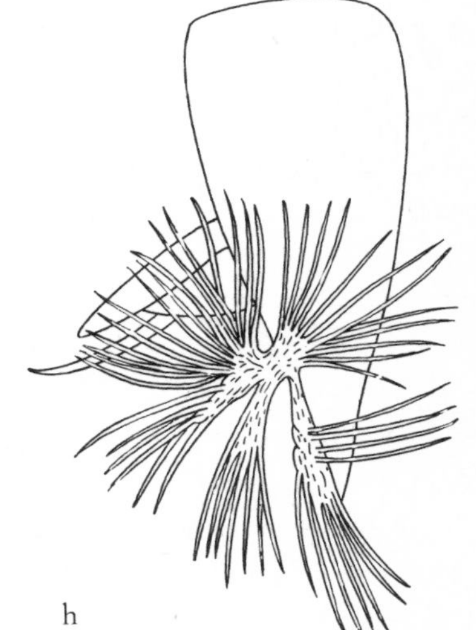

water. The plastron impedes swimming movements, so in general, the families of beetles equipped with them are those which clamber about on aquatic plants or other similar substrata. Some examples are Long-toed Water Beetles (Dryopidae), Elmid Beetles (Elmidae) and various Reed Beetles (Donaciinae, Chrysomelidae)—for instance, the genus *Haemonia* (Chrysomelidae). The plastron is supplemented by underwater air bubbles (assimilation bubbles). In theory, the system permits the beetle to remain submerged continually.

A second, quite different means of underwater respiration consists of carrying an external air bubble which is restricted to a particular region of the body and which must be renewed regularly at the water surface. This air bubble also functions as a physical gill. Let us look at some examples of this respiratory system. When Predacious Diving Beetles (Dytiscidae) come to the surface, air is taken into the tracheal spiracles, and in addition, the space beneath the elytra where the openings of eight abdominal and two thoracic pairs of stigmata are situated, is filled with air (Figs. 141, 142). The caudal extremity pierces the surface film of the water and respiratory exchange is effected by way of the space beneath the elytra. In many of the smaller Diving Beetles, an air bubble is carried at the extremity of the abdomen, being held in place by special chitinous ridges. The Crawling Water Beetles (Haliplidae) also have a supply of air beneath the elytra which they renew at the surface of the water through the caudal extremity. In addition they carry air under their broad, disc-shaped hind body. This air supply is in contact with the water and functions as a physical gill. An interesting adaptation is seen in the case of the Water Scavenger Beetles (Hydrophilidae) which have only a meagre supply of air beneath the elytra and so carry an air-supply bubble with them which extends along the ventral surface from the head, along the thorax to the front part of the abdomen. Respiratory exchange is carried out by means of the antennae. Contact with the surface of the water is established by the left or right side of the head, and the respective antenna is laid on the surface. By vibration of the antenna, air is carried in through a fine air channel along the antenna to the prothorax where it enters the respiratory spiracles.

Like the imagines, the larvae of Predacious Diving Beetles (Dytiscidae) and of many Water Scavenger Beetles (Hydrophilidae) also breathe atmospheric air. In their case, only the pair of spiracles situated at the end of the abdomen are functional. They too pierce the surface film of the water with the tip of the abdomen and thus a gaseous respiratory exchange takes place.

The articulated abdominal appendages have a supporting function in this. Smaller species probably subsist by cutaneous respiration. A number of Water Beetle larvae have gills, for instance, the larvae of the genera *Berosus* and *Hydrophilus* (Hydrophilidae). The gills are filamentous processes which are supplied with closed tracheae. Similar organs are also found in the Whirligig Beetles (Gyrinidae), in which the tracheal gills extend their surface area by a dense covering of hairs. The larvae of Screech Beetles (Hygrobiidae) also have tracheal gills which are situated ventrally on the thorax and on the first three abdominal segments. The larvae of some Crawling Water Beetles (Haliplidae) have similar organs of respiration, and in the larvae of Elmid Beetles (Elmidae) they are situated around the anus in a hollow that can be closed by a cover. The tracheal gills, concealed and protected within, are arranged in bunches and consist of a series of filaments which can be projected for respiration. The larvae of Marsh Beetles (Helodidae) obtain the oxygen they require at the surface of the water, but at the end of the abdomen they have eversible utricles known as branchial organs, the primary function of which is probably the disposal of CO_2 (carbon dioxide). A special method of obtaining oxygen has been evolved by the larvae of Reed Beetles (Donaciinae) (Chrysomelidae). Arising close to the paired spiracles of the 8th abdominal segment are a pair of horn-like processes which can penetrate the air-containing cavities of submerged aquatic plants. The air passes along channels inside these horns into the respiratory orifices. This process makes it possible for the larvae to remain inside the waterplants throughout the entire period of their development without ever needing to come to the surface. Various Weevils (Curculionidae) which have a similar mode of life, also obtain all the air they require from inside plants.

Beetles useful to man

At many points in this book it has been shown that beetles live by predation on other insects. Other species feed on plants which man calls "weeds," or else they dispose of carrion or dung. In these ways, as far as man is concerned, they are valuable links in living communities.

Many species of beetles, and particularly those which occur as pests in stored materials are used in experiments as laboratory animals. They are employed in the testing of chemicals suspected of being insecticidal and also in investigating other substances. Beetles also play a part in laboratory tests in work being carried out on hormone regulation and in genetic experiments.

Many species of beetles visit flowers, particularly Longicorn Beetles (Cerambycidae, Figs. 86, 90, 159, 184), Blossom Beetles (Nitidulidae), Soldier Beetles (Cantharidae, Fig. 189), Rose Chafers (Cetoniinae, Fig. 152) and others. Specialized pollination agents are rare among beetles, but nevertheless, the large numbers of beetles frequenting flower blossoms undoubtedly make a perceptible contribution to their successful pollination.

Many species of beetles play an important part as scavengers in the removal of waste materials in the natural environment. Numerous species of Longicorns (Cerambycidae), as well as representatives of other families, contribute vitally to the natural process of decomposition of dead wood. Other beetles destroy carrion, and the great army of dung eaters only really draws attention to itself when it is not present, as happened not very long ago in Australia. The indigenous Dor Beetles (Scarabaeidae) are adapted to the relatively dry dung of marsupials, and were unable to deal with the soft excretions of cattle that had been introduced. As a result, some 400 m^2 of grazing land per cow was being lost annually in Australia. Apart from this serious loss of pasturage, there were further harmful consequences, since various species of blood-sucking flies were able to breed in large numbers in the neglected cowpats. After intensive tests, African dung beetles (Scarabaeidae) were introduced, and since that ime, they have largely solved the problem. *Onthophagus gazella* has proved particularly successful, since in two to three days it is able to bury cowpats completely, as a result of which, in those regions where it has been introduced, the density of population of the Buffalo Flies has decreased by 80 to 100 per cent.

The origins of biological control using beetles as a means of combatting insect pests are clearly very old, since already in the 17th century Réaumur recommends the introduction of the Caterpillar Hunter *(Calosoma sycophanta)* (Carabidae) to deal with caterpillars, since it causes dreadful devastation among them like a wolf among sheep. Linné (1707–1778) attempted to follow up this suggestion, and writes:

"I have tried to obtain the seed of the latter, in order to spread it among the trees, but when I caught fair-sized Carabids and put them into boxes, with the intention of obtaining seed from them, they consumed one another. But if you go into dense woods, in summertime, where rotting trunks and stumps are lying about, and tear them apart, you will find a number of quite large Carabids living and laying their eggs there. You should take these up, as far as possible lifting whole pieces of wood, and place them in the garden, near to trees, preferably in a north-facing position, in such a way that the rotting wood lies half in the soil and half out of it. In this way you get Carabids in the garden which will do no harm to plants, but every night will climb on to trees and deal ferociously with the caterpillars there, annihilating them completely within a short time. It is one of the most effective of remedies which, even if it does not work in the first year, will certainly do so in the second and third; but after a few years, it should be renewed."

The great advance that had been made in man's knowledge of this beetle's biology is clear when one compares this with what the Scholastic Albertus Magnus (1193–1280) wrote about the Caterpillar Hunter, which he called *Spoliator colubri*. "This Ground Beetle which shimmers a greenish-gold colour, runs in the dust of country lanes and attacks beetles, sucking out their bodies. It derives its name from its habit of tearing open the skull of adders. It has been reported that it is fed first of all by its parents, and then lies motionless for a long time without food, until it is able to seek food for itself."

The idea of biological control, which originated with Réaumur, was later put into practice. For example, between 1905 and 1910, some 6,000 Caterpillar Hunters (Carabidae) were introduced from Europe to America where they were employed to control the Gipsy Moth and the Gold-tail Moth. Before their release, the imported Caterpillar Hunters were multiplied further by propagation. In assessing the probable results, the organizers of the scheme worked on the assumption that a single beetle, in its two to three-year life span, will destroy 1,000 caterpillars. The insects that were introduced established themselves and spread rapidly.

Beetles harmful to man

Because of their tendency to massive and rapid population increases, many species of beetles have achieved the status of major pests and have conquered almost every sphere of activity. Both in agriculture and horticulture as well as in forestry, and through the damage they cause to timber and other materials as well as to stored goods of all kinds, they have proved themselves very unwelcome visitors.

The classic example of a serious pest is the Potato or Colorado Beetle *(Leptinotarsa decemlineata)* (Chrysomelidae; Figs. 32, 104, 105, 180). These beetles were discovered in 1824 by the American entomologist Say, in the Rocky Mountains in the State of Colorado on wild *Solanum rostratum*, a plant of the Nightshade family. At first, this attractive beetle was a considerable rarity. With the building of the Pacific Railroad in about 1850, potato cultivation was also introduced to these regions and the Colorado Beetle changed its host plant. There followed a truly explosive increase in its numbers, which was accompanied by an extension of its territory eastwards. In 1859, the first report of great damage came from the State of Nebraska. Inexorably, the advance continued through the central and northern States of the U.S.A. In 1874 the Colorado Beetle reached the Atlantic coast. For the moment, it seemed that its spread was halted. But by 1877, in spite of the imposition of strict measures of control, the beetle was found in the dock areas of Liverpool and Rotterdam. In the same year, it was reported in Mühlheim on the Rhine, across the river from Cologne, and at Torgau in Saxony. By strenuous efforts and at great expense it was possible to destroy both hordes, although the outbreak in Saxony consisted of as many as 16 individual sites of infestation. Referring to this period, Horion writes: "The Colorado Beetle was a great sensation in those years, upon the subject of which the newspapers reported incessantly, and for the control of which the authorities issued new orders continually. Industry was not slow to exploit the beetle's notoriety; the firm of Stollwerck packaged chocolates in boxes carrying splendid pictures of the pest, and within a very short time, 135,000 of them were sold. Cuff-links and other items of jewellery in the form of Colorado Beetles appeared in the shops; in Mühlheim there was even a special 'Colorado Bitter' for the beer-drinker." In 1887, 1914 and 1934 there were new infestations, but in each case it was possible to contain and eradicate them. The suppression of the 1914 outbreak on the Lower Elbe cost 60,000 gold marks. Now the beetle was advancing from the west on a broad front. By 1922, approximately 250 km^2 near Bordeaux were contaminated. Some years the beetle covered 200 to 300 km in its advance eastwards. Having crossed the Rhine in 1936, it reached the Elbe in 1945, the Oder in 1950 and by 1960, had already crossed the whole of Poland. Today the Potato Beetle has extended into the farthest regions of the Ukrainian and Byelorussian Republics. The extent of the damage caused has been immense, although today, thanks to the development of chemical pesticides with which it is possible to combat the beetles, crop damage on a catastrophic scale rarely occurs.

Just as today we are much preoccupied with the problem of pests on living plants, in addition to the Potato Beetle for example the Rape Beetle (*Meligethes* spec.; Nitidulidae), various Click Beetles (Scolytidae), the Japanese Beetle (Scarabaeidae), many of the Weevils (Curculionidae), Bark Beetles (Scolytidae) and Leaf Beetles (Chrysomelidae), in past centuries it was mainly beetle pests in stored materials which were the subject of special attention. The storing of food supplies was already an established practice at a time when the development of beetles as pests, as a result of the practice of monoculture in crop farming, had as yet hardly started. The means that were used to combat one of the most serious pests to threaten stored grain, the Granary Weevil *(Sitophilus granarius)* (Curculionidae); at a time when there were no poisons available and even mechanical methods were still rudimentary, are described for us below in writings from a number of historical sources.

In his book *De re rustica,* the Roman politician Marcus Porcius Cato (234–149 B.C.) recommends the following: "If the corn worm is not to harm the grain, and if mice are not to touch it, it is a good measure to knead together some clay and some chaff very thoroughly with the liquid which is produced when oil is pressed, spread it thickly on the granary floor and then sprinkle more of the liquid on it. The grain is laid on this base only when the latter is completely dry again."

Another method is recommended by the Roman scholar Marcus Terentius Varro (116–27 B.C.) in his book, also entitled *De re rustica.* "In some countries, grain is stored in earth pits. Wheat will keep fresh in this way for up to 50 years, millet for more than a hundred. The corn-worm never penetrates grain of this kind. If corn in an ordinary granary has been infested by corn-worms, it should be brought into the open air and placed in the sun with vessels full of water beside it; the grain weevils will of their own accord make their way into the vessels and drown."

And finally we would like to add to this series one final remedy contained in the *Housekeeping Book* by Johann Colerus published in about 1590. "To drive out these worms, take a good portion of vermouth, pour water on to it and allow it to boil hard in a cauldron. Take out the water and pour herring pickle into it, and once again bring to the boil; any time there are large numbers of worms in the corn or in other grain, sprinkle a little of the liquid on the ground, toss the grain on to it and then sprinkle more liquid on the grain and mix it well together."

In a large volume published in 1665, Conrad Tiburtius Rangoni, a Professor of Theology at Greifswald also deals with the problem of grain pests and measures of control. He considers the causes for such infestations to be sins committed in the course of trading in grain and the farmer's ingratitude to God.

Such passages in old books not only reveal to us the vain attempts that were made in early times to control pests, as we see from the example of the Granary Weevil, but they also sometimes enter the realm of the fantastic. An instance of this can be seen in quotations from early sources on the subject of the Cockchafer (*Melolontha* spec.; Scarabaeidae). Today, this popular and universally known insect has in many places been almost completely exterminated by man, although certain people believe that it will continue to recur in 38-year cycles. But in the meantime, the Cockchafer lives on in the memory of that time when the creatures could be bought in "Zoological Stores" of Berlin, and not least, as a pest to agriculture and forestry in all the relevant text books and manuals. Reports in old books tell how in 1911 in the Rhenish Palatinate, 22 million Cockchafers were gathered up in an area of 1,750 hectares. At the same place in 1915, 14 million insects were caught. In 1939, some 15,000 kg of Cockchafers were gathered up on the Bergstrasse in Hesse, which represents about 18 million individuals. On the Baltic coast near Boltenhagen, huge numbers of Cockchafers were washed up along the shore, estimated to have numbered about 26 million specimens. Numbers on this vast scale represent, of course, immense potential for destruction. In France, the damage they caused was estimated to amount to 250 million to one thousand million gold francs per year.

Enemies of beetles

Like all insects, beetles also have large numbers of natural enemies. These may be insectivorous mammals, such as the mole, hedgehog or shrew-mouse. Beetles flying at night often fall prey to bats or night-jars. Well-known enemies of beetles are insectivorous birds like woodpeckers, tits, red-backed shrikes, common rollers, bee-eaters, even falcons. Many lizards and other reptiles feed on beetles. Frogs and even fish catch beetles, the latter particularly the larvae of aquatic species. Large numbers of beetles end their life enmeshed in spiders' webs, and there are many predacious insects that eat beetles, such as mantids, robber flies and, not least, predacious beetles themselves.

Apart from the enemies that prey on them, beetles have a large number of parasites. No phase of development, be it egg, larva, pupa or imago, is safe from infestation by parasitic insects. Only the tiniest eggs avoid being infested by minute egg-parasitic hymenopterons. Indeed, hymenopterous insects of a wide variety of species, are instrumental in controlling the density of population of beetles. In addition to the hymenoptera, various flies and particularly tachina flies play a role as enemies of beetles. The tachina flies live parasitically on the imagines in particular. Apart from insect parasites (parasitoids), mites also live on beetles, and especially if they occur in the tracheal system, can prove fatal to the beetle. The intestine and the body cavity are inhabited by various thread-worms (nemathelminthes).

Beetles can also fall ill. Numerous viruses, bacteria, fungi and sporozoa are able to develop within beetles. The symptoms and clinical picture of the diseases are very varied and little research has been carried out into them. Many of these diseases have been deliberately exploited in measures of biological pest control in which the agent of the disease is introduced among beetle pests.

How Do Beetles Multiply?

Sexual characteristics

External sexual characteristics and sexual dimorphism

Certainly in the majority of beetles, the sexes can be distinguished by external characteristics. But very often the distinctive features which separate male from female are only minute. In some instances, however, the external differences between the sexes are very great (Figs. 10, 11, 23, 44, 66, 69, 94, 150, 151, 156, 204). It is to these cases in particular that the term sexual dimorphism is applied. Within the individual groups of beetles there are many, very varied features which occur as secondary sexual characteristics. Generalizations are difficult, but it is usually found that all kinds of horn formations, enlargements of the mandibles or extensions of the antennae are typical of the male sex. Sometimes an enlargement of the whole body can also be observed in males, but there are also very many species in which the females are decidedly larger than the males.

Probably the most extreme case of sexual dimorphism is that found in the family of Net-winged Beetles (Lycidae). Ever since 1830, coleopterists have been familiar with the "larvae" of this beetle which grew to 7 cm in length and which were given the name of "trilobite larvae" on account of their curious form (Fig. 63). But no one succeeded in obtaining an imago from such a larva. It was not until 1924 that the creatures, which came from Indonesia, were shown to be the females of a Net-winged Beetle, *Duliticola paradoxa*. Finally the males were discoverd, and they are only about 1 cm long, and winged. They are like dwarfs when seen against the female, and scarcely anyone would take them to be a pair.

Sexual dimorphism with wing reduction in the female occurs quite frequently, not only in this family but also among Fireflies and Glowworms (Lampyridae), Drilid Beetles (Drilidae) and even in the Skin Beetle *Thylodrias contractus* (Dermestidae) which is parasitic on black beetles (oriental cockroaches).

Among the Oedemerid Beetles (Oedemeridae), particularly those of the genus *Oedemera*, the males have conspicuously swollen hind femora, but are not able to jump. The striking enlargement of the mandibles in Stag Beetles (Lucanidae) is restricted to the males. The various forms of horn-like processes in the Lamellicorns (Scarabaeidae) are reserved for the male sex. Female Straight-snouted Weevils (Brenthidae) have a narrow head with a rostrum which is often very long. The rostrum of the males is relatively short and instead, the mandibles are greatly enlarged and pincer-like. Also in the Snout Beetles or Weevils (Curcu-

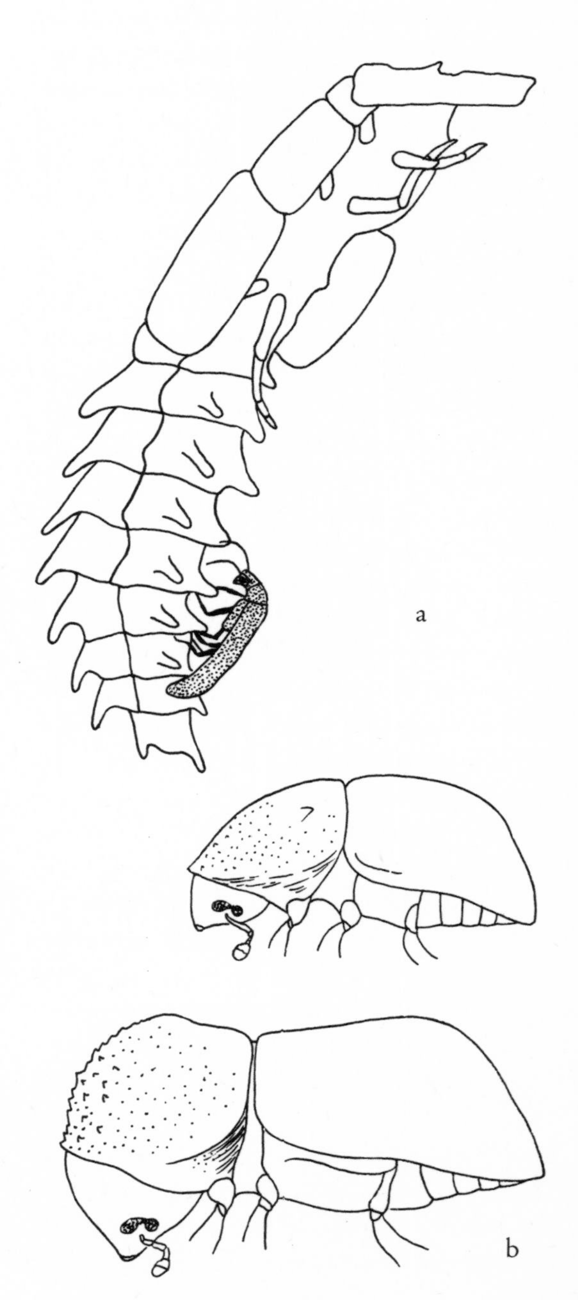

Sexual dimorphism
a) "Trilobite larva"; the wingless female of the Indonesian Net-winged Beetle *Duliticola paradoxa* Mjöberg (Lycidae) seen from side, mating with the small male (dotted).
b) The Pear-blight Beetle *Anisandrus dispar* F. seen from the side. Below female, above male (Bark Beetles, Scolytidae).

lionidae), the females often have longer rostrums than the males, a feature associated with their mode of life. A very striking example of sexual dimorphism is that found in certain Bark Beetles (Scolytidae). The male of the wood-boring Pear-blight Beetle (*Xyleborus dispar*) is 2 mm long and flat-bodied, the female 3 to 3.5 mm long and convex.

A great many other differences between the sexes are found. In the Longicorn Beetles (Cerambycidae), the males usually have longer antennae and their colour often varies according to sex. In the genus *Acanthocinus*, the females have an oviduct projecting forward which is otherwise found only rarely among beetles. Male Ground Beetles (Carabidae) are furnished with adhesive hairs on the underside of the segments of the fore tarsi (1,000 to 4,000 hairs per tarsus) which enable them to maintain their hold on the female during copulation. Sucker-like extensions on the same part of the leg are characteristic of the males of many species of Diving Beetles (Dytiscidae) (see Fig. p. 62) and Whirligig Beetles (Gyrinidae). The male, using these sucker pads and probably aided by adhesive glandular secretions, is enabled to retain its hold on the pronotum of the female while pairing. The males of many Click Beetles (Elateridae) have strikingly serrate or toothed antennae. Among certain species of Blister Beetles (Meloidae), there are considerable sexual differences in the structure of the antennae. The male of the Metallic Woodborer *Yamina sanguinea* (Buprestidae), found in Spain, has dark blue elytra with large yellow spots, while the female has dark red elytra with blue spots. These are, of course, only a few selected examples of sexual dimorphism. It would be possible to write a whole book on this subject alone. It should also be pointed out that conspicuous sexual differences make themselves obvious even in the pupal stage. A male Stag Beetle pupa has already developed its large mandibles. In the male pupa of the Timberman, the extremely long antennae are arranged in intricate curves within the pupal case. Even the larvae occasionally show sexual differences (for example, in the Drilidae). Male larvae of the Leaf Beetle *Phytodecta quinquepunctatus* (Chrysomelidae) have a colourless, transparent haemolymph, while that of female larvae has a cloudy appearance.

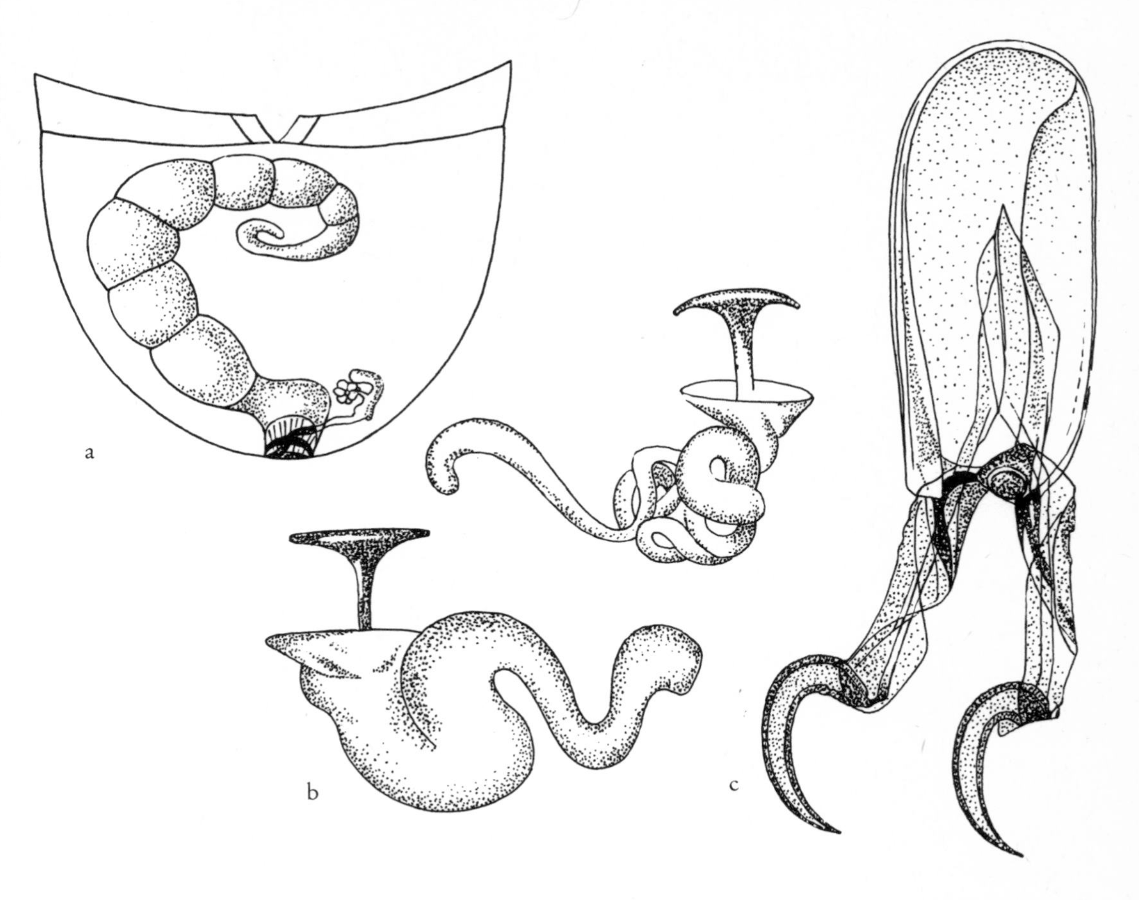

Sexual organs
a) Female of *Onthophagus fracticornis* Preissl. has only a single ovariole. Abdominal covering removed (Lamellicorns, Scarabaeidae).
b) Female sexual organs of two Fringed Ant Beetles (Ptiliidae) of the genus *Acrotrichis*, which are almost indistinguishable externally.
c) *Cyphon coarctatus* Payk., penis (Marsh Beetles, Helodidae).

Tertatological beetles

Occasionally unilateral hermaphroditism occurs in beetles. The gynandromorphs or sexual mosaics can be recognized clearly only in those species which exhibit sexual dimorphism. For example, a gynandrous specimen of *Ergates faber* has been described, which showed male characteristics on the left side and female characteristics on the right. Physiologically, the individual in question was probably a male, since the penis was developed normally, although situated in an abnormal position.

Internal male and female sexual organs

The renowned scientist Antony van Leeuwenhoek was probably the first to examine the sperm of beetles. Let us hear what he has to say: "An acquaintance who used to have many curiosities sent to him from abroad, once received an insect unknown to us, which had the name of kevers or molenaars [perhaps a specimen of *Melolontha* (Scarabaeidae); the Author]. When he brought them to me, I saw that a couple were in the process of pairing, and he kindly left them with me so that I could examine the male semen for the presence of spermatozoa. And indeed, I am convinced that I found some, which were of roundish shape with a long tail, but in the liquid substance in which they lay, were mixed with many other minute particles."

The internal sexual organs of beetles scarcely differ in structure from those of other insects, so we shall not describe them in detail here. Only a few particular features require mention. The females of all beetles have within the body cavity, on either side, a bunch-like, clustering ovary (ovarium) which consists of several egg tubes or ovarioles.

In various of the dung-eating Scarabaeidae which practice brood-care, a single ovariole is adequate for the production of those few eggs which are laid. The other ovary and its ovarioles are atrophied. In addition, the remaining ovarioles of the functioning ovary are also reduced. Similar conditions appear to exist in the majority of species in the sub-family of the Coprinae, that includes in particular the Tumblebugs or Pill-rolling Beetles of which frequent mention has already been made.

The penis and its accessory structures show an unusual degree of variability. As a single example, the family of Marsh Beetles (Helodidae) might be cited. The female sexual organs are also to some extent ectodermal. The minute Fringed Ant Beetles have a chitinous spermatheca (receptaculum seminis) of very specific form. The structure of the chitinous portions of male and female reproductory organs plays an important part in the classification of species. In many cases, species can be recognized from penial structure alone.

Finding a partner

For beetles, as for other insects, the finding of a sexual partner is one of the primary functions of the sense organs. In many species the process is carried out so inconspicuously that it is hardly to be noticed at all by the observer, and so, on the whole, very little is known in detail about the ways and means of selecting a partner. Usually we register only the more obvious phenomena, such as the emission of light or the production of sounds. In the majority of cases, the partners perceive one another by means of their chemoreceptors, the organs for the perception of smell and taste. But the photoreceptors or visual organs also play a large part in finding a mate. Very often beetles of one species concentrate around particular landmarks or features of the terrain, as a result of which the probability of meeting a suitable mate is greatly enhanced. A typical landmark of this kind might be umbellate flowers, for example. These are highly attractive to many Longicorn Beetles (Cerambycidae) and Soldier Beetles (Cantharidae), which in part frequent them for the purpose of obtaining pollen and other flower parts, but most of all in order to find a partner. Another phenomenon known as hypsotaxis consists of location of direction by taking bearings form an outline or silhouette. The focus of attraction is a silhouette which stands out at a high point on the horizon, such as a hill or group of trees. Cockchafers (Scarabaeidae), for instance, locate direction in this way. Bearings are taken from the silhouette and the direction, once established, is thereafter maintained. In this way, Cockchafers are able to make their way to their feeding places and, on the other hand, since relatively large numbers of individuals assemble, the likelihood of finding a partner is greatly increased. On the return flight to their egg-laying sites, the Cockchafers are able to use the earth's magnetic field in order to find their way. In experiments, they have been found to react to electrical fields. In addition, it was apparently found that their sense of direction was affected by the proximity of blocks of lead, 40 kg in weight, which permits the conclusion that they can also perceive gravitational forces. Below, let us consider in rather more detail the beetle's ability to produce light and sound.

The production of light

The remarkable ability of Fireflies and Glow-worms (Lampyridae) (Fig. 143) to produce light signals has always attracted the interest and attention of observers. Even in the earliest writings, we find references to Fireflies. For instance, there still exists an illustrated encyclopaedia from Ancient China, the *Erh-ya*, which is ascribed to a pupil of Confucius, Pu Shang (born 507 B. C.). This work contains the following information on Fireflies. "They have wings, and the abdomen produces fire. At the end of the summer when the grass is damp and wet, the worm grows; during the autumn the firefly flies out." Aristotle also mentions the Firefly under the name of Pygolampis (which means glowing with the hind part). In addition, Pliny gives a description of them, calling them Lampyrides, and says: "When in the summer evenings, the midsummer firefly begins to show its light, it is an important signal for the Roman farmer. It shows him that the barley is ripe and that time has come for him to sow common and foxtail millet." Pliny takes this opportunity to praise the great kindness of nature in giving mankind such valuable indications.

Fireflies are quite frequently mentioned in the writings of the Arabian culture group, such as in *Tractatus de simplicibus*, an alphabetically arranged encyclopaedia of Arabian pharmacology, written by the botanist Ibn al-Baithar (1197–1248). Here we read: "The firefly has wings like a common fly, and shines in the night. Pounded with attar of roses and dripped into the ear, it is said to cure suppuration of the ear. According to Massih Ibn al-Hakam, it resembles cantharidin, but is more active and produces greater heat." In his book *A Thousand Notable things, of sundry sortes* published in London in 1579, Thomas Lupton shows how to turn the light of the glow-worm to practical use. "To make a lyght that neuer shall fayle. Take the Woormes that shynes in the nyght, called Gloowoormes, stampe them, and let them stande tyll the shyning matter be aboue: then, with a fether take of the same shyning matter, and myngle it with some quycksyluer, and so put it into a Vyall, and hang the same in a darke place: and it wyll geue lyght. This I had out of an olde booke, which is not much unlike to the discription of Mizaldus."

In the writings of the great Italian scholar Ulysse Aldrovandi (1522–1605) we find some of the early results of the voyages of discovery to America. In his great Natural History of Insects there is a very interesting chapter on a luminescent beetle of Central America that belongs to the family of Click Beetles (Elateridae). "The Indians have various uses for it. They catch it by climbing a hill when twilight falls, as Peter the Martyr describes, swinging a lantern and shouting out in all directions 'Coccojus'. And these creatures come flying up at the call. But I believe that they are attracted there by the light, because here they find quantities of midges which they catch in flight and consume. When the Indian walks away with the light, they follow, falling to the ground as they do so, where they are easily taken up by hand. Others catch them in linen cloths. At home, it is useful to the Indians in two ways: it both catches mosquitoes and takes the place of a candle. It is allowed to fly about freely in the house within closed doors, and its light is no less than that of a candle. The Indians read, write and occupy themselves in other ways by its light. In the forest, the beetles shine so brightly that it is impossible to lose one's way. The Indians often tie 3 or 4 coccoji on a string round their neck, and while using this illumination, can cover up to three miles. Moreover, the light is not extinguished by wind. The light is emitted in part from the eyes, in part from the shoulders. For this reason, they emit more light in flight than at rest. Insects that are tired do not emit light, so closely is the capacity to emit light linked to the vital force."

Aldrovandi also took an interest in European fireflies and glow-worms, and made some very detailed observations of his own. The following is an extract from his comments on the habits of glow-worms. "I myself found a female glow-worm which was in the process of mating with a partner, and I kept them. The male did not leave the female even when it was touched. Next day they were still together and it was not until midday that they separated. By that evening, the female had laid a large number of eggs, out of which larvae hatched after only twenty hours. The male is winged and emits no light. Curiously enough, on touching the creatures, no sensation of burning is experienced."

In 1634, another important entomological work appeared in London, entitled *Insectorum sive Minimorum Animalium Theatrum* by Thomas Mouffet. Here we can read a good deal on the subject of lampyrids, including a very detailed description of the female imago. "The female is a slow-moving, wingless creature, the length of a finger. It is about the size of a medium-sized caterpillar, which it also resembles in other ways. The small, flattened head is hard, black, somewhat elongate and tapered towards the mouth. At the frons, two short antennae project. The six short legs are black and made up of three parts, and like those of caterpillars, they are joined on to the body near the head. The rather long, thick body is flattened almost like that of a tapeworm, with 12 distinct segments apart from the neck, which it can extend and retract at will . . . The white parts shine wonderfully in the night, having the appearance of earth stars, so that they seem to vie with the light of lamps or of the moon."

In the work *Sylva sylvarum* written by the English philosopher Francis Bacon, Lord Verulam, (1561–1626) we read the following on the subject of glow-worms (Lampyridae): "Glow-worms live only in summer, and they prefer darkness, country estates and blackberries."

One of the most important entomologists of all time was undoubtedly the Italian scholar Marcello Malpighi (1628–1694) who carried out anatomical examinations of insects with extraordinary skill and with unsurpassed precision. Malpighi was also concerned to discover the cause of the luminescence of glow-worms. He writes: "The outermost extremity of the body cavity, in the two hind segments, con-

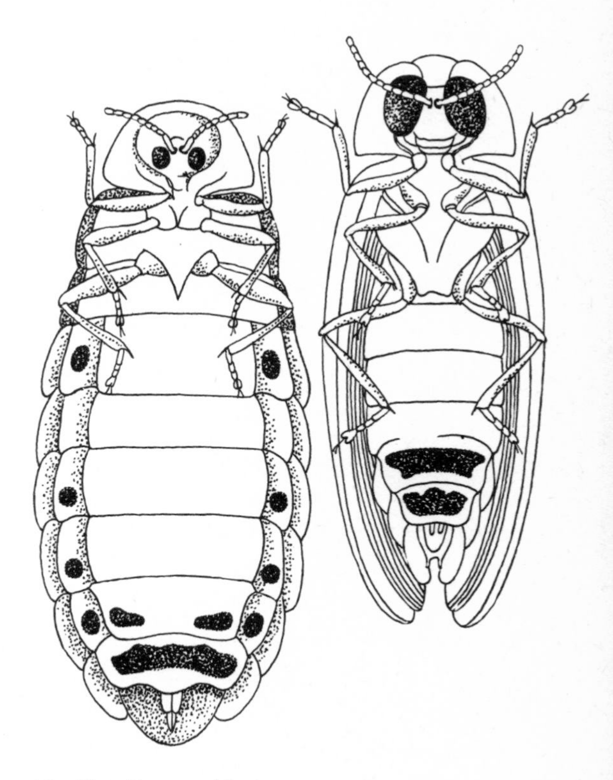

Fireflies (Lampyridae)
Lamprohiza splendidula L., Small firefly, left female, right male, underside, luminescent organs dotted in a dark shade.

tains a fluid which is the source of their luminosity. In the light it looks pale yellowish in colour shot through with a gleaming, milky substance; in the dark it shines out sulphur-yellow. This fluid seems to contain a mass of small yellow spheres in a similar, slimy substance, so that the whole thing appears semi-liquid. Now it is possible to make a number of statements on the subject of the light that the beetle emits at night and during the day in darkness. It is the two hind segments that emit the light. Sometimes it appears as a continuous gleam, but often as light pulses occurring rhythmically, similar to the beating of the heart. This periodic flashing stops if the insect's hind abdominal segments are removed experimentally; inside the segments that have been torn into, a continuous whitish luminosity remains like the continuous shining of the undamaged insect. The body of the undamaged living creature does not glow, but within the fluid mentioned, roundish bubbles develop which gleam out from the depths and sometimes disappear. When they increase again, there is a renewed luminosity. This comes about when, as a result of a movement of the intestines, large numbers of bubbles in the fluid are simultaneously forced outwards. During the period of luminescence, the quivering of these small bubbles can be observed clearly. Even outside the body, the fluid emits light, as long as the fluid remains liquid . . . If it dries out, the light disappears. The fluid retains its luminosity in water, vinegar and alcohol, indeed it even glows for a longer time and more intensely than in air. This emission of light lasts from May to mid June when it is lost."

In the descriptions of his travels written by the great Linné, we find another rather nice comment on fireflies, from which it can be deduced that much of the knowledge which existed in earlier times had been lost again by the time of Linné, and that the biology of the Lampyrids was something of a closed book to him. "Our great insect specialist, the Hofmarschall De Geer, has found that these females moult and metamorphose and that they emit light both before and after metamorphosis, as caterpillar, pupa and insect; from this we must conclude that this light cannot be a mating signal, for such a thing never burns in the immature stages, which still lack the oils required for it."

We have already seen that the production of light by beetles had attracted interest from early times. In addition to Fireflies and the Phengodidae, there are other beetles which also have luminous organs. Mention was made previously of the 2 to 6 cm long South American Click Beetle (Elateridae) of the genus *Pyrophorus* (Fire Beetle) which is known as the "coccojus." Its luminous organs are situated at the posterior angles of the pronotum and at the base of the abdomen. There is also an example of luminosity under water. The insects responsible for this are the larvae of the Firefly genus *Luciola* which inhabit streams and bodies of standing water in India, Indonesia and Japan, and which emit a very beautiful blue light. They are probably the only fresh water creatures in which luminescence occurs.

The main significance of light emission is certainly its role in bringing the sexes together. The light-producing organs function in a characteristic way in the different species. Many species emit light as a continuous glow, while in other species the light is intermittent, being "switched on and off" in a particular rhythm. The males actively seek out the females in response to particular spatial and temporal patterns of light which are characteristic of the species. It is possible to demonstrate this experimentally by setting up light traps that mimic natural light emissions. The females of many species often aid their discovery by the male by extending the abdomen upwards to make the luminous organs more clearly visible. A particularly spectacular phenomenon is the rhythmical flashing of lights which will sometimes suddenly illuminate a whole field and then as quickly die out. Other species rise vertically into the air as the light is produced and sink down again as if it fades. The natural effects produced in these ways can be extraordinarily impressive. Many tropical species assemble on particular trees. Then thousands of insects will weave back and forth in flight all the while emitting flashes of light. The tree stands visible for miles around enveloped in a cold, brightly-flickering light. There are also groups of male tropical fireflies which congregate on particular trees. They produce a synchronous flashing of lights which are then simultaneously extinguished. As if on the command of some unseen conductor, the tress appear suddenly, glowing brilliantly against the background of black tropical night for a brief moment and then are lost again in velvet blackness. *Photinus pallens* flashes its light twice in a second. Males of the genus *Pteroptyx*, which assemble in millions at certain points along the mangrove shores, flash synchronously three times in two seconds. Females ready for pairing, which are not themselves luminescent, are attracted by the light. Particularly those fireflies in which the males actively seek out the females on the wing have very well-developed eyes with 3,400 ommatidia. The eyes are so large they almost join together and have a binocular field of vision of 70°. In many species, for instance, *Luciola lusitanica*, the females respond to the flash of the male by emitting their own light. The great significance of the duration of the light signal has led to interesting cases of "abuse." The females of certain lampyrids for example, *Photuris versicolor*, mimic the light signals of other species of fireflies. And in addition, they give accurate responses to the flashing signals of foreign males. In this way, the latter are attracted and consumed. It is noteworthy that the females which make these foreign signals are said to be able to imitate the signal rhythms of quite a large number of species and by this means entice large numbers of males to their death.

Finally, one more eye-witness description of the brilliant effects created by tropical fireflies. "Those unforgettable evenings! When night falls, the primeval forest and in particular the open areas not far from the settlements, become alive with thousands of Lampyrids bearing whitish-yellow lights: brownish-black, broad-bodied *Lamprocera* (of which only the males glow), discoid *Hyas*, both with plumate antennae, slender *Aethra* and especially a wide variety of species of *Ludicotha* which are similar to our Midsummer Beetles. All of them are outshone by *Photinus,* a purely American genus. Like will-o'-the-wisps, this whole company of beetles, that during the day are inconspicuous and insignificant, flit about in the evening hours, at their most active between about 6.30 and 8.30, at which time they remain close to the ground on low shrubs and grasses. Later they rise to a much greater height until at about 10 o'clock, they disappear. In contrast, the luminous Elaterids, the Fire Beetles *Pyrophorus*, known as *cocuyos*, shoot up into the air like rockets, often rising from the ground right up into tops of the giant trees of the primeval forest. The twin fires they carry on the pronotum glow so intensely, and their ascent is so violent, that they describe a long, golden-red path of light." (Bürger, in: *Reisen im Brasilianischen Urwald* – Travels in the Primeval Forest of Brazil.)

Below, a few words on the physics and chemistry of light production. The emission of light by fireflies is carried out with a very high quantum yield. Fireflies convert 98 per cent of the energy used into light (an electric bulb in comparison only 3 per cent). The quantity of heat set free is exceedingly small. Therefore the radiance emitted is defined as a cold light. The bioluminescene of fireflies is described as primary luminescence, that is, it is generated by the insect itself, without the intervention of symbionts, within triple-layered luminous organs (reflector, photogenic cells, window) which are probably derived from the fat body. The light is produced within the cells (intracellular luminescence). The glow is initiated by a series of impulses from the abdominal medulla.

Two substances are involved in the light-producing reaction, the organic substrate luciferin and the enzyme luciferase. The light is generated when luciferin is oxidized by free oxygen in the presence of luciferase. Magnesium ions (Mg^{2+}) and adenosine triphosphate (ATP) also participate in the reaction, providing the energy required for the change. The oxidized luciferin is subsequently reduced again, whereby light is generated. The firefly's light comprises a wave spectrum of 500 to 600 nm. Attempts have been made to use the light-producing substances of fireflies as an indication of possible life on other planets. If the material samples obtained automatically contained any living matter in which ATP existed, they would create a flash of light which would be registerable.

The production of sound

Many species of beetles are able to produce sounds. Only in a few cases is the biological significance of stridulation clearly obvious. Apart from its function in bringing together the sexes which has been clearly illustrated for

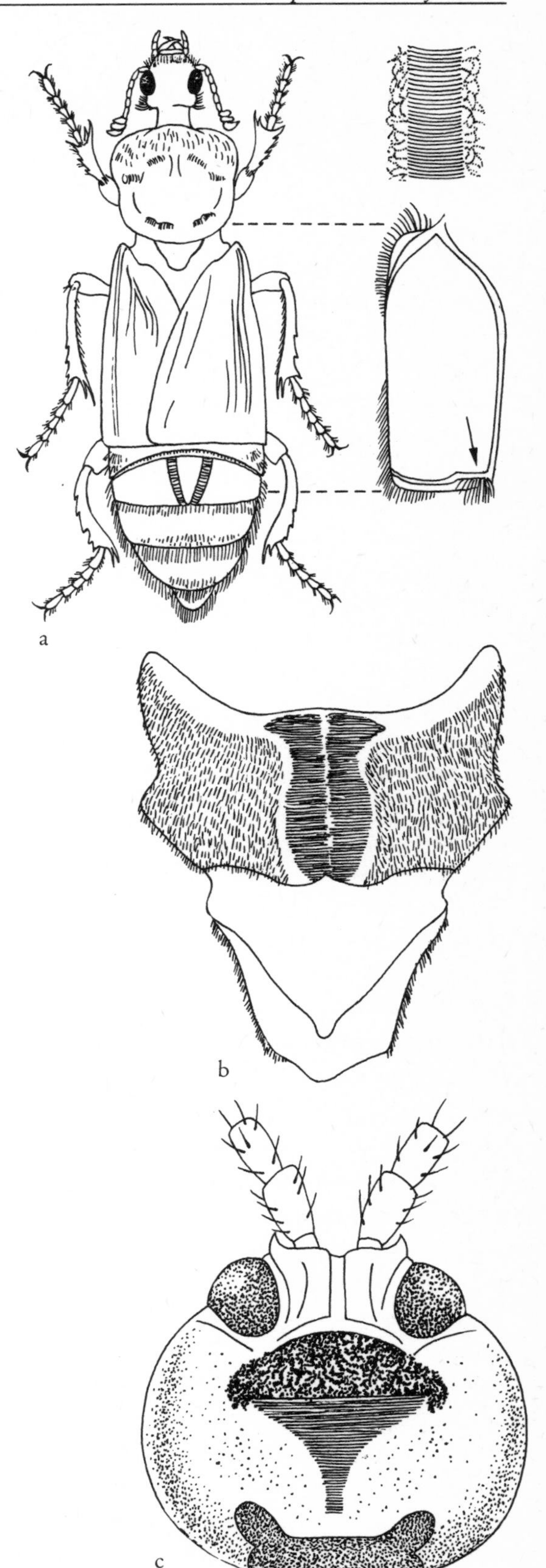

Sound production
a) Sound producing apparatus of the Burying Beetle or Sexton Beetle *Necrophorus vespillo* L. (Carrion Beetles, Silphidae)
left: Beetle with elytra removed to show stridulatory area on the abdomen
above right: Stridulatory area greatly enlarged
below right: Stridulatory edge or plectron on the inner side of the elytra
b) Mesonotum with stridulatory plate in *Rhagium inquisitor* L. (Longhorn Beetles, Cerambycidae).
c) Head of Southern European *Hispa testacea* L. (Leaf Beetles, Chrysomelidae) with stridulatory organ.

many species, the production of sound also seems to play a certain part in expressing sexual rivalry between males and to have a defensive function. For a long time it was thought that beetles were unable to hear. But today we know that noises can be perceived by the beetle as a response to vibration. Two sense organs are involved: sounds with a frequency of more than 300 Hz are perceived by means of a scolopale organ on the outer extremity of the tibia. Sounds with a lower frequency stimulate responses in hair sensilla on the tarsi. Dor Beetles of the genus *Geotrupes* (Scarabaeidae) can perceive sounds in the range of 600 to 1500 Hz.

Let us consider a few examples. Beetles produce a wide range of very varied noises, for instance, the humming or buzzing produced in flight, or the gnawing sounds of wood-eating larvae. Female Burying Beetles (*Necrophorus*, Silphidae) chirp softly as they engage in brood care. These sounds are produced by the friction of the posterior edge of the elytra (the sounding edge or plectrum) against a file-like area on the upper side of one of the abdominal segments. Pegor Bess Beetles (Passalidae) produce quite loud noises by rubbing the apse of the elytra against the upper side of the abdomen. The larvae of Pegor Bess Beetles can also stridulate. The chirping of larvae is very widespread among beetles, notably in the dung-eating Lamellicorns (Scarabaeidae).

Stridulation in Longhorn Beetles (Cerambycidae) was a phenomenon remarked by Aldrovandi. He writes that they produce "a chirping, quiet sound"; it was even turned to practical use (see p. 118). Here, as in the case of most other beetles, a stridulatory edge *(plectrum)* is rubbed against a stridulatory region (*pars stridens*) which consists of several teeth or ridges. The sharp edge of the pronotum functions as the plectrum, the *pars stridens* is well forward on the upper surface of the mesothorax. In the Capricorn Beetle *(Cerambyx cerdo)* the production of sound is linked with the main period of activity and occurs chiefly at night. Males also stridulate during fighting. A quite different means of sound production is found in the case of the Longhorn Beetles *Notorhina punctata*. These beetles wedge themselves into cracks of suitable width in the bark of pine trees and make vibrating movements with their body, which beats against the bark in a particular rhythm, creating a buzzing sound. The beetles have even been observed to reply to one another in this way.

Many of the Leaf Beetles of the family of Chrysomelidae, such as the Lily Beetles (*Lilioceris lilii*), are conspicuous for the loud chirping tones they produce. In the middle of the terminal abdominal segment is a stridulatory ridge, while the underside of the elytra forms the plectrum. The German popular name *Hähnchen* (Leaf Chickens) probably refers to this "crowing" sound made by the little beetles, that is, their name derives from the ability to produce sound. The Hedgehog Beetle *(Hispella atra)* is also capable of stridulation. It scrapes the front edge of the pronotum against the top of the head. So this beetle needs only to nod its head and it can produce sounds. Tropical species of *Hispa* are even able to vary the pitch of the sounds they make, as can be seen from the structure of their stridulatory organs. The May Beetle *(Polyphylla fullo)* (Scarabaeidae) can produce such a clamorous chirping, particularly if one strikes the trunks of the pines in which the creatures are sitting, that it really sounds for all the world like the twittering of young birds. It is less well known that Ground Beetles (Carabidae), for example, the snail-eating beetles of the genus *Cychrus*, can also stridulate. They do so by rubbing the side edge of the terminal abdominal segment back and forth against the tip of the elytra.

It is probably not generally known that Water Beetles are also able to produce sounds. The Screech Beetle *Hygrobia tarda* (Hygrobiidae) stridulates energetically by rubbing the hind abdominal segment against the back edge of the elytra creating a whistling sound. In *Spercheus emarginatus* (Spercheidae), both sexes are able to stridulate. On either side of the first abdominal segment is a modified stridulatory area which is moved across a striated area on the underside of the elytra. Many Water Scavenger Beetles (Hydrophilidae), such as *Hydrous* and *Berosus*, also possess an organ of stridulation of similar construction. The male of the Great Silver Beetle (*Hydrous piceus*) generates sounds which are answered by the female of the species.

And still numerous examples remain. We should not fail to mention that many Bark Beetles (Scolytidae) are also able to stridulate. *Blastophagus*, for example, chirps so loudly that its call can be heard from a distance of 2 m. Usually Bark Beetles stridulate within the breeding galleries. Hercules Beetles produce sounds at the mere sight of a rival. Pollen Beetles (Nitidulidae) and Darkling Beetles (Tenebrionidae) complete the list of sound-emitting beetles, to which Click Beetles (Elateridae), with their sharp, ticking noises can also be added. However varied in detail the mechanism of sound production may be, however variable the convex chitinous parts of the body that are used for the amplification of sound, beetles chirp, squeak, whistle, grate, rasp and creak in a wide variety of different ways, often producing quite a considerable volume of noise.

156 Pill-rolling Beetles from South America (Scarabaeidae)
above: Left male, right female of *Oxysternon festivus*
centre: Left female, right male of *Phanaeus imperator*, male of *Phanaeus difformis*
below: left female, right male of *Oxysternon conspilliertus*

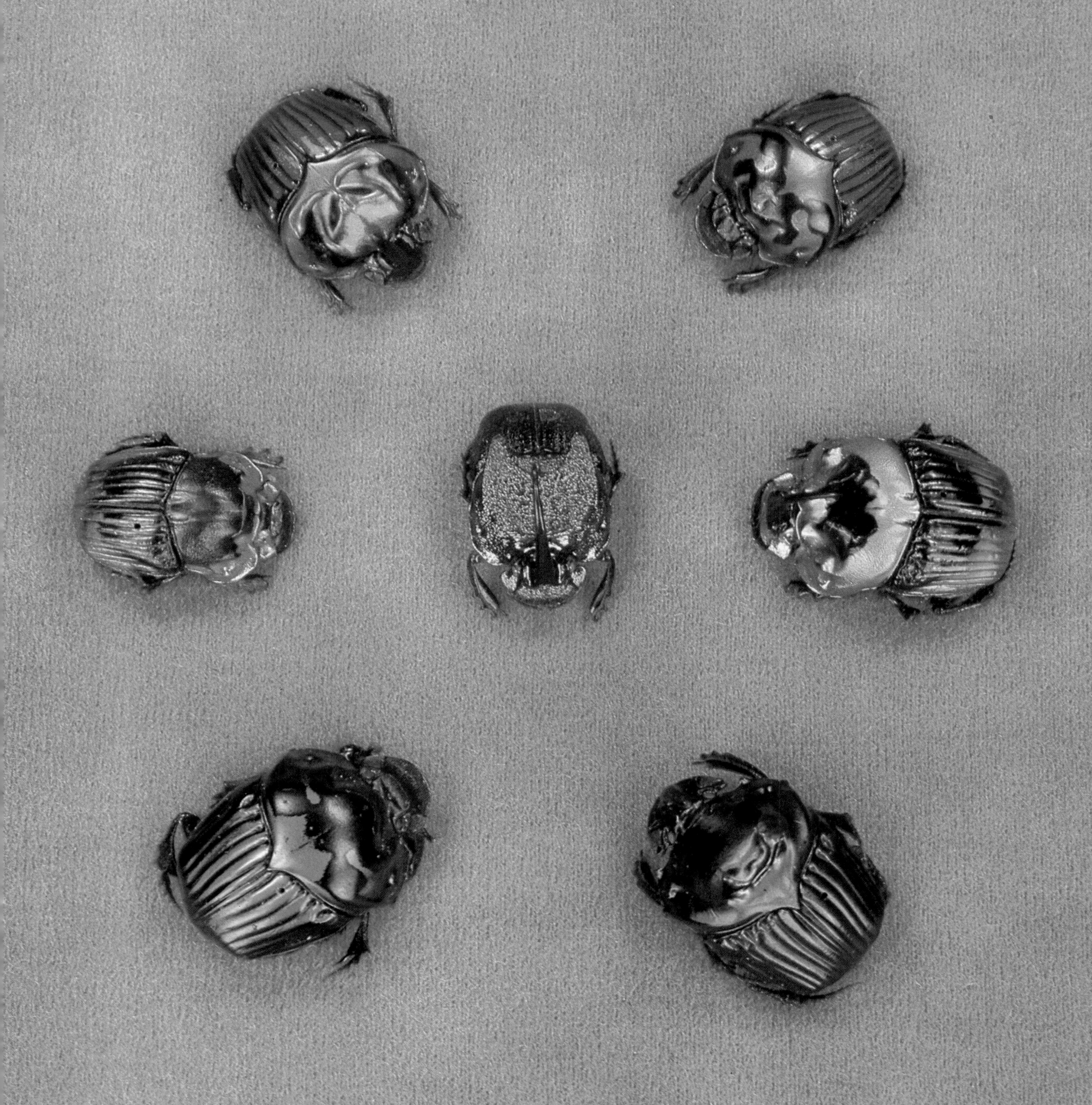

Unusual Longicorn Beetles (Cerambycidae)

157 *Gerania bosci* from Java
158 *Gnoma zonaria*, male from New Guinea (extended pronotum); *Gnoma zonaria*, female; *Enicodes schreibersi* from New Caledonia (elytra extended in swallow-tail effect).

159 The European Longhorn Beetle *Strangalia quadrifasciata* (Cerambycidae) drinking drops of water from a bindweed flower (Convolvulus).

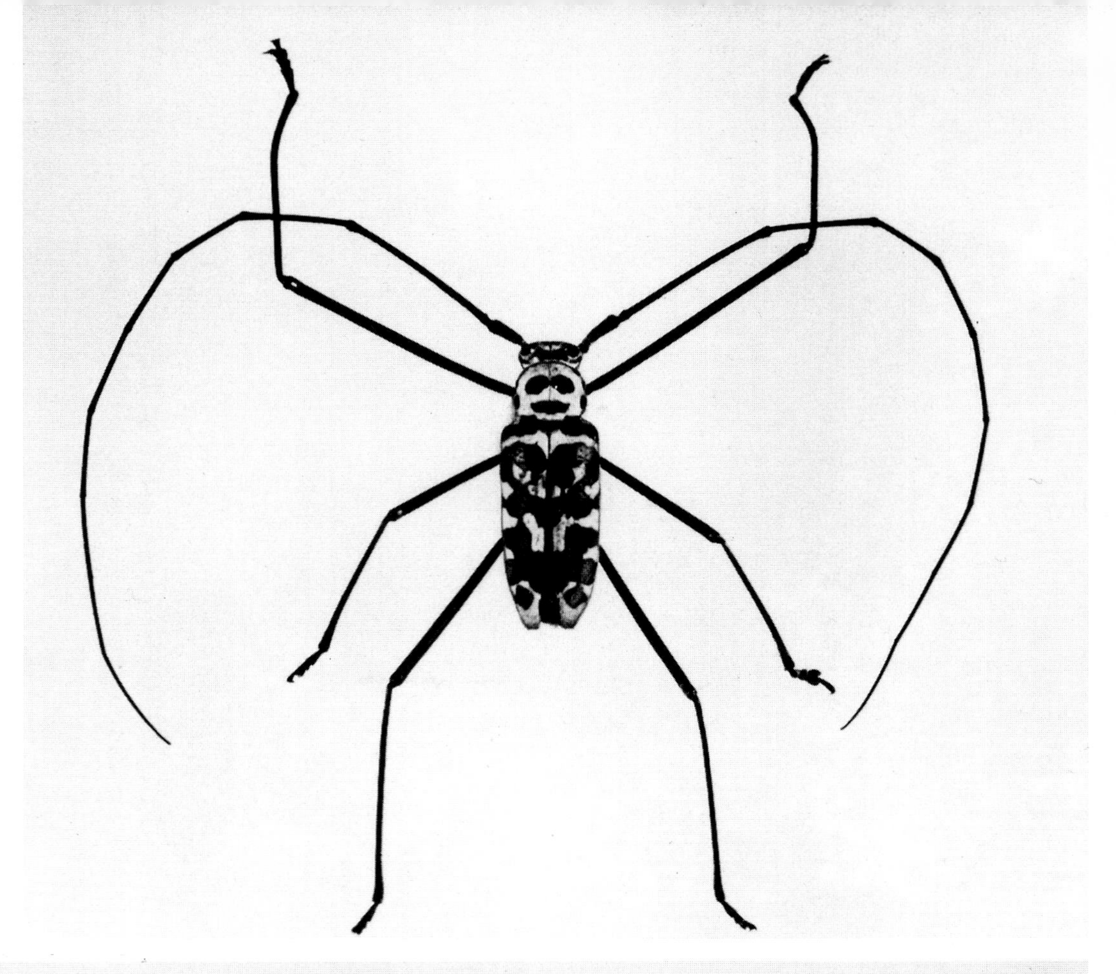

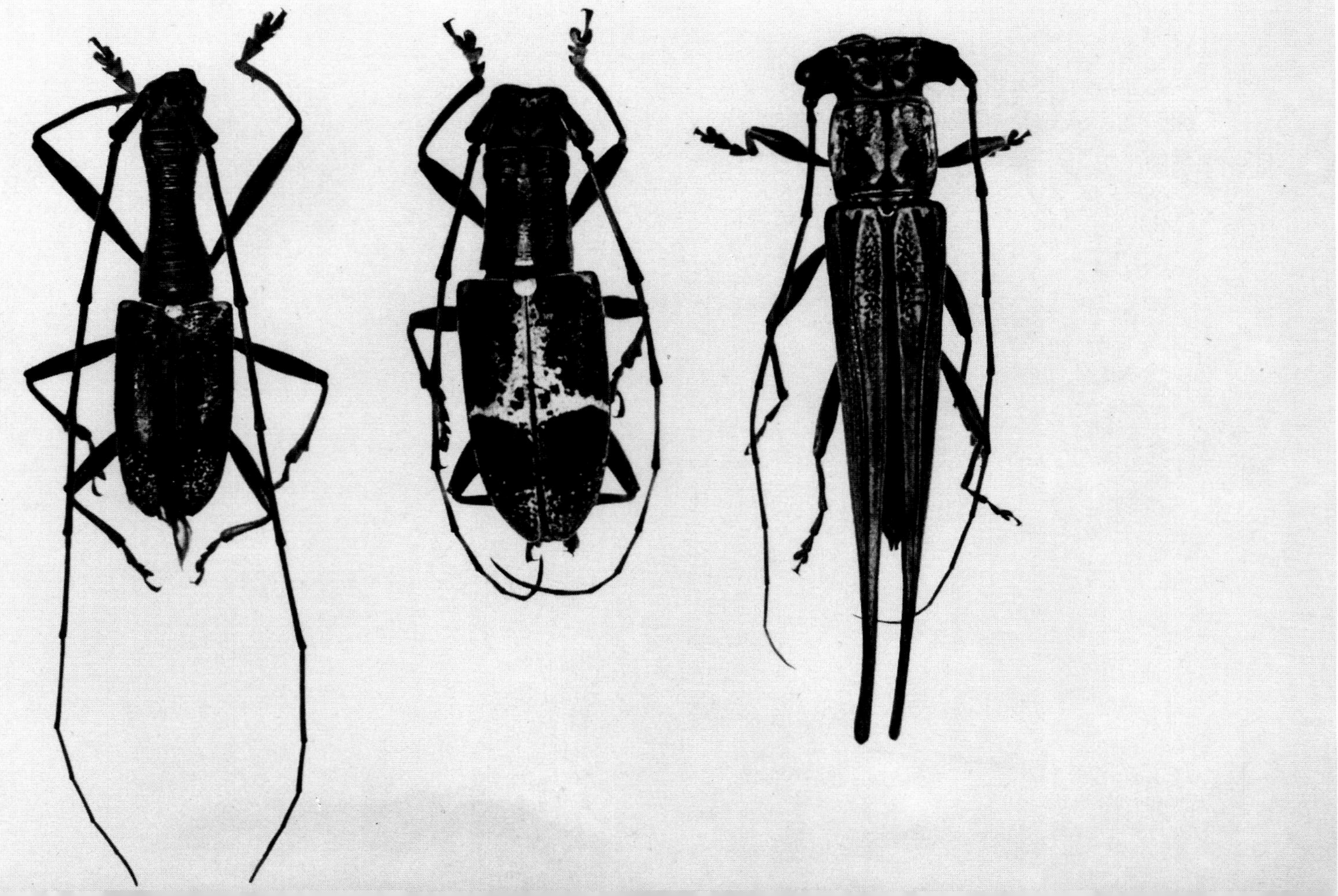

160 Some brilliantly coloured Ground Beetles (Carabidae)
left: *Carabus hispanus rutilans* from the Pyrenees
centre: *Carabus arcadicus* from Greece
right: *Carabus hispanus* from Southern France

161 Tropical Tortoise Beetles (Cassidinae, Chrysomelidae)
above: *Glima mirabilis* from Brazil
Tauroma casta from Central America
Pseudomesomphalia saundersi from South America
centre: *Oxynodera distincta* from Costa Rica
below: *Pseudomesomphalia pascoei* from Central America
Selenis sparsa from Central and South America
Pseudomesomphalia perimunda from Northwestern Mexico

Following pages:

162 Longhorn Beetle *(Callisphyris macropus)* (Cerambycidae) from Chile; length of body 2 cm

Some curious Weevils (Curculionidae)

163 *Eupholus albofasciatus* from New Guinea
164 *Entimus imperialis* from Brazil

165 Straight-snouted Weevil (Brenthidae) The male of *Brenthus anchorago* from Brazil is like some strange ghostly apparition.

Some curious Weevils (Curculionidae)

166 *Ozopherus muricatus* from Peru
167 *Diaprosomus magnificus* from Brazil

168 *Brachycerus fascicularis* from South Africa has very much the appearance of a brush. It is "coloured" in tones of grey ranging from white to black.

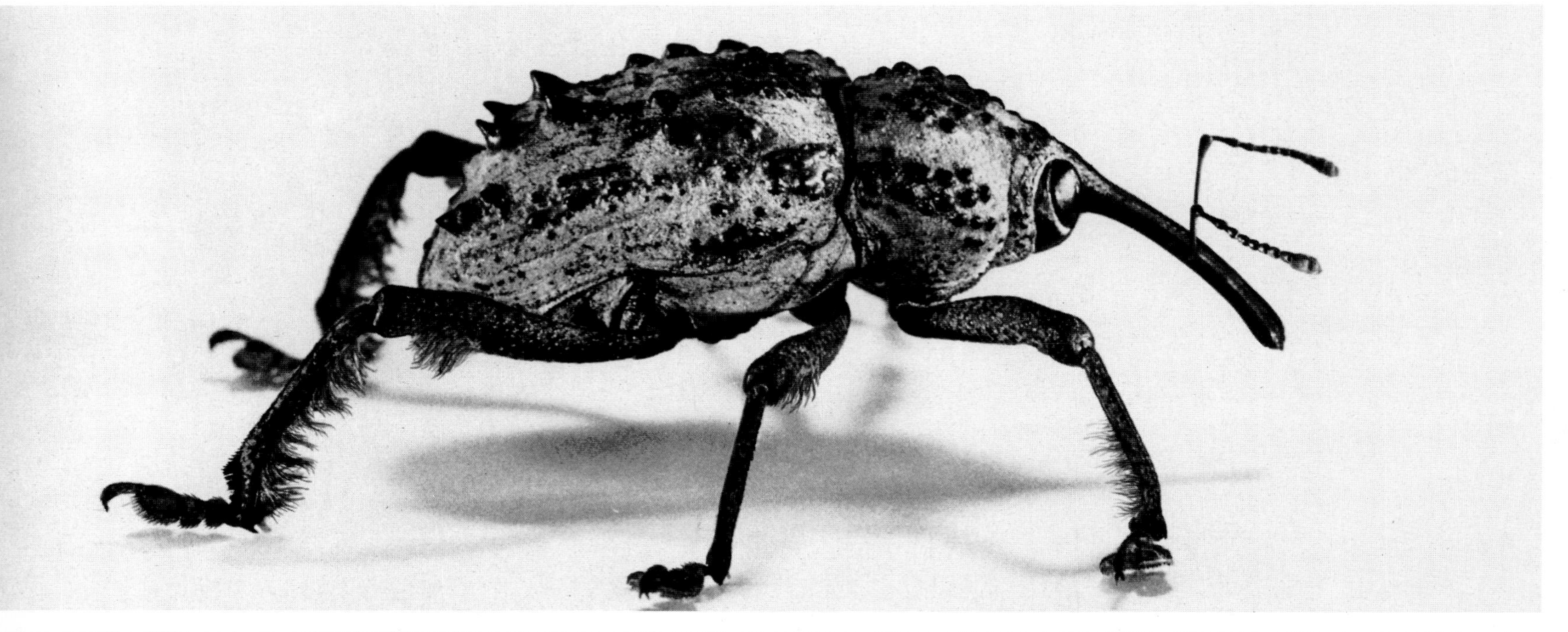

Some curious Weevils (Curculionidae)

169 *Gymnopholus weiskei*, male, from New Guinea
170 *Rhynastus sternicornis* from Argentina
171 *Rhigus schüpeli* from Brazil
172 *Phaedropus togatus* from Brazil

173 *Trichaptus mutillarius* from Brazil looks for all the world like a small soft toy. It is matt black with eight large creamy-white spots and two bright orange ones.

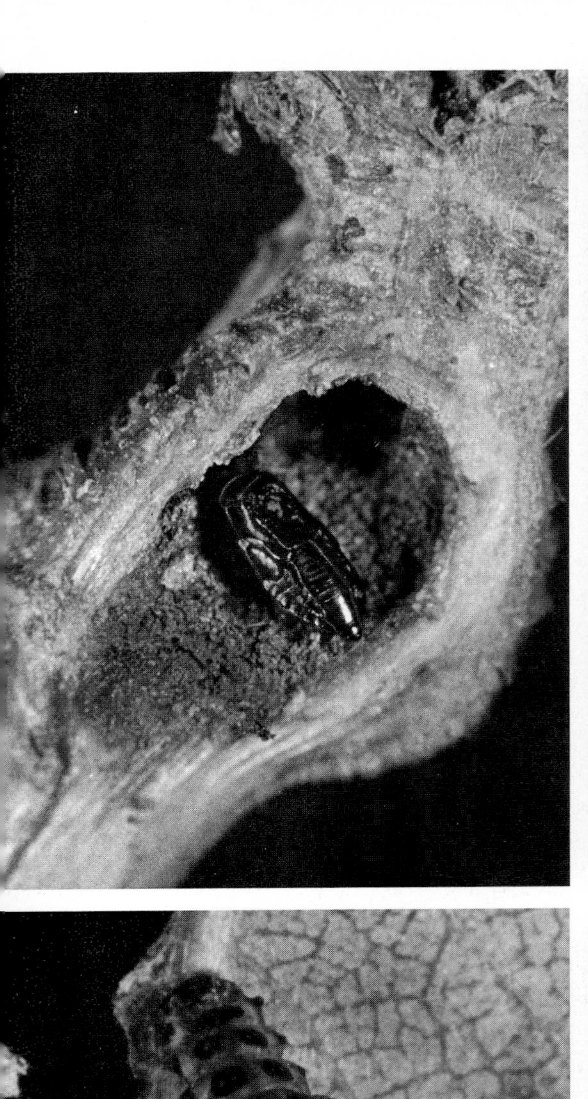

Pupae of various European beetles

174 Pupa of a Clover Weevil (*Apion* spec.; Curculionidae) inside a dissected gall in a stem of mugwort *(Artemisia)*.
175 The newly emerged Tortoise Beetle (*Cassida* spec.; Chrysomelidae) is still colourless; its curious pupal form can still be seen clearly.
176 *Melasoma vigintipunctata* (Leaf Beetles, Chrysomelidae). Note that the pupa is secured to the skin of the last larval instar.
177 Longhorn Beetle *(Rhagium mordax)* (Cerambycidae) inside a pupal cell bounded by wood chips.

Larvae of various European beetles

178 Lattice-like cocoon of the Snout Beetle *Cionus* spec. (Weevils, Curculionidae)
179 Great Water Beetle (*Dytiscus* spec.), head; note the mandibles traversed internally by a suction channel (Diving Beetles, Dytiscidae).
180 Potato or Colorado Beetle *(Leptinotarsa decemlineata)* (Leaf Beetles, Chrysomelidae)
181 Rhinoceros Beetle *(Oryctes nasicornis)* (Lamellicorn Beetles, Scarabaeidae)

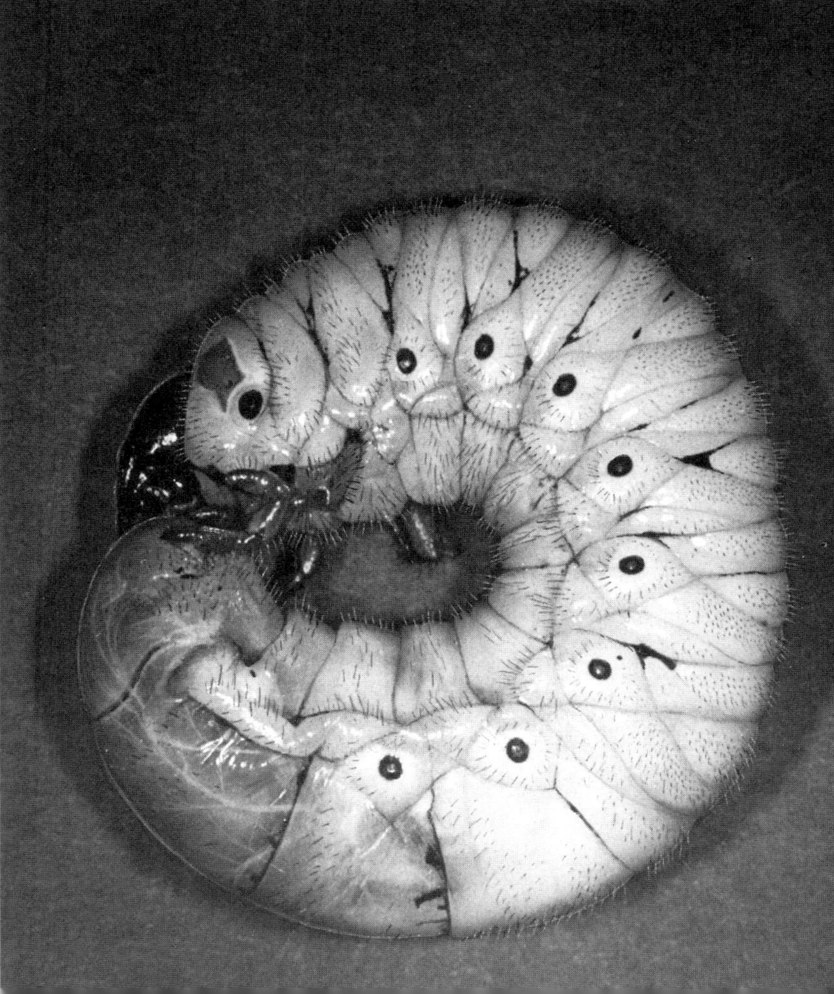

182/183 European Oil Beetle *(Meloe proscarabaeus* (Meloidae), female with egg-filled abdomen (up to 10,000 eggs).

Beetles feeding

184 Longicorn Beetles *(Strangalia melanura)* (Cerambycidae) feeding on flowerheads.
185 Carrion Beetle *(Phosphuga atrata)* (Silphidae) on dead bat (noctule).
Both species live in Europe.

Beetles copulating

186 Dock-leaf Beetles *(Gastrophysa viridula)* (Chrysomelidae). A male, already in the act of mating, is pulled down from the female by two rivals. The abdomen of the female is grossly swollen by the volume of well-developed eggs.
187 Two pairs of Oak-leaf-rolling Beetles *Attelabus nitens* (Attelabidae). The beetles are glossy black with pronotum and elytra red, and are about 6 mm in length.

188 *Stenocorus meridianus* (Scarabaeidae) from Europe
189 Soldier Beetles *(Cantharis fusca)* (Cantharidae) from Europe. During copulation, the female is consuming a second male.

Egg clutches produced by some European beetles

190 Alder-leaf Beetle *(Agelastica alni)* (Chrysomelidae), lemon-yellow
191 *Melasoma aenea* (Chrysomelidae), cream-coloured
192 Longhorned Beetle *(Hylotrupes bajulus)* (Cerambycidae), white

193 The saffron-yellow eggs of the Seven-spotted Ladybird *(Coccinella septempunctata)* (Coccinellidae) on a thistle

194 "Mealworms," the larvae of the Mealworm Beetle *(Tenebrio molitor)* (Tenebrionidae), a standard source of food, much used by terrarium keepers and bird breeders, which is produced and retailed literally in tons every year.

Larvae of various European beetles

195 Cardinal Beetle *(Pyrochroa coccinea)* (Cardinal Beetles, Pyrochroidae)
196 *Gnaptor spinimanus* (Darkling Beetles, Tenebrionidae)
197 *Phaenops cyanea* (Metallic Beetles, Buprestidae), drumstick larva
198 Carrion Beetle (*Blithophaga* spec.; Silphidae)

Pupae of various European beetles

199 The pupa of the Mealworm Beetle *(Tenebrio molitor)* (Tenebrionidae) looks as if it were moulded in wax.
200 Ladybirds (Coccinellidae)
left: *Anatis ocellata*
centre: *Harmonia quadripunctata*
right: *Exochomus quadripustulatus* inside its last larval skin

Measures of brood provision in European Leaf-rollers (Attelabidae)

201 A particularly successful funnel-shaped roll constructed by the Beech-leaf-roller *(Byctiscus betulae)*.
202 The canister rolls constructed by the Oak-leaf-roller *Attelabus nitens* look like the neat work of a saddler.
203 The Oak-leaf-roller *Attelabus nitens* is only about 6 mm long, its leaf roll about 2 cm × 1 cm.

Only in a few cases do we understand the "language" of beetles. But undoubtedly it is very frequently linked with finding a sexual partner. Fighting between rivals can be included here. But the significance of sound production in larvae remains uncertain. Whether they are sounds generated by maxillae and mandibles or, as in the case of *Geotrupes* (Scarabaeidae), by the back pair of legs, the question of who is supposed to hear the noises produced by larvae immured deep down in an earth burrow and moreover totally enclosed in a mass of food material, remains for the time being an inexplicable mystery.

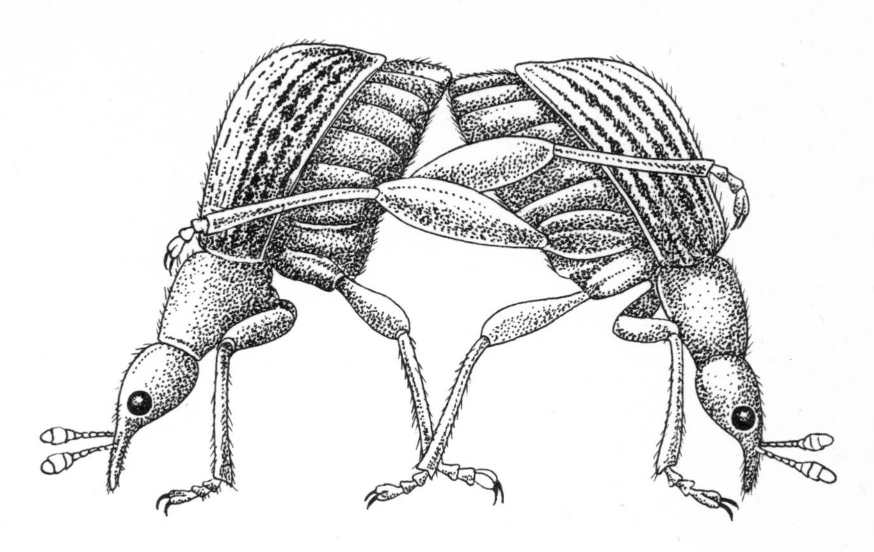

A fight between males of the Beech-leaf-roller *Deporaus betulae* L. Leaf-rollers (Attelabidae) the hind legs are used to clasp the opponent.

Courtship display and contention between rivals

It is known that courtship display and fights between males occur in many species of beetles. The series of movements performed by the Blister Beetle *Cerocoma schaefferi* (Meloidae) is known as a fanning display. When male and female meet, they remain at first standing in front of one another. Then the male climbs on to the female and moves his front legs up and down in a very rapid fanning movement. This activity alternates with short pauses in which the male strokes one of its front legs along its antennal or palpal segment which is furnished with glands. In this way, the leg probably takes up a quantity of aromatic matter. Then the fanning is continued, which clearly induces in the female a preparedness for mating.

Among the Soft-winged Flower Beetles (Melyridae) which are often very brightly coloured, the males possess organs known as excitators. These are organs into which glands open, and which in a distribution characteristic of species, can occur in various parts of the body, as on particular segments of antennae or palps, on the pro- or meso-throax, on the mid or hind tibiae, but most frequently on the frons or at the end of the elytra. During courtship, these organs, which at other times are concealed, are displayed to the females. The latter bite into the excitatory organs and are clearly stimulated. (It is possible that the organs emit a secretion. But the males also seem to be excited by the bite of the female. At a particular point in the courtship ceremony, which can in some cases be a long one, copulation occurs.

Courtship procedure is determined by the position of the excitators. In *Troglops albicans* they lie on the frons. When a couple meet, the male offers the female the frontal organ to bite into. If this is done, the male moves to the hind end of the female to investigate the degree of readiness for mating. If this has not yet been achieved, it once more offers the frontal organ. So it runs back and forth, until finally copulation is achieved. In another species, *Axinotarsus pulicarius* (Melyridae), the excitatory organs lie on the end of the elytra. When the partners have met, the male turns through 180° and the female bites into the excitators on the margin of the wing covers. Then the male turns again through 180° and the whole process is repeated for some time. Finally both partners turn throught 180° so that now the ends of the abdomens come into contact and copulation follows. Species of the genus *Malachius* (Melyridae), when alarmed, will project lateral protrusible vesicles, red in colour and of varying length, at the sides of the body between the head and thorax and between the thorax and abdomen. They are sometimes tubular and may be as long as the antennae. These organs possess single-celled glands. This behaviour has been interpreted as a defensive reaction which is believed to have the purpose of frightening off potential enemies both by the striking colour of the utricles and by the possible emission of an aroma. So far this is only speculation.

Fights between male Stag Beetles (Lucanidae) have often been described and illustrated (Fig. 149). Kästner describes one such contest in this way: "The males, meeting on the branch of a tree that is exuding sap, attack one another with their mandibles. Like wrestlers, they try to lock their rival within the circle of their arms. If one succeeds in doing so, it lifts its opponent, violently struggling, so high into the air that the latter cannot retain a hold with its tarsi on the trunk; it

204 The Longhorn Beetle *Petrognatha gigas* (Cerambycidae), right male, left female, from Central Africa

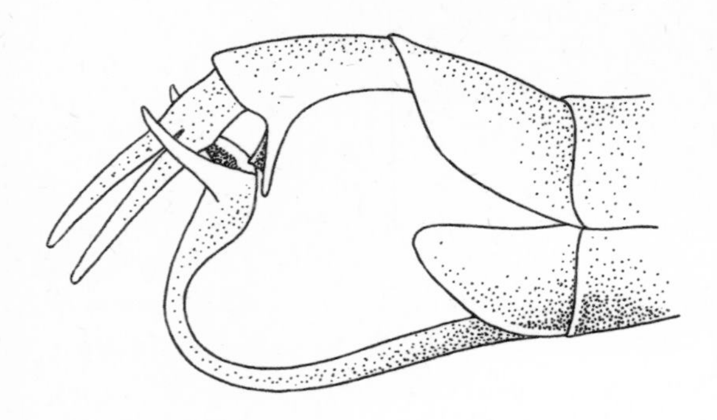

Copulation
Tip of the abdomen of a male *Malthinus* with the characteristic gripping organ (Cantharidae).

is thrown down from the tree. Of course, it can sometimes happen that the victor will tear off one of the tarsi or puncture an elytron of the opponent which, in its desperate resistance, has maintained a firm hold with the claws of its hind legs, but really serious injuries are never inflicted."

The largest of the Lamellicorns (Scarabaeidae) also take part in combat, for example, the males of the Elephant Beetles *(Megasoma elephas)*. First of all they try to pull at each other with the tarsi of their long forelegs. They are in no hurry and will remain standing in front of one another for a considerable period. Occasionally they try to seize and overthrow their opponent with the forelegs. Sometimes the attempt succeeds and the loser falls to the ground. Or perhaps one of the two rivals tries to force its fore body under its opponent by using its horns, and exerting all its power, to lever it upwards. If this tactic is successful, the other beetle is forced to relinquish contact with the base on which it stands, first with its fore and then with its mid legs, and finally it falls backwards from the tree. The males of Goliath Beetles (Scarabaeidae) are particularly pugnacious. Moving with surprising rapidity, each tries to gain a hold on the pronged cephalic horn of the other beetle and to toss it upward with powerful movements of the head. Between the pronotum and the elytra, Goliath Beetles have a sharp-edged joint which they open wide when threatened. An opponent attacking at this point is very quickly gripped and held fast. Curiously enough, this method of defence is not used in fights with other Goliath Beetles.

The mighty Hercules Beetles (Scarabaeidae) are also considerable fighters. Of the species *Dynastes hercules*, which is found in Venezuela, Kästner writes: "A male *Dynastes hercules* is eating the flesh of a banana, its head pushed deep into the fruit, when a second male approaches and with seesaw movements of the thorax, stridulates rhythmically. Immediately the other stops eating and turns towards the newcomer. In contrast to their usual leisurely gait, the two beetles now make for one another at a rapid pace, each attempting to seize the other with the horns of its head and thorax which it uses as pincers. Over and again they let go, retreat a few steps and then attack each other anew. Finally one of them moves a little to one side and tries to seize the opponent's abdomen in its grip. If it succeeds in doing so, it forces the pincers further and further across the abdomen so that the more basally situated teeth are now brought into action. Then it suddenly draws itself up almost vertically and throws the body of the opponent, which is struggling helplessly in the air, violently down from the tree, or else carries it a short distance and then flings it to the ground."

The males of other species, such as those of the Timberman Beetle *(Acanthocinus aedilis)* also fight among themselves. Standing head to head they brace themselves one against the other, their long antennae stretched out widely, and try to push each other away. The males of the Ground Beetle genus *Carabus* (Carabidae) bite one another violently. Male Pill-rolling Beetles (*Scarabaeus* spec.; Scarabaeidae) also indulge in frequent bouts of fighting. The immediate cause may be a ball of dung which the "owner" has to defend. It pushes its front legs beneath the body of its attacker and throws the latter aside with a jerk. Sometimes these beetles fight standing on their hind legs with their bodies drawn up high. Each then attempts to seize the other with its powerful fore legs. In the end, one of the two falls on to its back. The victor, seated upon the vanquished, compresses its body so forcibly that the chitin can be heard to crack. Sexton Beetles (*Necrophorus* spec.; Silphidae) and Scarabaeids of the genus *Lethrus* (Scarabaeidae) fight among themselves with considerable violence. The males of the leaf-rolling weevils of the genus *Deporaus* (Attelabidae) try to throw each other down from leaves using their hind legs. To do this they stand back and draw up the hind part of the body. Bark Beetles (Scolytidae) drive off intrusive males by stridulating excitedly and then, bracing themselves head to head with quivering antennae, they exert pressure until one of the rivals gives in. The victorious beetle then runs to the female for whose sake the contest was fought, and still stridulating, rubs its antennae along the female's abdomen.

Copulation

In early times, ideas about copulation in beetles were extremely confused. For example, Aristotle writes (after Bodenheimer, 1928) "that the female inserts its organ into the male and they remain united for a long time. Only cicadas behave in the contrary way. Thus we see that in pairing with the female, many males do not introduce any organ into the female, on the contrary, the female into the male, which is the case in certain insects. For that which in those insects that introduce an organ, is effected by the seed in the female, is effected in these insects by the warmth and strength in the creature itself. Whereby the female introduces the organ responsible for reception and secretion into the male. And therefore these creatures remain together for a long time, but as soon as they have separated, they procreate immediately; that is, they remain paired long enough for the germ to have formed, which is otherwise accomplished by the seed; but once they are separated, they immediately bring forth the germ; for they have generated an incomplete thing: all of this kind namely beget worms."

At the time of Aristotle, it was not known that there is indeed a family of beetles in which species exist, the females of which possess a penis-like copulating apparatus which they introduce into the male in order to receive the spermatophore. This is found in a few representatives of the genus *Cyphon* which belongs to the family of Marsh Beetles (Helodidae). But they are very much the exception. In the normal case, copulation consists of the introduction of the male penis into the female.

In the majority of beetles, copulation occurs with the male climbing on to the back of the female from behind and maintaining a firm hold with the fore and mid legs (Figs. 90, 147, 186–189). Sometimes the legs are furnished with special means of adhesion. The male organ of copulation is introduced into the female and sperms are transferred as free spermatozoa or sometimes enclosed in a proteinaceous sac, the spermatophore. In copulation, the organs are usually linked very firmly together.

For example, in the Cockchafer (*Melolontha* spec.; Scarabaeidae), the tip of the male copulatory organ has a spherical swelling which prevents its sliding out of the female's body. As a result, the male can fall backwards and be carried about by the famale (as also happens in Soft-winged Flower Beetles (Melyridae). Copulation lasts for a long time and during this period, the females feed.

In a number of cases, the act of mating shows certain special features. Among Carrion Beetles (Silphidae) of the genus *Silpha*, the males seize one or both antennae of the female with their maxillae, holding on to them like reins. A completely anomalous copulatory position is taken up by the species of the genus *Malthinus* in the family of Soldier Beetles (Cantharidae). These insects mate with heads facing in opposite directions and only the ends of the abdomens in contact. At the end of the abdomen, the male has organs shaped like gripping-tongs, which enable it to maintain a firm hold on the female. Most species of Bark Beetles (Scolytidae) copulate within the system of galleries they have excavated. For this purpose, a special area is constructed by the males, known as the nuptial or pairing chamber. Because of the extreme sexual dimorphism of the Pear-blight Beetle *(Xyleborus dispar)*, (Scolytidae) it is able to copulate within the breeding gallery without requiring a nuptial chamber for the purpose. The body of the male is so small and flat in shape that it appears as little more than an extension of the body of the female, and scarcely extends beyond the hind limit of her body. In many species of beetle, the act of copulation lasts for a very long time, many hours or even days. This is particularly striking among Soldier Beetles, notably in the very common species *Rhagonycha fulva* (Cantharidae). In the literature there are frequent reports of copulation having been observed between males. One example is that of the Lamellicorn beetle *Golofa pelagon* (Scarabaeidae) which occurs in Bolivia.

"*Marriage*"

There is, of course, nothing that could be termed "marriage" among beetles. However, in many groups, the pairs remain together throughout an entire season. In terms of animal psychology, this could be defined as seasonal marriage. A suitable example might be that of the Scarabaeid beetle *Lethrus apterus*. Sexton Beetles (*Necrophorus*; Silphidae) and Bark Beetles (Scolytidae) frequently live together with one partner for a season, the latter, indeed, with several females. Among many dung-eating Lamellicorn Beetles such as the species *Geotrupes* (Scarabaeidae), the Pill-rolling Beetle *Sisyphus schaefferi* and others, couples tend to remain together for a considerable time.

Stages of development and metamorphosis

The egg

Within a more or less short period of time after copulation, oviposition or egg-laying takes place. Among beetles, a wide variety of methods are involved in this process. In many species, eggs are laid singly, in others in batches, often containing up to 100 eggs (Figs. 190–193). In very many species, the egg is brought directly to the future larval food substrate. Many Weevils (Curculionidae) dig channels with their rostrum, into which eggs can be placed by means of the telescopically retractile, tubular ovipositor. And many Water Beetles, such as the Great Water Beetle (*Dytiscus*, Dytiscidae), lay their eggs in plant tissue, in incisions made by the ovipositor in the stems of plants.

Just as diverse as the process of egg-laying is the shape and colour of the eggs. From spherical to elongate-ovoid, and in Powder-post Beetles (Lyctidae) even rod-shaped, all imaginable variations occur. The surface can be smooth, spotted with droplets of secretion or covered with a honeycomb pattern. The eggs of many species are almost transparent, others white, yellow, orange, red or even speckled red. The size depends largely upon the size of the beetle and for that reason alone, is very varied. The eggs of *Carabus coriaceus* (Carabidae) are 8 mm long, those of the Great Water Beetle (*Dytiscus* spec.; Dytiscidae) 7 mm, while *Ergates faber* and the Capricorn Beetle *Cerambyx cerdo* (both Cerambycidae) have eggs 5 mm long. Just as variable as the size of the egg is the number of eggs laid. The highest record is held by the Blister Beetles (Meloidae) which are said to lay up to 10,000 eggs (according to other workers, 4,000). The Great Water Beetle (Dytiscidae) produces up to 1,000 eggs while a figure of 2,500 eggs is given for the Colorado Beetle (Chrysomelidae). Death-watch Beetles (Anobiidae) may lay 20 to 40 eggs, Forest Cockchafers 60 to 80, Bacon

Beetles *(Dermestes lardarius)* (Dermestidae) 100 to 120, Grain Weevils (*Sitophilus* spec,; Curculionidae) up to 250 and the Seven-spotted Ladybird *(Coccinella septempunctata)* (Coccinellidae) up to 800. The smallest numbers of eggs are laid by those species that practise brood care.

A curious structural feature is found in the eggs of Leaf Beetles (Chrysomelidae) of the sub-families Clytrinae and Cryptocephalinae. In these beetles, the female encloses the egg in a shell of excrement (scatoconch). After laying the longish egg, the female takes it between the hind legs. One end is pressed into a hollow at the end of the abdomen. Turning the egg as she does so, the female fastens several balls of excrement to it, securing them with a special glandular secretion. In this way, a casing of excrement somewhat in the shape of a fir cone is produced, which is of particular importance in the transmission of symbionts. It takes the female about three hours to prepare a covering of this kind for a single egg. Because of this measure of provision for the brood, the number of eggs laid by this species is very low, amounting to only about 30 in those cases which have been examined. Leaf Beetles of the genus *Phyllodecta* lay their eggs on leaves and cover each individual egg with scale-like secretal structures. The Leaf Beetle *Haltica oleracea* also covers the eggs with excrement as soon as they are laid. The eggs of Leaf Beetles of the genus *Polychalca* are also given a thick secretal covering, while the female of *Aspidomorpha puncticosa* encloses its eggs in a firm capsule or ootheca, much in the manner of praying mantids, Mantodea.

In most species of beetle, the female abdomen swells with the growth of the egg store. The intersegmental cuticle stretches, but in only a few cases is the female abdomen very strikingly distended (physogastry). An example of physogastry is found in the Sorrel-leaf Beetle *Gastrophysa viridula* (Chrysomelidae). The abdomen of the females reaches several times its normal volume. A similar phenomenon is found in the Tansy-leaf Beetle *Galeruca tanaceti* (Chrysomelidae). A particularly well-known and striking example of physogastry is seen in the female of the Oil Beetles of the genus *Meloe* (Meloidae; Figs. 182, 183).

The duration of embryonic development within the egg depends upon environmental factors such as temperature and humidity, and, of course, it also varies from species to species. No general rules can be given. Many species overwinter in the egg state, in which case this stage of development achieves a considerable duration. But in many cases, the egg seems to mature very quickly and the larva hatches within a few days or rarely hours. The process of eclosion, or hatching from the egg, can present quite a problem for the larva. In many species of beetles, the larvae have hatching spines or egg bursters. These are special structures by means of which the larva is able to force its way through or tear open the chorion. In many Ground Beetle larvae (Carabidae), they are located on the head. In Ladybirds (Coccinellidae) and various of the Scarabaeidae, they are on the upper side of the thorax. The larvae of the Asparagus Beetle *(Crioceris asparagi)* (Chrysomelidae) have tooth-like hatching spines on the first abdominal segment. Carrion beetle larvae (Silphidae) have paired egg bursters on the labium. All these structures help the larva in the process of hatching. Egg bursters are found only in the first larval stage. Since they are not needed for any purpose later on, they are shed at the first moult.

The larva

In beetles, as in all insects which undergo complete metamorphosis (holometabola), the larva is very different in appearance and structure from the imago. A study of the larvae proves them to be just as fascinating and varied as are the beetles themselves (Figs. 32, 110–115, 178–181, 194–198). Yet the world of the larvae is a much less familiar one than that of the imagines. It is estimated that so far, the larval stages have been examined for only about one tenth of all beetle species.

If we want to describe a typical larva, we immediately meet with considerable difficulties. Normally, a beetle larva has six legs, on which it moves about with a good deal of agility, but which may also be adapted for swimming or burrowing. Legs that are distinctly natatorial, for example, are found in the larvae of Diving Beetles (Dytiscidae), fossorial legs, for example, in the larvae of Hide Beetles (Heteroceridae). Many larvae need to be able to climb well on plants. Frequently the legs of such species are furnished with supplementary structures which provide adhesion, in the larvae of Ladybirds (Coccinellidae), for example, these take the form of tufts of bristles. Climbing is further facilitated by an organ formed by the anal segment of the abdomen known as the pygopodium which can function as a suction pad. Many beetle larvae even have supplementary abdominal processes used as legs, much like those generally known from the caterpillars of butterflies. A good example is seen in the larvae of many species of Water Scavenger Beetles (Hydrophilidae), such as *Enochrus*. We have already seen an example of specialized development of the legs for the purpose of maintaining a hold on living insect prey in the triungulin larvae, e.g. Meloidae. In a whole series of other beetles, the legs are more or less completely reduced or absent (Curculionidae, Cerambycidae). These are the groups that live in narrow systems of galleries within plants, such as, for example, the leaf-mining Leaf Beetles, many Longicorns (Cerambycidae), Bark or Engraver Beetles (Scolytidae), Metallic Beetles (Buprestidae) and False Click Beetles (Eucnemidae). The capacity of these larvae to move about within their feeding galleries is provided by folds on the back and underside which enable them to

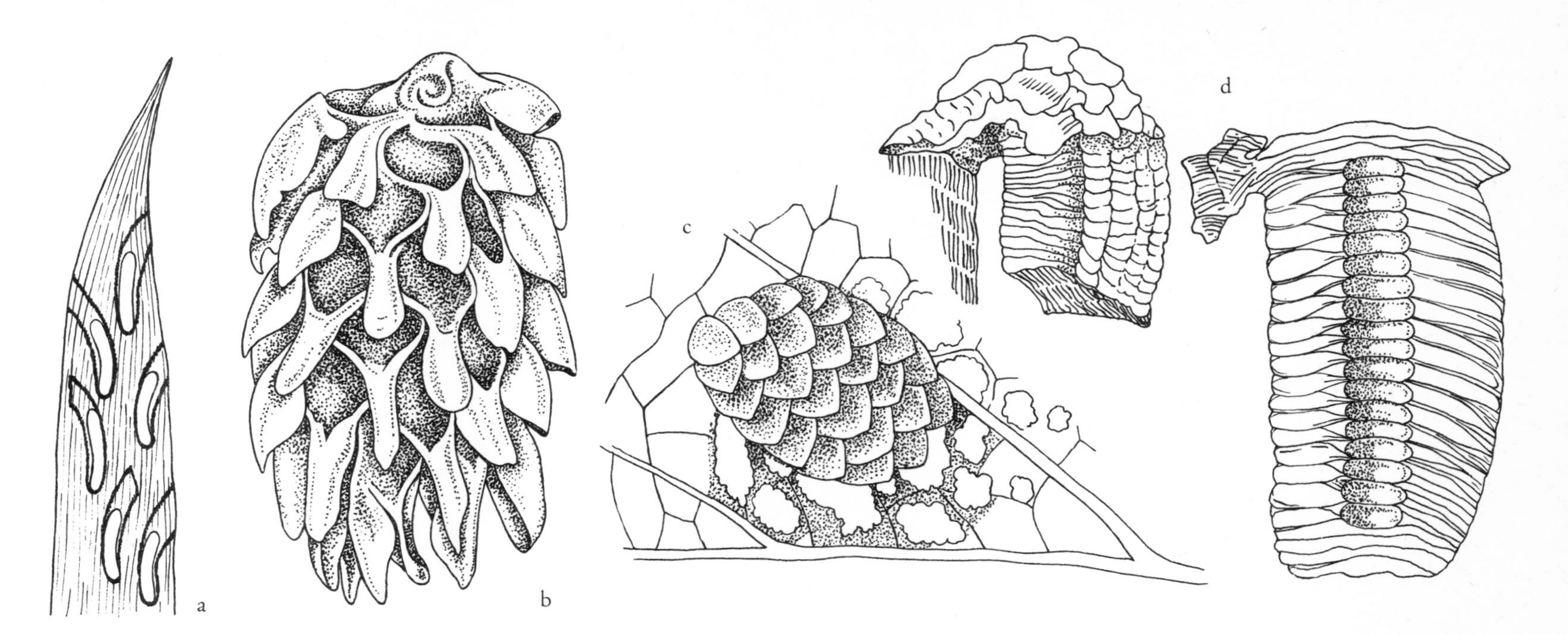

Beetle's eggs
a) Leaf of a water plant furnished with egg pockets by the female Great Water Beetle *Dytiscus marginalis* L. (Diving Beetles, Dytiscidae).
b) Egg case constructed by *Clytra quadripunctata* L. (Leaf Beetles, Chrysomelidae).
c) Clutch of eggs laid by *Polychalca* spec. (Leaf Beetles, Chrysomelidae). Each egg is covered by a scale of hardened secreta.
d) Ootheca of *Aspidomorpha puncticosa* Boh. (Leaf Beetles, Chrysomelidae)
left: Attached to a base
right: In longitudinal section, enlarged

crawl. Just as widely varied in construction as the organs of locomotion are the organs of feeding. The fine structure of the mouthparts displays an enormous range of variation and is very important in distinguishing individual species. On the other hand, the mouthparts are surprisingly uniform in their basic type. Larvae of Diving Beetles (Dytiscidae), Soldier Beetles (Cantharidae), Fireflies (Lampyridae) and Drilid Beetles (Drilidae) digest their food extra-intestinally. In all these groups, the mandibles are traversed by a fine groove, through which a secretion of the gut is emitted, and finally liquefied food is imbibed. The mandibles themselves are very varied in form, and are appropriate to the particular feeding substrate. Many groups exhibit some assymetry of the mandibles, for example, some genera of Water Scavenger Beetles (Hydrophilidae). Other beetle larvae have paired appendages on the 9th abdominal segment, called urogomphi. Their function is not really understood. They are, however, very varied in form and provide an important feature of identification.

At this point, mention might be made of the curious larval development of the genus *Lebia* belonging to the family of Ground Beetles (Carabidae). In the spring, these beetles live on the eggs and larvae of the Elm Leaf Beetle (*Galerucella* spec.; Chrysomelidae). They also desposit their eggs on the elm tree and the larvae seek out Elm Leaf Beetle larvae and pupae which they consume. After their first moult, their mobility is greatly limited. The *Lebia* larva spins a cocoon in which it also encloses an Elm Leaf Beetle pupa. Or sometimes it may place the cocoon next to such a pupa. Whatever may be the details of the case, the consequence is that the cocooned *Lebia* larva devours the Elm Leaf Beetle pupa. Then it moults into the third larval stage, which has extremely rudimentary mouthparts and legs. It remains lying immobile, entirely enclosed in the cocoon of the second stage. After some time, this larval stage changes into a pupa from which the beetle finally emerges (hypermetamorphosis).

Many larvae are able to construct special casings or cells. The larvae of Leaf Beetles of the genus *Lamprosoma* (Chrysomelidae) make hood-shaped casings out of splinters of wood and bark. The casing lies with its opening against a twig. The larva inside eats the bark. We should also mention the C-shaped, permanently curved larvae of the Scarabaeidae, which have also been reported for other families (for example, many Leaf Beetles (Chrysomelidae), Dascillidae, Stag Beetles (Lucanidae), Pill Beetles (Byrrhidae), Pulse or Seed Beetles (Bruchidae), Powder-post Beetles (Lyctidae), False Powder-post Beetles (Bostrychidae), Deathwatch Beetles (Anobiidae), Spider Beetles (Ptinidae)). Remarkable forms also occur in the hard, sclerous larvae of Click Beetles (Elateridae) which are popularly known as

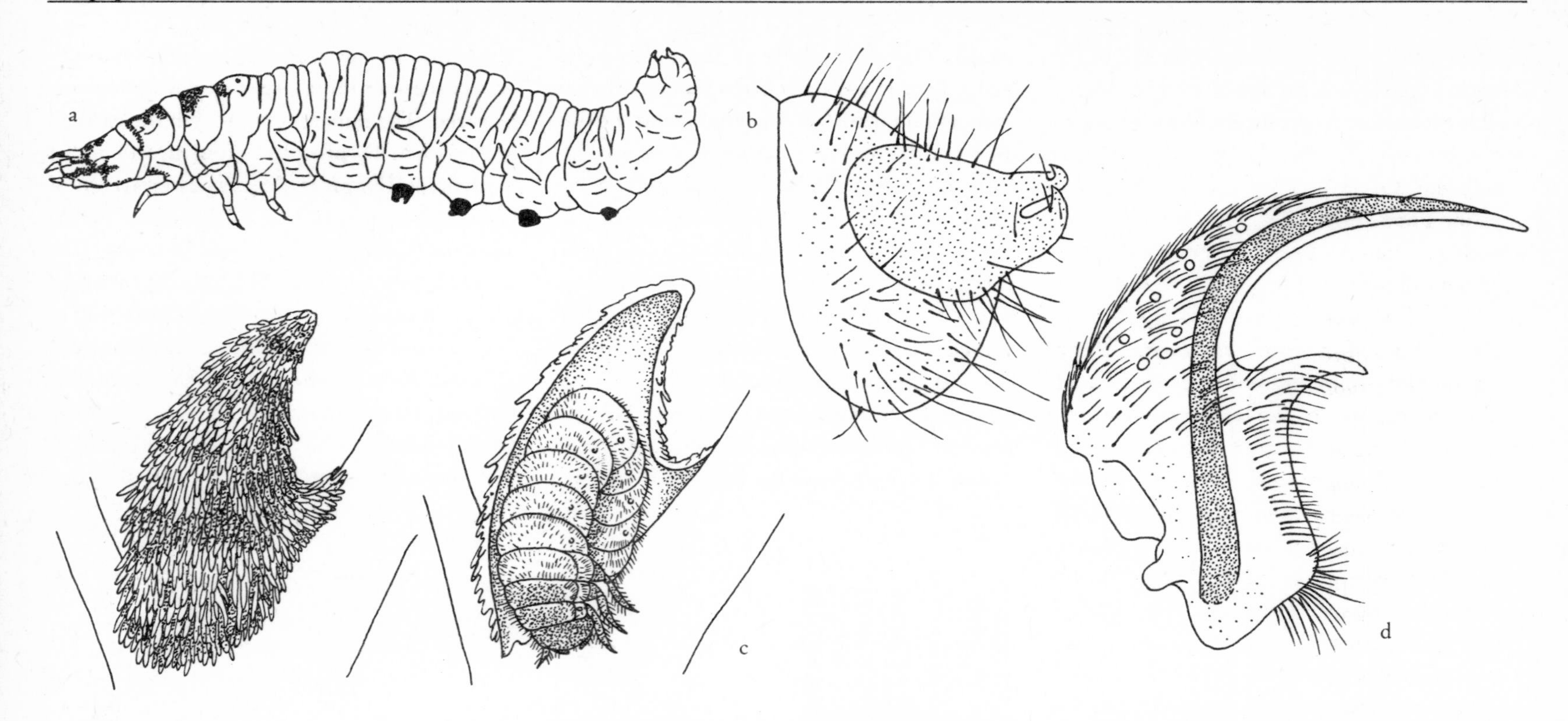

Beetle larvae
a) *Enochrus bicolor* F. (Water Scavenger Beetles, Hydrophilidae) with thoracic legs (marked in black).
b) Urogomphi of a Checkered Beetle (Cleridae) on the 9th abdominal segment
c) Larva of *Lamprosoma* spec. (Leaf Beetles, Chrysomelidae) inside its bonnet-shaped housing which is situated with its open end against a twig. From within this housing, the larva feeds on bark (right).
d) Grooved mandible of *Lampyris noctiluca* L. (Fireflies, Lampyridae)

"wireworms," and of many Darkling Beetles (Tenebrionidae). Particularly noteworthy are the larvae of Carrion Beetles (Silphidae) which are like woodlice in shape, and of certain other families, for example, Stone Beetles (Scydmaenidae).

Growth in beetle larvae alternates with periods when moulting occurs and the intervals between one moult and the next are known as stages or stadia. The total number of moults varies greatly. Hister Beetles (Histeridae) have only two larval stages. Very many species of beetles have three larval stages, for example, many Ground Beetles (Carabidae), Diving Beetles (Dytiscidae), Rove Beetles (Staphylinidae) and Snout Beetles (Curculionidae). The maximum number is probably that achieved by Darkling Beetles, with 10 to 16 larval stages. Each time, the newly-moulted stage is larger than the previous one, but at the same time, more or less conspicuous alterations in proportions also occur. The duration of larval development is very varied. Many beetles such as Carrion Beetles (Silphidae), many species of Leaf Beetles (Chrysomelidae) and Ladybirds (Coccinellidae) have very short larval periods. Larvae of beetles living in wood require the longest time for their development. Stag Beetles (*Lucanus cervus;* Lucanidae), for example, take four to six years (with a maximum of eight). The larvae of Deathwatch Beetles (Anobiidae) often require several years. In laboratory conditions, Longicorn larvae (Cerambycidae) were reported to have taken 25 to 31 years to complete their development, but this could hardly happen in natural conditions outdoors. The longest periods required for development in the open, in rather exceptional conditions (extremely dry wood and at the same time, a diet lacking in nutrients) were found to be 12 years for *Ergates faber* and 11 to 12 years for the Longhorn Beetle *Hylotrupes bajulus* (Cerambycidae).

The pupa

Larval development culminates in the pupal stage (Figs. 116, 174–177, 199, 200) in which metamorphosis into the beetle imago takes place. Typical of beetles is a freely articulated pupa in wich the extremities, antennae and mouthparts are already visible externally (Figs. 116, 177, 199). Looking at the pupa of the Timberman Beetle (*Acanthocinus aedilis*; Cerambycidae), it is possible to discern the long antennae intricately coiled; or on the pupa of the male Stag Beetle (Lucanidae), the antler-like development of the mandibles. A number of families deviate from this "normal" pupal form, in that they produce an obtected or mummy-like pupa. In these pupae, like those of most Lepidoptera, no sign of wings or legs is visible externally. As prototype of such a pupa, we might well take that of the Ladybird (Coccinellidae). Other families also have a mummy-like pupa (Figs. 176, 200), for example, Handsome Fungus Beetles (Endomychidae), Corylophid Beetles (Corylophidae) and some of the Leaf Beetles (Chrysomelidae), for instance, species of the genus *Melasoma*. Many such mummy-like pupae are even located within the remains of the last larval skin, for example, those of Ladybirds of the genus *Exochomus*. The pupae of Hide or Skin Beetles (Dermestidae) also remain concealed by the old larval skin, although in this case, the pupa is not of the mummy-like type.

A large number of larvae construct special pupal cells. These are well-known among Longicorns (Cerambycidae) which, for example, prepare a plate- or bowl-shaped niche beneath bark, enclosed by a ring of wood chips (e.g. the genera *Rhagium* and *Acanthocinus*). Many other species living in timber prepare a special cell which may lie at the end of a straight or hooked gallery. The pupal cell is always constructed in such a way that it will afford the larva the freedom from disturbance necessary for pupation, and the pupa similar conditions necessary for metamorphosis. In the construction of a pupal cell, provision is always made for beetles to emerge without difficulty. This is particularly important in species living in wood, since very often the imago would not be capable of gnawing a passage through wood. Therefore the larva must prepare an exit gallery in advance, often leaving no more than a thin membrane between it and the outside world. Pupal cells are not only constructed in wood but also below ground in the earth. The illustration on p. 181 shows the elaborate care with which the larva of the Diving Beetle (Dytiscidae) sets about this task. First, it constructs a circular rampart, one wall of which it arches over into a dome-like roof. At first it works from the outside of the dome, and then completes the work from the inside. The final result is a sphere of soil inside which a smooth hollow cavity houses the larva and, later on, the pupa. In this way, the specific microclimate necessary for this species' development is ensured. The pupae, lying within the earthen cell, are usually protected from direct contact with the soil by protuberances, ridges, tufts of hairs and so on. Beetles of the genus *Rhynchaenus* (Curculionidae) mine in leaves. The larvae produce secretions by means of which they join together the upper and lower skin of the leaf, and then, above and below, cut a small disc out of the leaf, with which they fall to the ground, to pupate within it. The leaf looks as if a punch had been used to perforate it. For pupation, many larvae are able to pene-

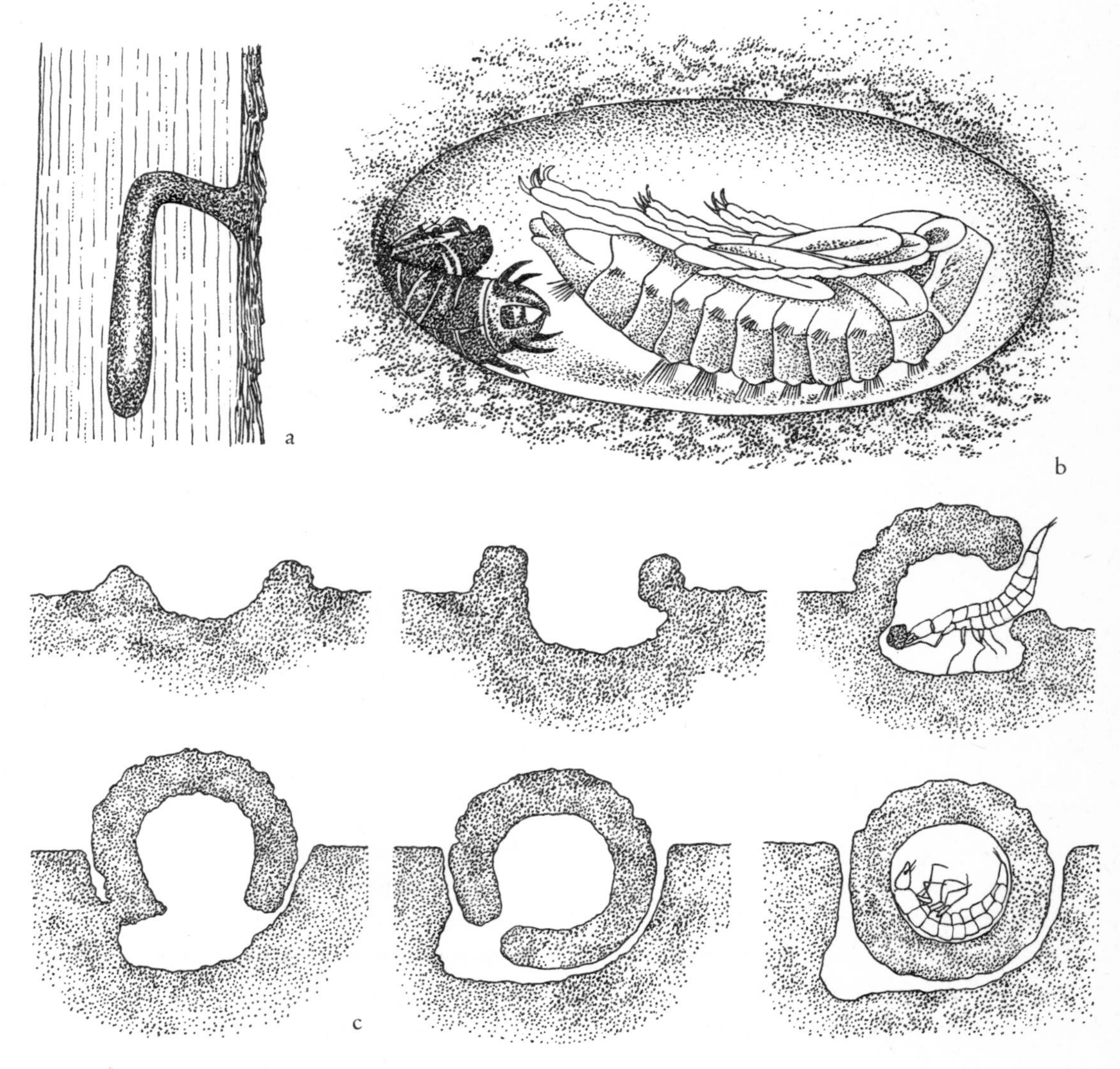

Beetle pupae
a) Uncinate (hamular) gallery with pupal cell of *Tetropium castaneum* L. (Longhorns, Cerambycidae)
b) Pupa of Ground Beetle (Carabidae) inside its earthen cell. The pupa lies on the tufts of bristles on its back. On the left, the discarded larval skin can be seen.
c) Larva of the Diving Beetle *Agabus bipustulatus* L. (Dytiscidae) constructing its pupal couch.

trate a quite hard substratum, even such as lead. The larvae of Hide or Skin Beetles (Dermestidae) have been observed to pupate within lead and pewter. False Powder-post Beetles (Bostrychidae), for example, the Capuchin Beetle *(Bostrychus capucinus)* have, as larvae, been known to penetrate the lead sheath of an electric cable in order to pupate. The larvae of the Meal Beetle *(Stegobium paniceum)* are also able to pupate in lead.

The larvae of some species form cocoons by means of secretions from special spinning glands. Weevils and Snout Beetles (Curculionidae) of the tribe of Cionini spin secretal cocoons which are thin as parchment (Fig. 178). These are attached to the food plant or to the ground. Similar ones are found among Leaf Beetles (Chrysomelidae) of the sub-families Donaciinae and Criocerinae, among Ground Beetles (Carabidae) of the genus *Lebia* and among various Longicorns (Cerambycidae) of the sub-family Prioninae, which pupate in the soil. The secretal cocoon can range from fine, net-like to coarse-meshed material.

The duration of the pupal period varies greatly, it is species-characteristic and also depends upon environmental factors. The shortest time to have been observed was three days for a Rove Beetle *(Paracymus aeneus)* (Staphylinidae). In their natural environment, many Leaf Beetles (Chrysomelidae) and Ladybirds (Coccinellidae) also require only 9 to 10 days for the beetle to emerge. But very often pupation can last several weeks or even months. In many species, the pupal stage overwinters, so that as a result of the diapause, pupal periods of six months can occur. It is not unknown for a pupa to remain in that state for an entire year.

Eclosion of the beetle

Emergence of the beetle from the pupal case (eclosion) is usually a rapid process requiring no more than 15 to 30 minutes. After eclosion, many species remain for hours, days or months within the pupal cell. Very often, the most favourable conditions for the hardening and coloration of the chitinous exo-skeleton (Fig. 117), which at first is soft and colourless, are those provided by the pupal cell (Figs. 116, 177). After eclosion, the Stag Beetle (Lucanidae) remains in the ground for several months. In many species, the process of developing and laying down pigments in the chitin can be concluded very rapidly, while in other species, it may take a considerable time. When the Ladybird *Sospita vigintiguttata* (Coccinellidae) emerges from the pupal case in summer, it is brown spotted with white. It is not until after the winter that it acquires its full coloration, and in spring is black with yellowish-white spots.

Exceptional reproductive patterns

The normal development of the beetle starts with an egg, from which, after a specific time, the first larval stage emerges. The larva grows, with several intervening periods of moulting, and then pupates. From the pupa, a beetle emerges. Male and female beetles copulate and the female lays a fertilized egg. There are several exceptions to this "normal" cycle, the first of which is viviparity or ovoviviparity. By these terms we mean respectively the production of live progeny and the laying of eggs which hatch immediately. Ovoviviparity is found in certain Leaf Beetles (Chrysomelidae). The larvae of the Alpine Leaf Beetle *(Chrysochloa alpestris)* which lives at altitudes of 800 to 1,000 m, hatch immediately the eggs are laid, and are already quite large. The development of the egg has taken place within the abdomen of the mother. Obviously ovoviviparity is an adaptation to the short period of vegetation occurring in the mountains. (Similar phenomena are also found among other animal groups.) In these species of Leaf Beetles, the number of progeny is exceptionally small. One female produces only 10 to 11 larvae. But many Leaf Beetles that live at low altitudes are also viviparous, such as *Chrysolina varians*, the eggs of which hatch two or three minutes after they are laid. The myrmecophile *Atemeles* (Staphylinidae) is viviparous (see p. 135).

A second exceptional phenomenon in individual development in beetles is that of hypermetamorphosis (or heteromorphosis). By this we mean the phenomenon by which individual larval stages undergo major changes in their way of life and consequently the instars which succeed one another have very different external forms (see p. 123).

A third major deviation from normal development is that of parthenogenesis (reproduction without fertilization). The female lays unfertilized eggs which undergo full development and from which larvae hatch. A process of this kind occurs in many Weevils (Curculionidae) of the large genus *Otiorhynchus*. Apart from that of the genus *Otiorhynchus*, obligate parthenogenesis has been observed in *Trachyphloeus*. These Weevils lay unfertilized eggs and only female progeny result. This type of parthenogenesis is called thelytoky. In the beetle kingdom, it is probably quite widespread among other families as well, possibly in certain Leaf Beetles (Chrysomelidae), Skin Beetles (Dermestidae), Darkling Beetles (Tenebrionidae) and Rove Beetles (Staphylinidae). A second form of parthenogenesis known as arrhenotoky, in which male progeny are produced from unfertilized eggs, while on the other hand, females result from fertilized eggs, is one we have already met with in a Bark Beetle (Scolytidae) (see p. 182), while the particularly interesting condition of paedogenesis occurring in the genus *Micromalthus* (Micromalthidae) is described in detail on p. 112.

Life span and manifestations of ageing

Many readers have probably wondered how long a beetle may be expected to live. If, in answering such a question, the whole cycle of development is taken into consideration, a life span of as long as six to eight years may be claimed, particularly in the case of beetles living in timber. But probably the question really refers to the age achieved by the imaginal stage. In general, beetles do not reach any great age. Most species live as imago for only some weeks or months. Only a few exceptions are known. In some cases, Darkling Beetles (Tenebrionidae) as well as Carabidae and various of the Scarabaeidae have been observed to live for several years. Even in early literature, there are records of such instances. For example, in 1598, Johannes Bauhin wrote about a Rose Chafer *(Cetonia aurata)*: "I caught one such beetle near Kirchen on 24 September 1596 and kept it in captivity. It lived until 15. 1. 97." And that probably without any food. In 1739, Henry Baker told how he kept a beetle—clearly it was *Blaps mortisaga*, belonging to the family of Darkling Beetles (Tenebrionidae)—for three years without food.

In more recent literature, we also find information on the life span of beetles. The Pine Weevil *(Hylobius abietis)* (Curculionidae) can live for up to three years, *Hetaerius ferrugineus* (Histeridae) for four. Under laboratory conditions, the life span can be extended very greatly, particularly if the insects are not allowed to propagate. A Water Scavenger Beetle *(Cybister laterimarginalis)* (Dytiscidae) lived for five and a half years, a Great Water Beetle (*Dytiscus* spec.; Dytiscidae) for five years, a Ground Beetle *(Carabus auronitens)* (Carabidae) for six years. In very old beetles, signs of degeneration occur. For example, the chewing surface of the maxillae alters with increasing age. In Darkling Beetles (Tenebrionidae) especially, individual tarsi are sometimes lost, and very old Tenebrionids run on the tibia only. Moreover, the waxy lustre which characterizes many beetles diminishes with increasing age, since the activity of the cuticular glands is restricted.

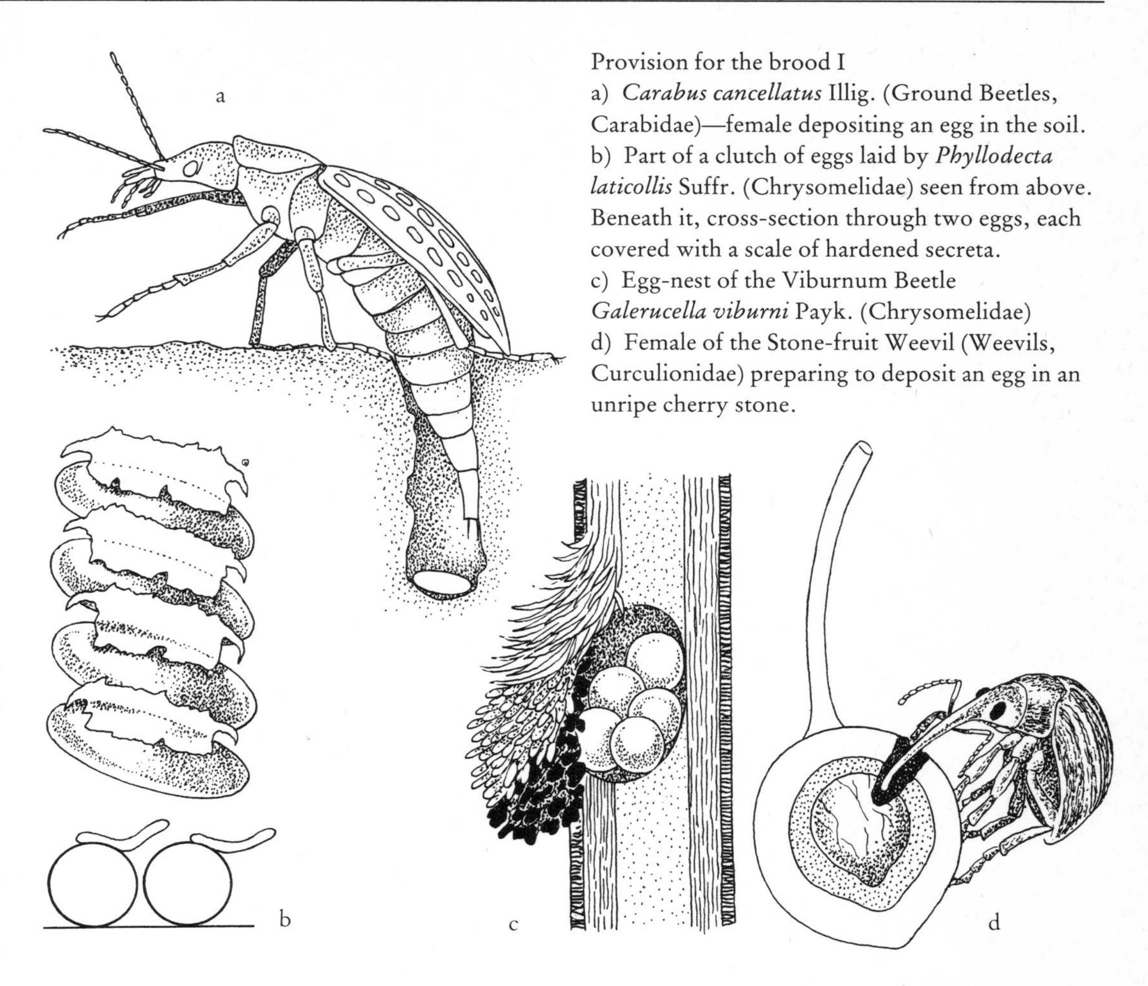

Provision for the brood I
a) *Carabus cancellatus* Illig. (Ground Beetles, Carabidae)—female depositing an egg in the soil.
b) Part of a clutch of eggs laid by *Phyllodecta laticollis* Suffr. (Chrysomelidae) seen from above. Beneath it, cross-section through two eggs, each covered with a scale of hardened secreta.
c) Egg-nest of the Viburnum Beetle *Galerucella viburni* Payk. (Chrysomelidae)
d) Female of the Stone-fruit Weevil (Weevils, Curculionidae) preparing to deposit an egg in an unripe cherry stone.

Provision for the brood and brood care

The conspicuous measures of provision for their offspring carried out by many species of beetles could not fail to attract the notice of early writers. In his book *De animalibus Insectis*, Ulysse Aldrovandi describes the measures of provision for the brood taken by Dor Beetles (*Geotrupes* spec.; Scarabaeidae) and a Leaf Roller *(Byctiscus betulae)* (Attelabidae). "From the Capuchin friar Gregorius, I received two nests of a different species. Both consisted of a fragile mass largely of animal dung mixed with soil. I presume that these were the nests of beetles, because in one of them, I found an almost dead Scarabaeus. They are constructed in the form of a long tube with two or three nests at the extremity, in which the beetles protect their progeny from the rigours of the winter and rear them." "It [*Byctiscus betulae*, the Author] is found on vine leaves. It develops from reddish-coloured eggs which are similar in size to those of the silk worm. At the time of propagation, it is present in large numbers, and rolls up the leaves, depositing its eggs there."

An attempt at a systematic classification of brood care

Most species of beetles make some provision for their brood. Even the simple action of taking the egg to the appropriate food source is a measure of brood provision. Brood care (parental or maternal care), on the other hand, is practised by relatively few species of beetles.

Brood care also embraces the action of watching over and tending the eggs and sometimes even feeding the young larvae. Hanns von Lengerken (1889–1966) attempted to systematize the instincts of brood provision and brood care. Below is an abridged version of his survey.

1. Provision for the brood
1.1. Protection of eggs
1.1.1. The eggs are deposited at a favourable site, for example, in cracks in bark (Longicorns—Cerambycidae, Metallic Beetles—Buprestidae), in small cavities in soil (Blister Beetles—Meloidae, Ground Beetles—Carabidae) or else in special egg pockets which are excavated in plant tissue.
1.1.2. The female prepares special protective coverings for the eggs. These may consist of a special secretion, as in the case of Leaf Beetles of the genus *Phyllodecta* (Chrysomelidae), or a casing of dung (scatoconche) is formed. This can be extended to the development of egg capsules (oothecae), as for example, in the case of the Tortoise Leaf Beetle *Aspidomorpha puncticosa* of Natal, Tortoise Beetles (Cassidinae, Chrysoelidae) cover an entire batch of eggs in a highly specialized secretion, as does the Leaf Beetle *Galeruca tanaceti* (Chrysomelidae). Special nest covers are constructed by *Galerucella viburni* (Chrysomelidae) using dung, glandular secretions and chips of wood. The female gnaws an elongated-oval hole in thin twigs of the host plant, into which 4 to 12 eggs are deposited and then covered over by a lid. It takes the insect some two to four hours to prepare a protected clutch of this kind. On average, one female produces 50 clutches of eggs which overwinter under their protective covering. Special casings round eggs may also consist of fragments of bark (many *Lamprosoma* species; Chrysomelidae). Many Water Scavenger Beetles enclose their eggs in special cocoons which they spin.
1.2. Brood provision in respect of food for the future larvae. This includes the action of placing the eggs on or immediately next to a source of food. Many beetles do this. An extension of this measure of provision exists among those beetles (Scolytidae and Platypodidae) which cultivate ambrosia fungi, supplying spores for the eggs.
1.3. Measures of provision for the brood which ensure both protection for the eggs and the provision of future nourishment for the larvae. These measures can be subdivided into two main groups:
1.3.1. Food for the larvae not prepared by the beetle. Many Longicorns (Cerambycidae) and Weevils (Curculionidae) place their eggs in the tissue of the larval food plant. Usually, simple hollows are drilled in which eggs are deposited. In the case of Long-nosed Weevils, the rostrum provides a particularly suitable instrument for this purpose. The females of those species of Bark Beetle (Scolytidae) which breed within bark, cut out an elongated egg gallery or "mother gallery." Along its sides, the eggs are placed in niches in the walls. When the larvae hatch, they eat out their own tunnels at right angles to the egg tunnel. In many species, the communal feeding activity produces blotch-shaped patterns of tunnelling.
1.3.2. Food for the larvae prepared by the beetle. Four large groups belong to this category, first of all those beetles that penetrate wood and herbaceous plants, including leaf-rollers (Attelabidae), and secondly, species that "girdle" a leaf or shoot. An example of the latter is found in the African Weevils of the genus *Alcides* (Curculionidae). These species cause a shoot to die, providing withered material for the development of the larvae. The larva is specialized to feed on the decaying wood and lives within the plant tissue prepared for it by the female. Longicorns (Cerambycidae) of the North American genus *Oncideres* behave in the same way, girdling twigs and even stout branches (up to 12 cm in diameter), thus preparing food for their larvae in a very specific way. The Hazel-nut Beetle *(Oberea linearis)* (Cerambycidae) gnaws a small hole between the wood and bark of a shoot that is still green. After an egg has been placed in this aperture, the branch is girdled at a point a few centimetres above the place at which the egg lies, so that the shoot withers and finally breaks off. Almost immediately the egg has been laid, proliferation of tissue occurs, which initially provides food for the larva. After a while it eats into the

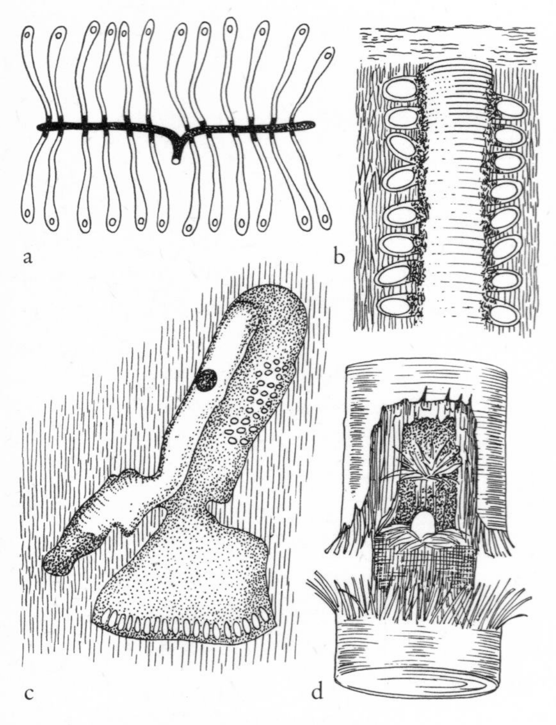

Provision for the brood II
a) Diagram showing breeding tunnels of a Bark Beetle (Scolytidae).
b) Part of the parent gallery of a Bark Beetle (Scolytidae) with eggs placed in egg niches along the walls. Each niche is covered over with wood chips.
c) Blotch-shaped pattern of tunneling made by *Dendroctonus micans* Kug. (Bark Beetles, Scolytidae).
d) Measures of brood provision taken by *Alcides brevirostris* Boh. (Weevils, Curculionidae) which "ring" or "girdle" bark.

pith of the branch right up to the point at which the shoot broke off. From there it eats its way on, moving in the direction of the base of the branch. Probably the larva is dependent upon a specific physiological condition of the branch brought about by the girdling action of the beetle. A third kind of food preparation is that illustrated by the Lesser Poplar Borer (*Saperda populnea*; Cerambycidae). The fourth method of preparing food is extremely extensive and comprises the storage of larval food (plants, dung) in tunnels or mines in the ground.

2. Brood care

Those measures which fall within the category of brood care can be divided into two main groups.

2.1. Larval food not prepared by the beetle. Included here is, for example, the supervision of the eggs by the female of the South American Tortoise Beetle *Selenis spinifex* (Chrysomelidae). This species attaches its eggs, about 30 in number, like grains of seed, to a thread made out of secretions. The thread with the eggs hangs down from the underside of a leaf, and the female sits at the top of the thread until the larvae have hatched. Other species of Tortoise Beetles conceal the eggs during the day under their body, and only during the night do they disperse across the plant to feed. The female of the indigenous Leaf Beetle *Phytodecta rufipes* (Chrysomelidae) lays its eggs on a leaf. The larvae remain together on this leaf. The parent sits head downwards on the branch and is said to repel approaching ants and other insects. Only the younger larval stages are guarded. The South American Tortoise Beetle *Omaspides pallidipennis* (also *Neomphalia*) has elytra that extend widely to each side, underneath which about twenty larvae can be accommodated. The larvae insert their fore body beneath the elytra of the mother. And of course, initially the females guard the clutch of eggs. The females of various species of Water Scavenger Beetles (Hydrophilidae) look after their eggs by carrying them about until the young larvae have hatched. As an example, we might take the indigenous *Spercheus emarginatus* (family Spercheidae). Beneath the abdomen, the female has a spun sac containing about 60 eggs. The basket-like web is attached to the back edge of the femur of the hind leg. When the insect is disturbed, the egg sac is raised high, drawn up by the pressure of the hind tibiae. The woven tissue has a firm base on which the eggs lie, embedded in loose web tissue. When the female is undisturbed, it allows the egg pouch to hang down behind her, in order to ensure an optimal supply of oxygen. The female *Spercheus* prepares a succession of several of these egg containers. Brood care of a similar kind is found in Water Scavenger Beetles of the genus *Helochares* (Hydrophilidae). Here again, the female spins an egg pouch to hold 60 to 70 eggs, which are arranged in strict order. The egg pouch is carried beneath the abdomen and is attached by spun tissue to the hind femora and trochanters.

2.2. Measures of brood care in which the beetle prepares the larval food.

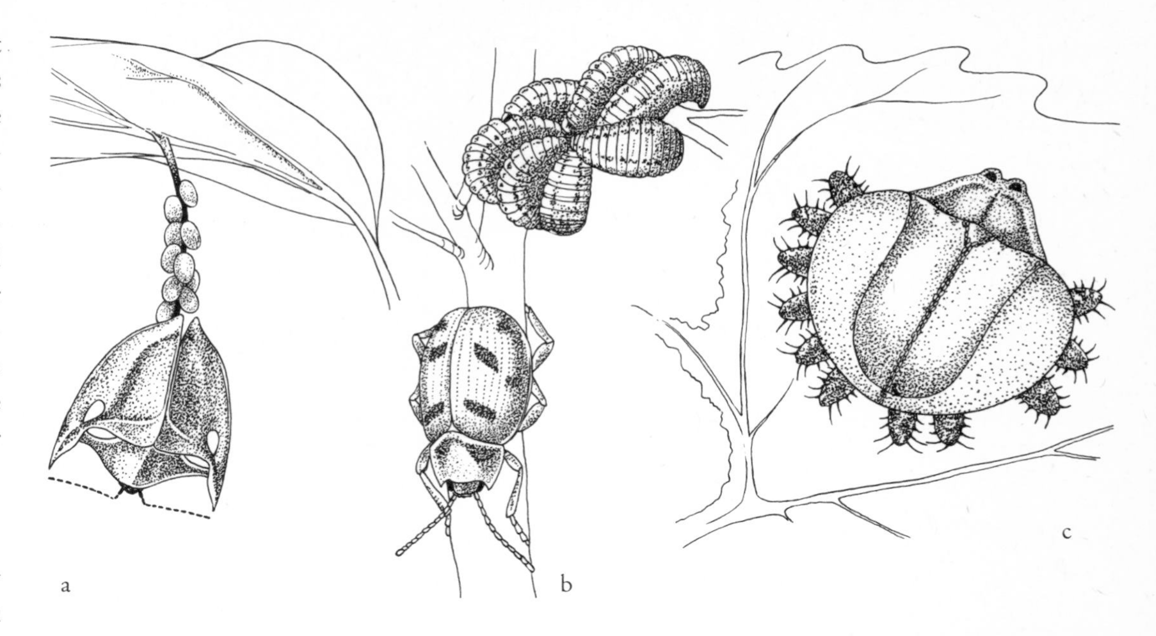

Brood provision in Leaf Beetles (Chrysomelidae)
a) Female of *Selenis spinifex* L. guarding its clutch of eggs.
b) A mother beetle (*Phytodecta rufipes* F.) keeps watch while above, the young larvae huddle together in a mass.
c) Female of *Omaspides pallidipennis* Boh. with its larvae which rest during the day with the forepart of the body concealed beneath the broad margins of the mother's elytra.

This category contains probably the most advanced instincts for brood care. We might first mention the Bark Beetle *Coccotrypes tanganus* (Scolytidae). This species is a native of Africa, living in the hard kernel of palm nuts (even sometimes in buttons manufactured from them). Within a single nut, up to 4,400 individuals can develop as the progeny of a single female. The female bores a main tunnel or mother gallery into the nut, at the end of which it lays its eggs and remains inside the tunnel. The larvae eat out a blotch-shaped mine. The female removes excrement and remnants of larval moults. In this way, the development of mould is prevented. After about three weeks, the beetles of the new generation emerge. These are all females, and they construct new breeding galleries and lay unfertilized eggs, from which only males hatch. Now the mother insect copulates with one of these "grandsons" and prepares a second main tunnel in which it deposits eggs; all of these are fertilized eggs and once again produce exclusively female progeny. It is probably the only known instance among beetles in which males result from unfertilized eggs and females from fertilized. It is, however, typical of hymenopterons (for example, honey bees). In this way, the inside of the nut becomes an increasingly intricate network of interwoven tunnels, although even in cases of excessive over-population, a thin outer wall of husk remains intact. The total of *c.* 4,400 individuals can be produced as the result of many generations. This succession of generations comes to an end only when the source of food within the palm nut is exhausted. Incidentally, the mother insects eat the superfluous males unless the latter manage to get away from the nut in good time. Other representatives of this type of brood care are those beetles (Scolytidae, Platypodidae) which cultivate "ambrosia" fungi. The females of the Scarabaeid genus *Copris* tend their eggs and larvae until the young beetles have emerged. In species of Burying Beetles (*Necrophorus* spec.; Silphidae), the females are known to feed the larvae directly (see p. 194).

Below we shall consider some examples of brood care in rather greater detail.

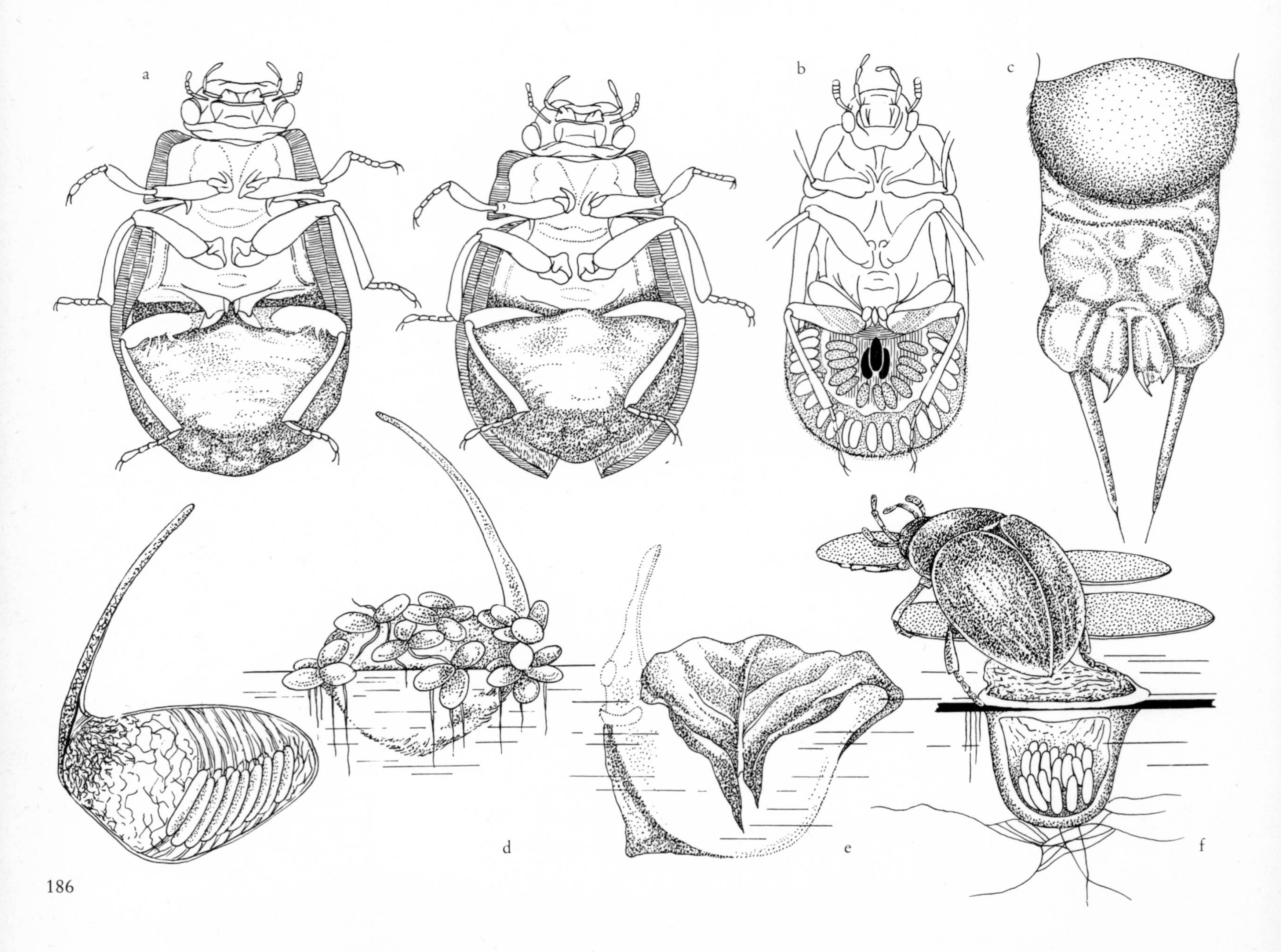

Egg Cocoons spun by Water Scavenger Beetles (Hydrophilidae)

The female of the Great Silver Beetle *(Hydrous piceus)* possesses a special spinning apparatus at the end of the abdomen. Accessory or collaterial glands of the reproductory organs produce the special secretions which are exuded from the vagina. At the back of the abdomen are two thin processes known as spinning rods which are mobile and thus able to draw out the silk thread. By means of this equipment, the Great Silver Beetle spins an egg cocoon which is about 2 cm long and 1 cm high and wide. This cocoon is usually attached to the underside of the leaf of an aquatic plant. One end of the egg container is extended upward above the water surface like a small mast or chimney projecting into the air. It is traversed by a longitudinal channel and is important in ensuring a supply of air to the eggs. At first, the female spins the covering plate, trapping a quantity of air beneath it. Then the floor and sides are constructed. Finally, the female deposits about 50 eggs vertically, one after the other, into the lower half of the cocoon. The upper half is filled with loose spun material. In this way, the cocoon is given stability in the water. The female constructs several cocoons of this kind. Another water beetle *Hydrophilus caraboides* (Hydrophilidae) weaves a similar cocoon to that of the Great Silver Beetle, but always works a leaf firmly into the structure, for example, a leaf of *Lysimachia*. Water beetles of the genus *Enochrus* produce a basin-like cocoon some 2 to 4 mm wide and deep, which hangs at the surface of the water from a carpet of aquatic plants that have been woven together. An egg-bowl of this kind contains about 30 eggs. Almost all species of Hydrophilids construct a protective cocoon covering of some kind, but for our purpose, perhaps the examples already mentioned will suffice.

Egg cocoons spun by Water Scavenger Beetles
a) Female of *Spercheus emarginatus* Schall. (Spercheidae) with spun egg pouch attached beneath the abdomen, left showing position when insect is undisturbed, right when disturbed.
b) *Helochares griseus* F. female, (Water Scavenger Beetles, Hydrophilidae) with eggs. Black central eggs, shaded mid-position eggs, unshaded principal row, later to be covered over with spun tissue.
c) Female of the Water Beetle *Hydrophilus caraboides* (Water Scavenger Beetles, Hydrophilidae); the spinning apparatus.
d) *Hydrous aterrimus* Esch. (Water Scavenger Beetles, Hydrophilidae); egg cocoon, incised on the left.
e) Cocoon like a small boat fashioned by *Hydrophilus caraboides* L. (Water Scavenger Beetles, Hydrophilidae) in a leaf of *Lysimachia*.
f) Structure of the basin-shaped cocoon spun by *Philydrus quadripunctatus* Hbst. (Water Scavenger Beetles, Hydrophilidae).

Weevils that pierce plants

Among weevils, which practise measures of provision for their brood by protecting the eggs and at the same time preparing a supply of food for the larvae, there are two biological groups: those that pierce holes into vegetation and those that roll leaves. Within the first category, we can distinguish between those which bore into timber and those which pierce herbaceous plants. Included among timber borers is, for example, *Lasiorhynchites cavifrons* (Attelabidae) which pierces oak twigs. The female of this beetle excavates on oval-shaped egg cavity inside lignified oak shoots. Into the cavity, which lies at a depth of about 1.5 mm, it deposits an egg. The larva mines into the medulla of the dying twig. Those beetles that cut into herbaceous plants can again be subdivided into four groups, according to their biological habits. Firstly there are those which pierce holes in buds, including, for example, *Coenorhynus aeneovirens* (Attelabidae), which attacks the buds of oak trees. The female of this species first makes a cut at the base of the bud which severs the vascular bundle of the bud axis. Now the bud is unable to unfold. Then a second hole is made in the centre of the bud, and in this, the egg is laid. The larva develops inside the oak bud which slowly dries up but does not fall from the tree.

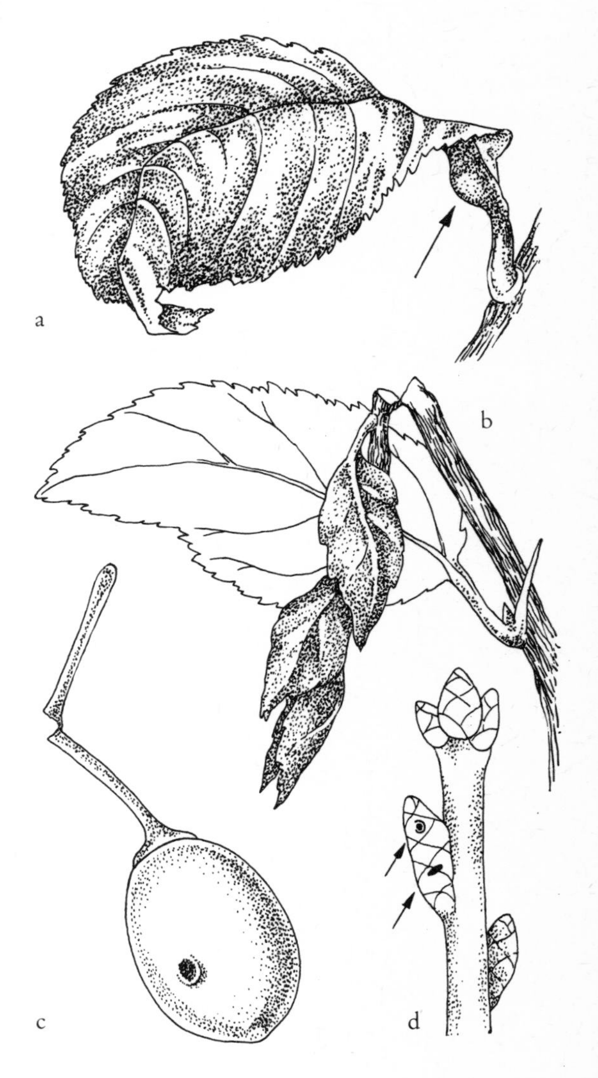

Leaf-rollers (Attelabidae)
a) Pear leaf with eggs deposited by *Coenorhinus interpunctatus* Steph.
b) Tip of growth-shoot of a fruit tree cut off by *Rhynchites coeruleus* Degeer.
c) Unripe green plum with a hole pierced by *Rhynchites cupreus* L. for oviposition and an incision made into the stalk.
d) Hole pierced in bud by *Coenorhinus aeneovirens* Marsh.

A second subsidiary group is represented by those weevils which pierce a hole into the ribs of leaves, including *Coenorhinus pauxillus* (Attelabidae), a beetle that attacks leaves of fruit trees. The female alters the physiological condition of the leaf by cutting an egg hole in the central rib of an apple, pear or strawberry leaf. Thickening occurs at the egg-laying site and the larva mines within the central rib. Finally the leaf falls off.

The third group consists of those beetles which cut holes in young shoots. Here we include, for example, *Rhynchites coeruleus* (Attelabidae) which attacks the shoots of fruit trees. These beetles deposit their eggs on young shoots of the host plant, and then eat at the shoot above and below the egg-laying site. The larvae develop within the pith of the withering shoots.

A fourth and final group of weevils which make holes in vegetation are those which pierce fruit, an example of which is the copper-red plum piercer *Rhynchites cupreus* (Attelabidae). The egg is placed by the female inside young fruit while it is still green. Then the female eats through the fruit stalk. The fruit finally falls and the larva develops within it as it lies on the ground.

Weevils as leaf-rollers (Attelabidae)

Leaf rolling beetles can be divided, according to the method of rolling they use, into those which roll the leaf lengthwise and those which roll it crosswise. In both groups there are species that make an initial cut in the leaf blade and species that do not. But the feature common to all leaf-rollers is that they roll up a leaf to form a container in which they place the eggs (Figs. 201, 202). The withering leaf serves the larva as food.

Among the lengthwise rollers, we can distinguish between those that make cone-shaped and those that make funnel-shaped rolls. As an example of the first, we might take the Grape Curculio *(Byctiscus betulae)* (Attelabidae) which occurs on several broad-leaved trees. The female of this beetle pierces the leaf stalk and hollows it out. As a result, the leaf begins to wither. The beetle, often aided by the male, now begins to wrap the leaf into a cigar-shaped lengthwise roll with the underside of the leaf on the outside. In the process, four to six eggs are deposited between the folds. Secretions from the anal glands help to keep the layers of the leaf in position. In one day, the insect can construct two such leaf rolls. In all, it makes 20 to 30 of them. Sooner or later, the rolled leaf falls to the ground, where the further development of the beetle takes place. Among the lengthwise rollers, there are also species that start off by making an incision into the leaf, and these are known as funnel rollers. The Beech-leaf-roller *Deporaus betulae* (Attelabidae) might serve as an example. Starting from the margin of the upper surface of the leaf, the female makes a shallow S-curved cut as far as the central rib. A notch is made in the central rib and then another cut in the leaf across to the opposite margin. When the cutting is completed, the female returns to the point from which it started. Beginning at the underside, the leaf is rolled up toward the central rib (constructing the inner funnel). Around this inner funnel, the other half of the leaf is rolled to make the outer funnel. The whole package is secured by turning up the tip of the leaf and "sewing" it in place by piercing the outer layers of the funnel with the rostrum. Within the leaf tissue, one to six eggs are laid. In this way, a centrally situated funnel-shaped roll is produced. Similar rolls are constructed by the Maple-leaf-roller, *Deporaus tristis* (Attelabidae), but in this case the roll is situated at the side.

Let us now turn to the transverse rollers. In Japan, there is one species *(Taiwanobyctiscus pavici)* which constructs a crosswise roll working from the tip of the leaf, without making a cut into the leaf. This principle is known as cylinder rolling. All indigenous species of transverse rolling Weevils make a cut into the leaf, and are known as box rollers. As an example, we might take the Hazel-leaf-roller *(Apoderus coryli)* (Attelabidae). The female makes an incision from the side edge of the leaf blade to beyond the central rib. Or else, on many leaves, the cut is made from the edge of the leaf to the central rib, which at this point is left untouched, and then from the central rib to the edge of the leaf. Only at the end, is the central rib deeply notched. But whichever of these two initial methods is used, the next step is to notch the side ribs, and then one half of the leaf is turned over on to the other half with the central rib as the hinge, so that the two upper surfaces are brought together. Working from the tip of the leaf, the leaf roll is now constructed, and then secured by a series of stabs with the rostrum. Whereas the structure produced by the Hazel-leaf-roller is situated to one side of the leaf, that of the Oak-leaf-roller *(Attelabus nitens)* (Attelabidae) lies on the mid line. Six to seven centimetres from the tip of the leaf, the female makes a cut from the margin to the central rib, and then from the opposite side, once again carrying it up to the central rib. Then the central rib itself is nicked. As a result of the cuts made into the central and subsidiary ribs and the consequent withering, the leaf becomes flexible. Finally the two halves of the leaf are folded together across the central rib, with the upper sides lying on top of one another. The roll is constructed from the tip of the leaf, and the end of the rostrum is used to secure it firmly. The side lobes are also folded in and secured. During the rolling process, the female deposits one to three eggs within the leaf roll. The completed structure is severed by the female and further development takes place on the ground, the larva remaining inside the wrappings throughout the winter.

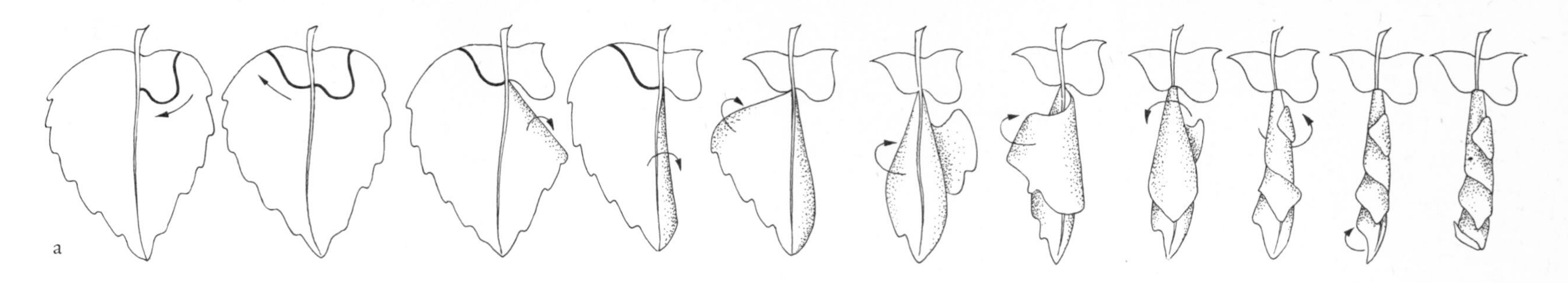

Cuts made into bark

Cutting into bark can also be a method of preparing larval food, as can be seen from the example of the Lesser Poplar Borer *(Saperda populnea)* (Cerambycidae). Working head downward, the female cuts shallow crosswise furrows into the bark of the branch it has selected. Then below these furrows, a hole is cut into the bark, extending inwards as far as the sapwood. Starting from this hole, two upward curving incisions are then made in the bark, with the female turning to the left and to the right at an angle of 90° to the original point. When the female has completed the horse-shoe shaped incision, it turns through 180° and deposits an egg under the small peninsula of bark that it has formed. Then the parent leaves the egg-laying site. The plant tissue around the blackening egg-island reacts by rapid cellular proliferation. These rank growths close in on the egg from all sides forcing the peninsula of bark upward. The gall-like growths thus produced serve as the initial source of food for the larva that has hatched meanwhile. Later on, the larva penetrates the pith of the branch and conspicuous thickenings of the branch result (galls).

Burying algae

The habit of carrying larval food into galleries and mines in the soil shows an almost infinite range of variations. The Rove Beetles (Staphylinidae) of the genus *Bledius* live in the shore zone of the sea and of inland bodies of water. They dig systems of burrows in the ground in which they deposit algae. The system of subterranean tunnels they construct is a typical feature of the species. At first the larvae live with the mother in the main gallery, and later in galleries of their own. Excrement is compacted into the lower part of the passageways. The supply of algae is usually stored in an upper extension; in the central zone the egg chambers extend radially, and within them the eggs are placed on a special plinth. The *Bledius* galleries can be up to 40 cm deep.

Leaf-rolling Weevils (Attelabidae)
a) Birch-leaf-roller *Deporaus betulae* L.
b) Hazel-leaf-roller *Apoderus coryli* L.
c) Poplar-leaf-roller *Byctiscus populi* L.
d) Oak-leaf-roller *Attelabus nitens* Scop.

Carrying in plant material

Many of the Scarabaeids (Scarabaeidae) gather in fresh or rotting plant tissue; a good example is that of the species *Lethrus apterus* (Scarabaeidae). Using their very powerful mandibles, the beetles tear off parts of living plants which they then carry into soil burrows. These fragments of plant material serve in part as food for the beetles themselves, in part for the future progeny. Male and female work together as a pair. The female digs a side gallery which terminates in a cavity the size of a pigeon's egg. Then one egg is laid. After this, fragments of green plants are brought into the cavity. They are carried in by the male, moving backward, then taken over by the female and stamped down into the egg cavity. Then

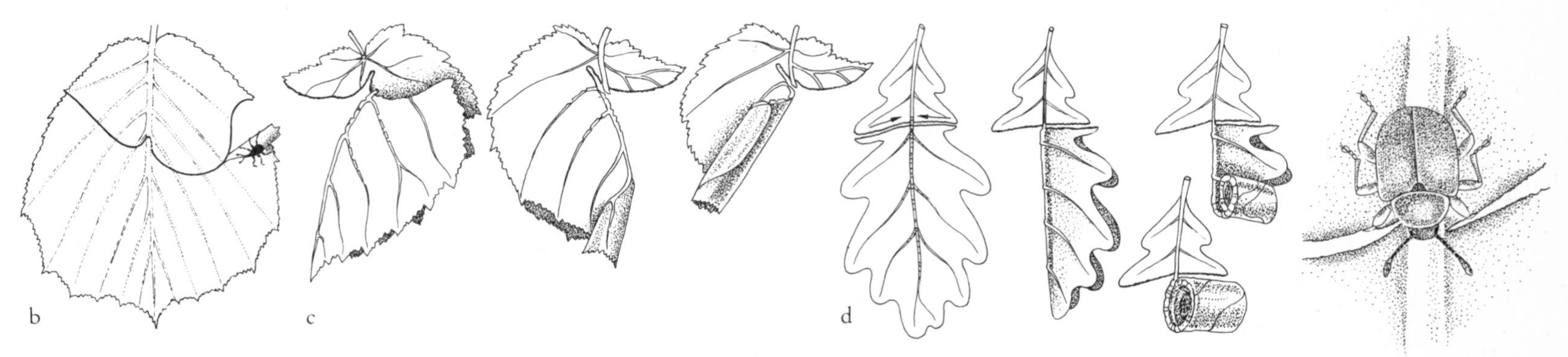

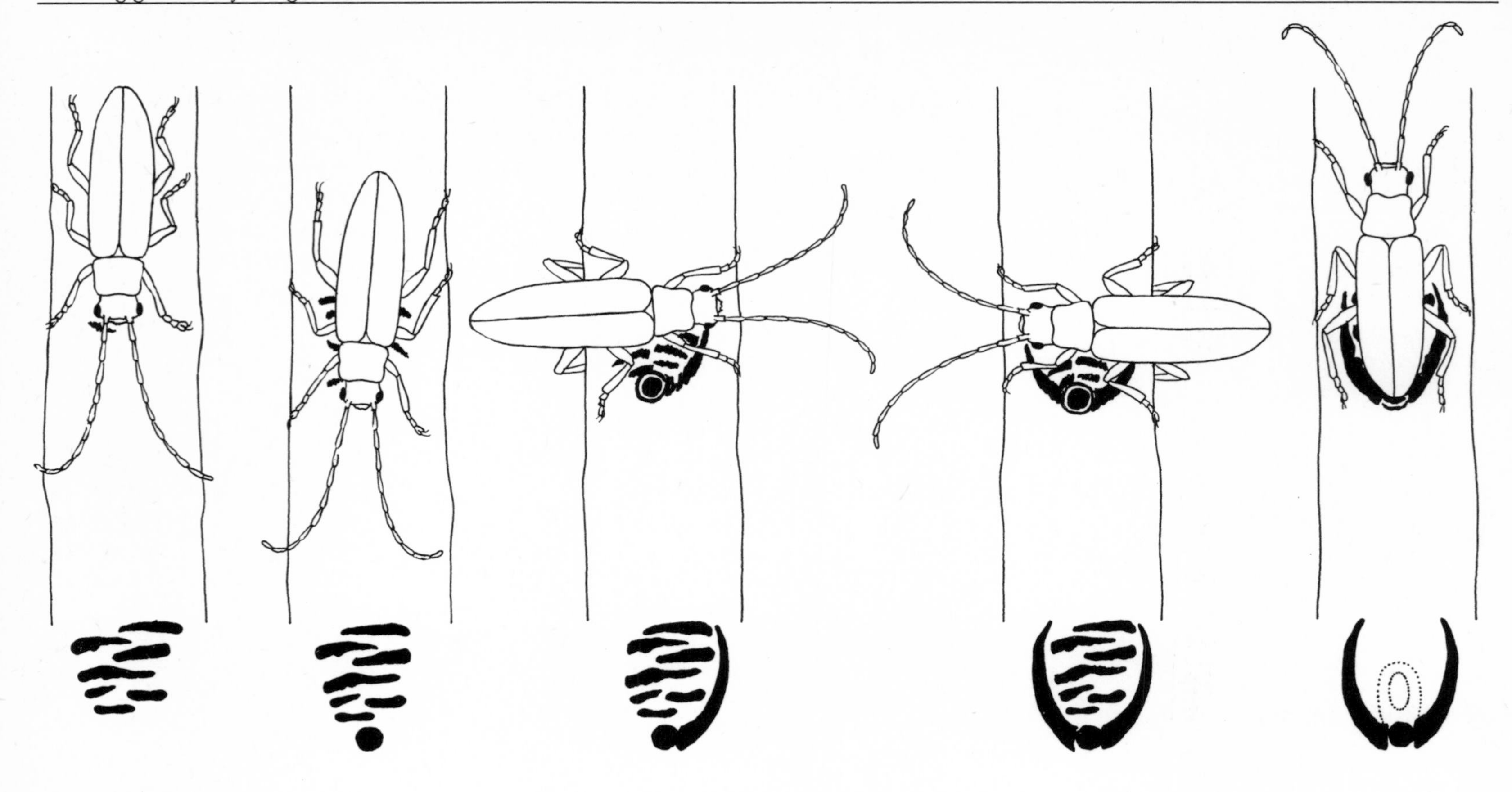

Brood provision (an incision made into bark) by *Saperda populnea* L. (Longicorn Beetles, Cerambycidae).

the side gallery is closed off with a plug of soil, and work begins on a new side gallery. The larvae feed on the supply of plant material and also pupate within the food cavity. The young beetles overwinter there, and dig their way out the following spring. The male guards the entrance to the burrow and also keeps the area in front of it clear. A special process on the mandible proves particularly useful for this purpose. Before the larval food is consumed, it probably undergoes a process of fermentation. Similar brood provision is also practised by certain South American and North American Dynastinae (Scarabaeidae).

Choeridium granigerum, a member of the Coprinae sub-family of the Lamellicorn Beetles (Scarabaeidae) shows special adaptation in its method of providing for its brood. To construct its breeding galleries, it seeks out remnants of abandoned nests of Leaf-cutting ants *(Atta)*. Decayed plant material that is usually also highly infested with fungus is used as the feeding substrate for the larvae. Starting from the waste storage chamber, the beetle excavates galleries into the earth, at the end of which an egg is laid, and which are later filled completely with food material.

The breeding galleries of dung beetles

A great many of the Scarabaeids bury dung in the soil, and in order to do this, construct a wide variety of systems of tunnels. Undoubtedly the action of burying the dung helps to preserve it for a certain length of time. Perhaps best known of all are the Dor Beetles of the genus *Geotrupes* (Scarabaeidae), and in their case, male and female work together to build underground galleries. The pair start by digging a principal gallery several decimetres deep, bringing the soil that they have loosened up to the surface. Then, working from this main gallery, they construct side galleries, filling them to a length of about 10 cm with dung. For the most part, it is the female that is responsible for carrying in the dung and also for treading it down firmly. When the length of dung has been prepared, the female lays an egg at the end of the supply. The larva feeds on the dung supply and overwinters in the ground. In the summer of the following year, it pupates, and the young beetle makes its way out through the main gallery. In most species, no more than eight galleries are constructed. Measures of provision for the brood similar to those of the *Geotrupes* species are carried out by the indigenous Three-horned Dor Beetle *(Typhoeus typhoeus)* (Scarabaeidae). With breeding galleries at a depth of 1.50 m, these beetles achieve the greatest depth of any of the

European species. The members of the very widespread genus *Onthophagus* also construct extensive tunnelling systems. The beetles, which are relatively small (6 to 9 mm in length) dig a tunnel 5 to 11 cm deep down in the soil, next to a cowpat. At the end of this, a breeding cavity is excavated, which is then filled with dung, and an egg deposited there. Finally it is sealed up and work is started on the next nesting burrow, as a result of which, the breeding system appears a somewhat irregular one.

Pill-rolling beetles

A further extension of the measures of brood provision described so far can be seen in those species which construct an individual pyriform brood ball or cell for each egg. This is the case in a great many of the Coprinae (Scarabaeidae), for instance, members of the genera *Euristernus, Phanaeus, Canton* and others. This category also includes the group of pill-rolling beetles, for instance, the genus *Scarabaeus* (Figs. 12, 17–22, 97, 98, 100, 101, 156). These insects construct two kinds of dung balls: feeding balls for their own consumption, and brood balls for the larvae to feed on. The mass of dung is either cut from a larger quantity of dung, or made up of several smaller quantities of dung that are combined (by kneading). The pills are trundled away backward. The front legs of the beetle are on the ground and walk in a backward direction. The hind legs hold on to the ball and move forwards. Feed pills can be constructed by both sexes. They are buried and consumed. The brood balls are formed and transported by the impregnated female alone. And it is the female which buries them in a spacious cavity. Here, the spherical pill is remoulded into a pyriform shape, narrowing toward the apex, and standing upright. In the upper part of this cell, an egg chamber is constructed and an egg deposited in it. In the case of the Sacred Scarab *(Scarabaeus sacer)*, the brood cell is about 4 cm × 5 cm in size and weighs some 40 g. In all, the female constructs about six of these brood balls. In beetles that practise brood care, fertility is relatively low, since the probability of survival of the larvae is high. The larvae also pupate within the brood ball.

Behaviour in reaction to contact with members of the same species varies within a wide range. Where both beetles have no dung-pill, there is no reaction. If one of the two has a feeding-ball in its possession, the owner takes up a defensive position, the newcomer cowers in an attitude of submission. If the newcomer is of the same sex, it is pushed away or there is a fight for the possession of the dung pill. If the newcomer is of the opposite sex, it is tolerated. A female Pill-roller will permit a newly-arrived male to roll the pill further. The male then buries the dung pill and the two beetles consume it together, after which they

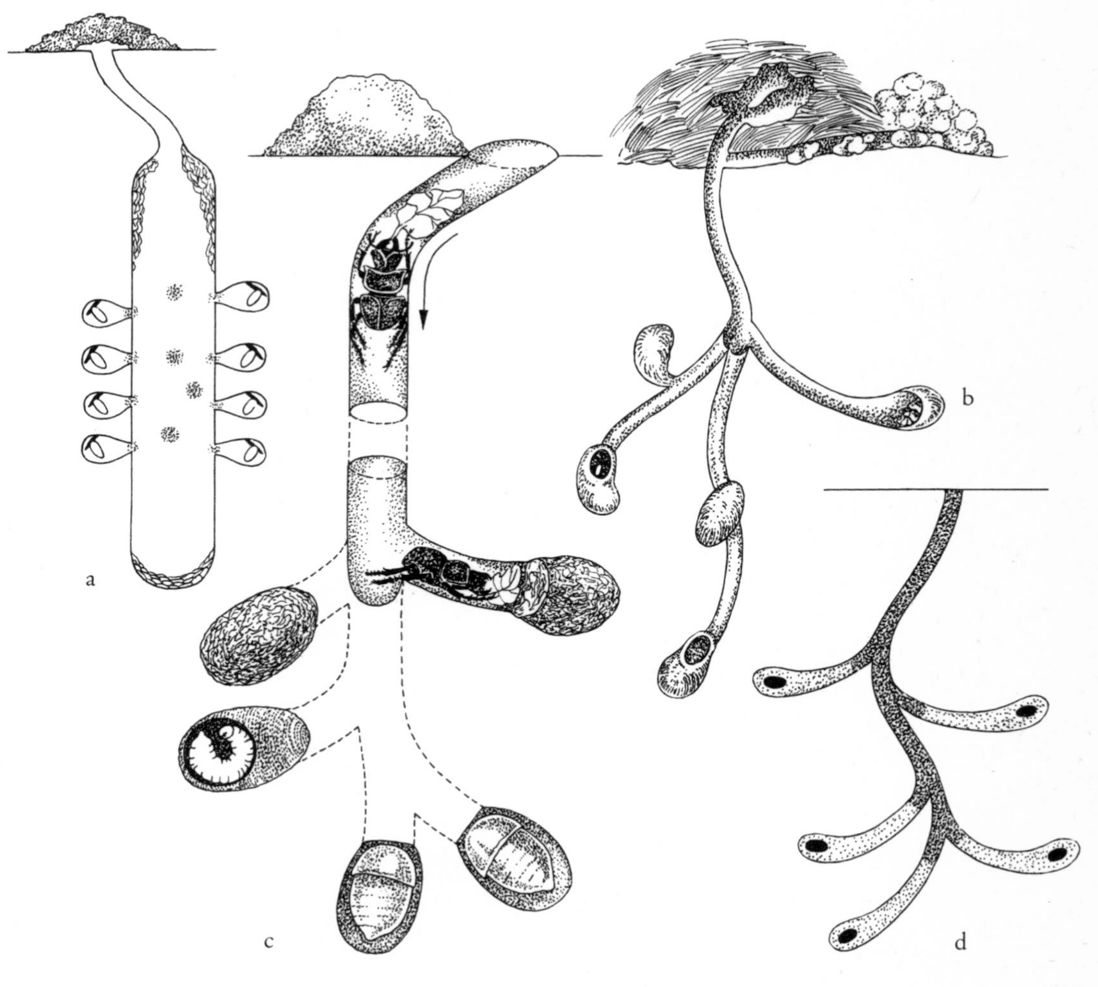

Breeding galleries
a) Breeding gallery constructed by *Bledius spectabilis* Kr. (Staphylinidae) in sand on a beach.
b) Breeding gallery of *Onthophagus nuchicornis* L. (Scarabaeidae)
c) Breeding gallery of *Lethrus apterus* Laxm. (Scarabaeidae).
d) Diagram showing a breeding gallery constructed by *Geotrupes stercorarius* L. (Lamellicorn Beetles, Scarabaeidae).

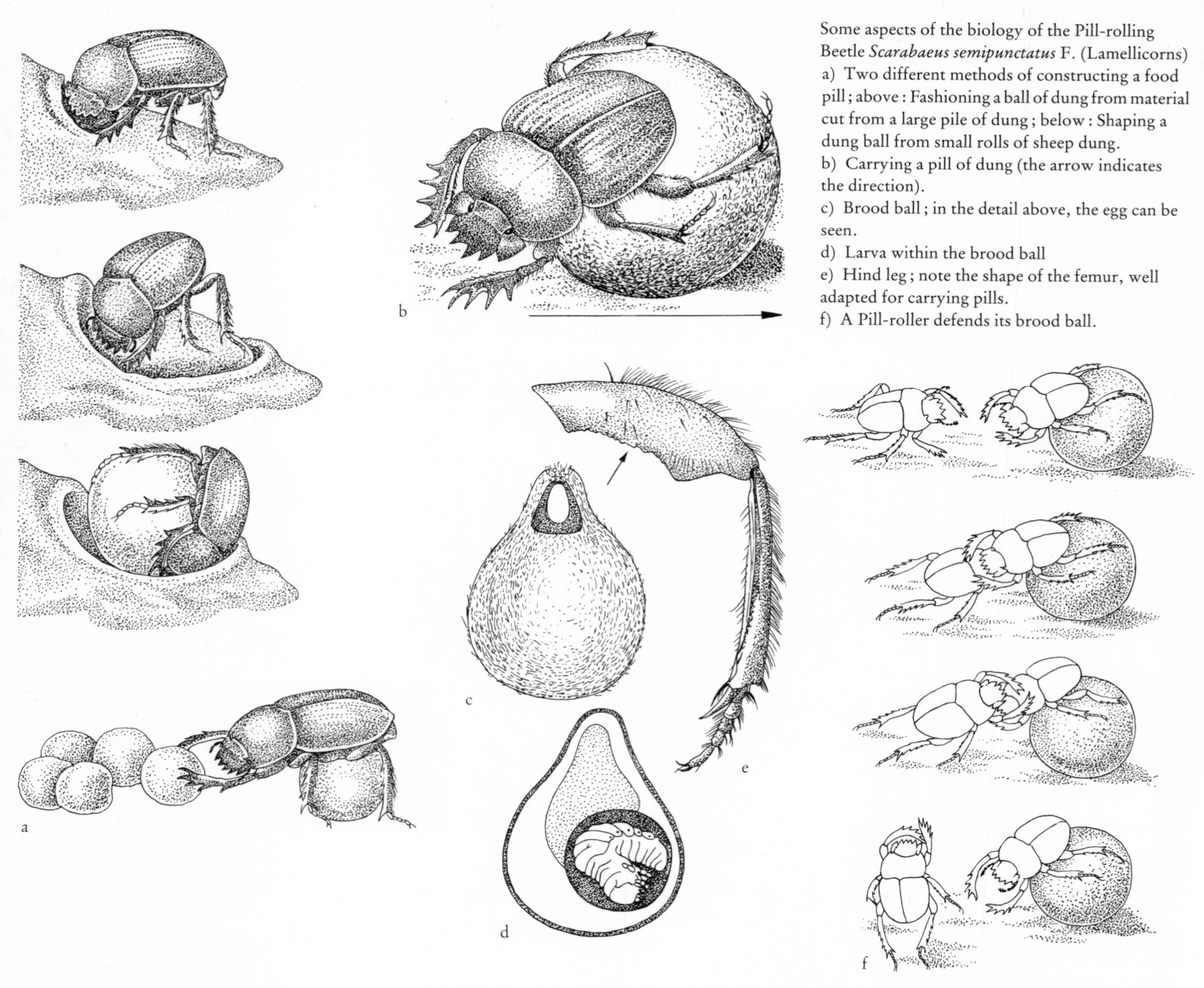

Some aspects of the biology of the Pill-rolling Beetle *Scarabaeus semipunctatus* F. (Lamellicorns)
a) Two different methods of constructing a food pill; above: Fashioning a ball of dung from material cut from a large pile of dung; below: Shaping a dung ball from small rolls of sheep dung.
b) Carrying a pill of dung (the arrow indicates the direction).
c) Brood ball; in the detail above, the egg can be seen.
d) Larva within the brood ball
e) Hind leg; note the shape of the femur, well adapted for carrying pills.
f) A Pill-roller defends its brood ball.

probably mate. Pill-rollers are well adapted for handling and transporting dung pills, particularly in the structure of the hind legs.

A similar pattern of behaviour is found in many other genera of Pill-rollers (Scarabaeidae), such as the indigenous species of *Gymnopleurus* and *Sisyphus*. In *Sisyphus schaefferi*, which is found in Central Europe, male and female often transport the brood ball in common, with one of the two standing with the forelegs on the pill, drawing it backward, while the partner pushes from the opposite side, with its back legs on the ball and front legs on the ground. In the case of the South American Pill-rolling Beetle *Phanaeus milon*, the brood ball consists of carrion. Other beetles, for example, certain South American species of *Canton*, are able to construct brood balls both of dung and of carrion. In addition, a characteristic feature of the *Canton* species is the combination of several brood balls in a

g) A Pill of dung is buried by a pair of beetles. The female sits on the ball, the male excavates beneath it.

single subterranean chamber, rather as in a nest. We might also mention here another rather more anomalous type of brood provision, as exemplified by the South American Dynastine beetle *Scatophilus dasypleurus* (Scarabaeidae). Under the soil, this species constructs a large sausage-shaped roll of dung in which it deposits eggs at intervals of about 2 cm. Another interesting habit is that of the North American Dung Beetle *Deltochilum gibbosum* (Scarabaeidae) which constructs a brood ball out of feathers or hair with a covering of rotting leaves and soil. This brood ball is placed in a shallow depression and only loosely covered with soil. The species *Deltochilum dentipes* forms brood balls of dung which it then encloses in a covering of clay, again providing them with no more than a superficial covering of soil.

Brood care in the Dung Beetle Copris lunaris (Scarabaeidae)

Among dung beetles, *Copris lunaris* has progressed from provision for the brood to actual brood care. In the late spring, *Copris lunaris* lays up a supply of dung in an underground chamber for its own use. A male makes its way into the supply chamber built by the female, and together they construct a brood chamber. In a natural division of labour, the male carries away the soil and brings in portions of dung. The female works these fragments of dung together, finally forming them into a large "dung loaf" weighing between 50 and 180 g. After about eight days, the female re-forms it into several pyriform brood cells (five at most), into each of which an egg is deposited. The female constantly guards and tends the brood cells, preventing any growth of fungus on them. During the entire period of development of the larvae and right until the young beetles have emerged after pupation, a period which extends over four months, the female continues to show this intensive maternal care, during which time it takes no food. It constructs only a single brood chamber. Sometimes the male remains with the female. In other cases it is driven away.

The "tomb" or "larder" of Burying Beetles (Silphidae)

A particularly highly developed form of brood care is found among Burying Beetles (Silphidae), also known as Sexton Beetles or Gravediggers, species of the genus *Necrophorus*.

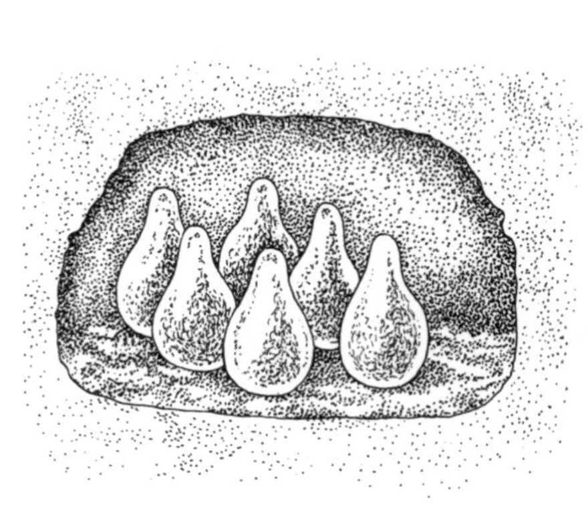

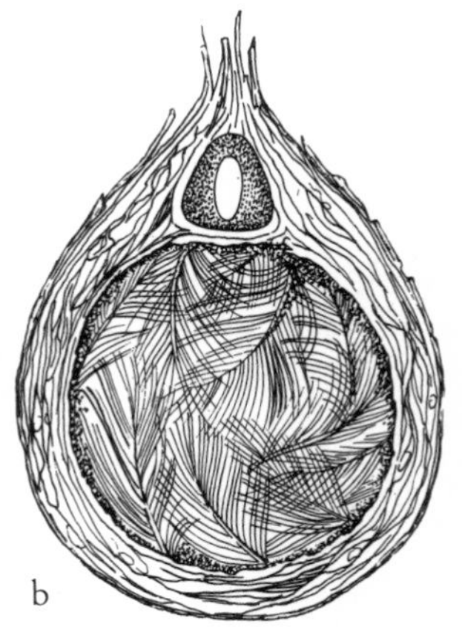

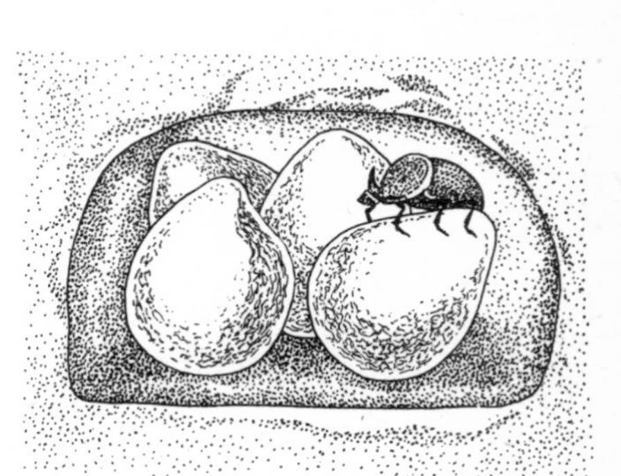

Brood balls made by Scarabaeidae
a) Brood chamber constructed underground by *Canton muticus* Har.
b) Brood ball of *Deltochilum gibbosum* F.; above, the egg
c) Brood balls of *Copris hispanus* L.; left, a mass of dung not yet treated

Using their sense of smell, these beetles track down a piece of carrion. If a single male is the first to arrive, it takes up its position on the carrion with the abdomen raised high, and may remain so for some hours. Apparently an attractant chemical substance is secreted, the smell of which attracts a female. If several beetles arrive, males and females fight among themselves, until only a single pair is left. The two beetles bury the carcase by digging earth away from beneath it and then pushing the corpse into a narrow shaft sunk underneath it. In the process, the carrion is progressively folded together and rolled into a ball, until, after many hours of digging, it finally lies in a cavity, which is known as a tomb or crypt. Then the male is driven off by the female. Straight away, the female lays up to 24 eggs in the wall of a gallery leading from the chamber. The eggs take five days to hatch, and during this time, the female tends the ball of flesh, finally cutting a funnel-shaped opening into the top of it, which is opened and closed several times. Probably the female secretes digestive juices into the funnel. Immediately before the larvae hatch, the funnel is opened. The larvae are attracted by the smell, or by sounds produced by the female, and gather in the funnel. The emission of sounds seems to play an important role among Burying Beetles, since both sexes can stridulate, and can also answer one another. The young larvae in particular appear to make use of these noises to find their way about. The larvae now inside the funnel do not, however, immediately feed on the carrion. Instead, the female comes to the larvae and feeds them individually apparently with partly digested meat regurgitated from the intestine. The larvae actively seek out the fore end of the female and stretch up their head towards the parent's mandibles. After about five or six hours, the young larvae are able to eat the carrion independently. However, immediately after the two following moults, it is necessary for them to be fed again by the mother. After only seven days, larval development is complete, and the larvae pupate in the soil in the vicinity of the crypt. Within these seven days, the larva of *Necrophorus vespillo* grows from 0.5 to 2.8 cm in length. At the same time, the weight of the insect increases to one hundred times the original weight, indeed, after the first seven hours, its weight has already doubled.

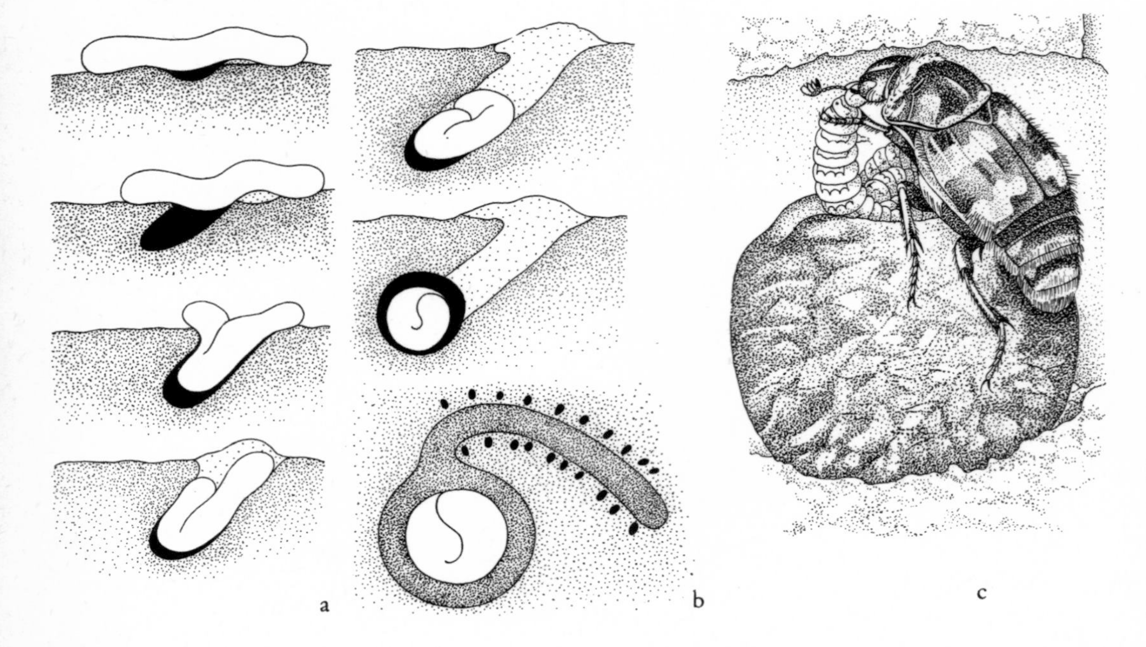

Burying Beetles (Carrion Beetles, Silphidae)
a) Method of burying a carcase used by *Necrophorus vespillo* L.
b) Diagram showing horizontal section through the crypt, parent gallery and egg chambers of *Necrophorus vespillo* L. The rolled and folded carrion is shown as white.
c) Female Burying Beetle (*Necrophorus* spec.) feeding its larvae.

The Beetle in Creative Art

Beetles in painting and the graphic arts

Pictorial representations of beetles exist in great abundance. Various species of beetles appear as the sole subject of or elements within numerous works of art. In addition to those portrayals carried out by the creative artists, we have technical illustrations made primarily for scientific purposes. And between the two there are many transitional stages.

Albrecht Dürer (1471–1528) often depicted insects, including beetles. For instance, in his symbolic painting "The Virgin with Animals" there is a stag beetle (Lucanidae), and we might also recall Dürer's very famous individual study of a stag beetle. Obviously the stag beetle has proved a considerable stimulus to artistic representation. In a miniature painting in the Posch Missal (1526) a stag beetle is shown attacking two putti which are fleeing before it. In the painting "St. John on Patmos" by Hans Burgkmair the Elder (1473–1531) a species of *Polyphylla* (Scarabaeidae), which is a kind of cock chafer, is to be seen at the feet of the saint.

The Flemish painter Jan Brueghel the Elder (1568–1625) often ornamented his flower studies with insects. For instance, on his "Large Flower Study" he has painted cockchafers (Scarabaeidae). Noteworthy too are the book illustrations of the period which were intended primarily as "scientific" material, and which, although their scientific value may be slight, are of great artistic and historical interest. For example, in Joachim Camerarius' *Moralische Zoologie* (Moral Zoology) published in 1605 we find a drawing of a rose, from which visiting dung beetles (Scarabaeidae) are falling down dead. But even in later periods, beetles remained as popular motifs in painting and the graphic arts. The Swiss painter Martin Disteli (1802–1844) is very well known for his portrayal of animals. Although grasshoppers were undoubtedly his special favourites, nevertheless we also find beetles depicted in his work. In a water colour illustrating "The Grasshopper's Sermon" by the Swiss poet Abraham Emanuel Fröhlich (1796–1865) we see a stag beetle listening attentively to the words it hears issuing from the mouth of a grasshopper:

> "And you, so long with us in true alliance,
> you bat, stag beetle and nocturnal moth,
> who praise our happy state with hearts and voices,
> are still the doughty guardians of our realm . . ."

None of the animals named, apart from the bat which might occasionally catch a grasshopper, has any great connection with that insect, but neither in this poem nor, indeed, in the illustration that accompanies it, is it necessary that they should do so.

The French graphic artist and caricaturist Jean Ignace Isidore Gerard (1803–1847) published under the name of Grandville a great many illustrations which embodied criticism of contemporary society. Particularly well known is his book *Scenes from the Family Life of the Animals* (1842), to which Honoré de Balzac (1799–1850), Alfred de Musset (1810–1857) and George Sand (1804–1876) contributed texts. In it we find the depiction of a marriage in which the registrar is a stag beetle, the notary a cockchafer and the best man a dung beetle. The caption to the picture runs: "The husband gives his wife protection, the wife her husband obedience."

The work of Wilhelm Busch (1832–1908) is alive with pictures of beetles. One need only recall the Fifth Escapade of *Max and Moritz* and *Hänschen Däumling*. The collection of stories in pictures *Schnurrdiburr or the Bees* also contains depictions of longhorn beetles, rhinoceros beetles, stag beetles and cockchafers.

Perhaps we might now make a leap to a modern artist who in her etchings has made frequent use of insects, including beetles, as a means of expression, namely Lieselotte Schober (born 1915). Special mention should be made of her "Escape from the liquid resin" (1976) and "Variations on Snow White" (1976). In addition, there is a whole series of pictures by this artist in which beetles also feature, for example, her "Variation on Genovefa" (1976). Other artists of recent times have portrayed beetles, for example, Wolfgang Hutter (born 1928) in his etching "Beetles." Contemporary depictions of beetles often show a certain propensity for the fantastic and the mystical.

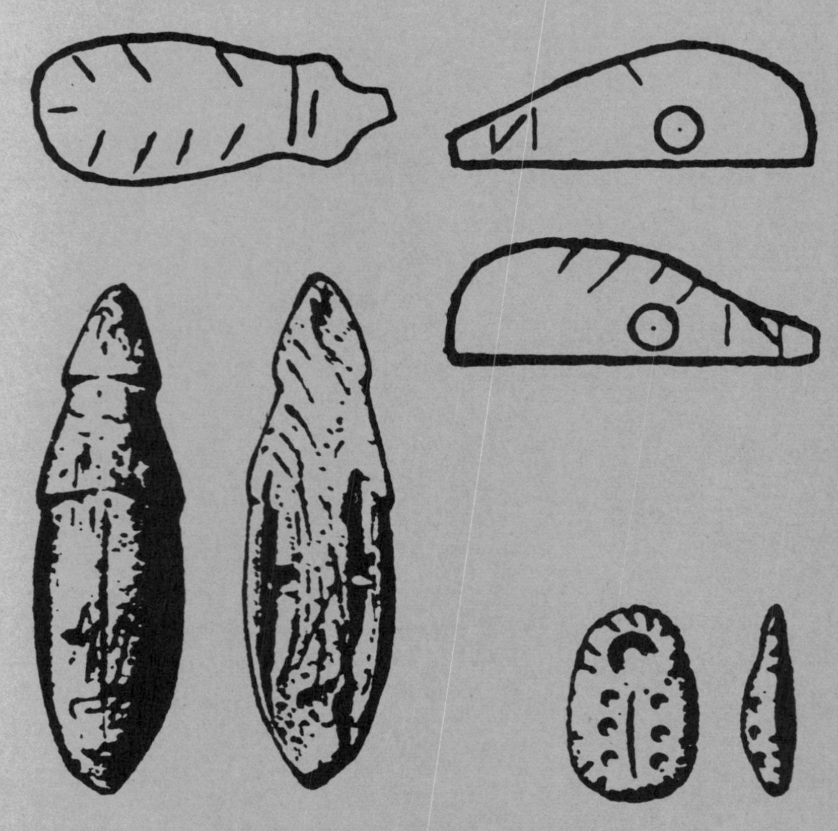

205 Earliest known representations of insects from the Magdalenian period
above: Beetle in Tertiary coal, probably a *Necrophorus*, worn as a pendant. Engen in the Hegau, Baden, 25,000–30,000 B.C.
below left: Beetle in lignite, a Buprestid, mounted as a pendant. Grotte du Trilobite à Arey-sur-Cure, (Yonne)
below right: Ladybird in fossil ivory, fashioned as a pendant. Laugerie-Basse (Dordogne)

Sculptures of beetles

The oldest known sculpture of any insect portrays a beetle, probably a Burying Beetle *(Necrophorus)*. This sculpture, fashioned out of coal was made 25 to 30,000 years ago in the Magdalenian cultural epoch, and was found together with other sculptures in coal. In a description of this, the earliest statue of a beetle, we are told the following facts: "The figure is completely rounded, it has a high lustre and a hole has been made through it. To judge by the extensive polishing that has rendered the base completely smooth, it must undoubtedly have been worn as a pendant, and on its own." Other sculptures of beetles from the Magdalenian period are known. One of them is the representation of a buprestid beetle (Buprestidae) some 5 cm in length. This sculpture was worked in lignite. A hole has been bored through it as well, and it was certainly worn as an ornament. A sculpture of a ladybird (Coccinellidae) in mammoth tusk ivory has also been found, and it was also holed so that it could be worn as an adornment. The ladybird is 1.5 cm long, and may have been regarded as a symbol of good fortune. Sculptured beetles also play an important part in advanced civilizations of a later period. On Crete, hand-sized representations of rhinoceros beetles (Scarabaeidae) have been excavated, which date from about 1700 to 1600 B.C. and which were found in a Minoan shrine. It is assumed that these finds, which can be attributed to the Mycenian cultural complex, were dedicated to a deity to entreat divine protection of the crops.

It is not possible here to give a complete survey of the use of beetles as motifs in the plastic arts. In later periods as well very many examples of sculptured beetles can be found. Perhaps in conclusion we should mention a modern sculptor, Hans Jähne (born 1926). He created an extremely impressive sculpture of a stag beetle in fine steel, which is over 70 cm high. Ground beetles (Carabidae) and longhorn beetles (Cerambycidae) have also been subjects of his works. From these creative sculptures it is but a short step to the scientific model, and here it might not come amiss to mention that in many museums throughout the world there are extremely well-made models of beetles which provide illustration of a high scientific standard of the finer details of their physical structure.

Beetle dances

A masked dance of the Kaua of the Upper Aiary (Brazil) is known as the "Dance of the Dung Beetles." Koch-Grünberg (1921) described this dance in the following way: "Hand in hand and singing, two masked dancers walked forwards and backward, one beside the other. They held ceremonial staffs tightly clasped under their outside arms, using them to roll back and forth a stick which represented the ball of dung." The idea of a magic power of purification lies behind the dance. It is believed to be capable of driving off demons and bringing about fertility. The movements of the dance portray the behaviour of the pill-rolling beetle.

Koch-Grünberg, who spent several years among the Indians of northwestern Brazil, and saw them perform the "Dance of the Dung Beetles," interprets it as follows: "By trying to imitate the beetle as closely as possible in movements and actions, the dancer identifies himself with that creature. The mysterious power inherent in the mask is transferred to the dancer, transforming him into a powerful demon and

206 Snuff pouches from Africa, made from the foreparts of Weevils. The Weevils *(Brachycerus apterus)* (Curculionidae) shown alongside illustrate the material used.

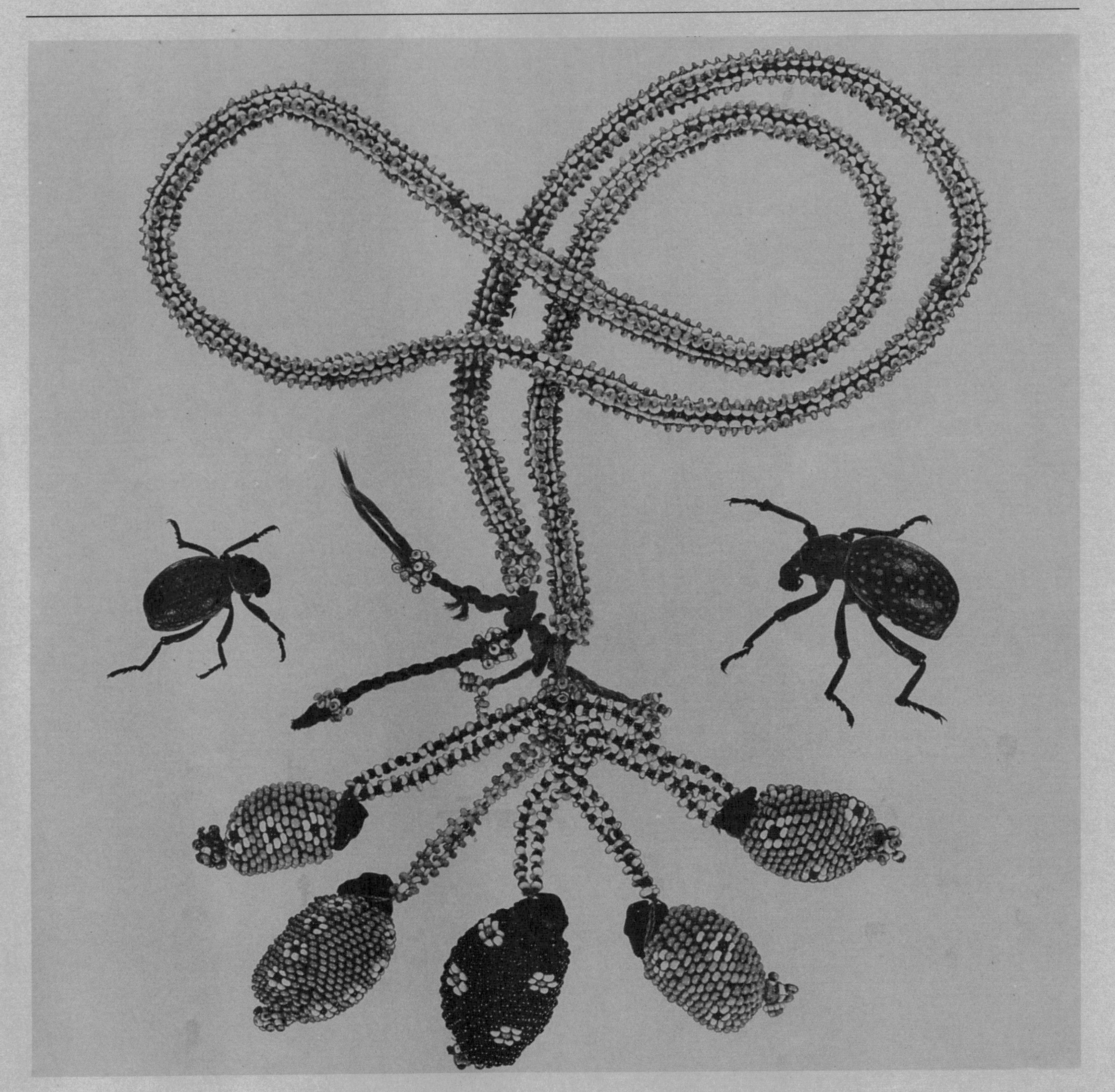

207 Ear pendants (detail) from Montana (South America), as made by several Red Indian tribes, using the elytra of beetles, here *Chrysophora chrysochlora* (Scarabaeidae).

giving him the ability to drive off demons or to dispose them favourably towards him. Particularly the demons of growth, the spirits of animals, which play a part here, and the animal spirits of hunting and fishing are believed to be brought by a spell into the power of man."

Beetles in applied art

The famous batik textiles of ancient Java use beetles as well as other insects as motifs. Ever since that time, and right up to the present day, beetles have frequently featured in patterns decorating various kinds of material.

The wing cases of beetles have quite often been used in various kinds of handicraft work (Figs. 50, 51, 207, 210). An early reference to this was made by Johann Leonhard Frisch (1666–1743). "A good friend who saw how beautiful this beetle is [the beetle in question is the Rose Chafer *Cetonia aurata* (Scarabaeidae); the Author], decided to collect a quantity of them and to cover the drawer of a small box or container with their elytra, which looks as beautiful as if it had been lacquered, it can easily be wiped clean of dust, and anyone who can draw, can make patterns with them. Particularly because one can assemble all the colours of heraldry from among beetles of this kind, coats of arms of all kinds look very well when they are inlaid with them."

209 Chain made from the mandibles of Stag Beetles (Lucanidae) from India.

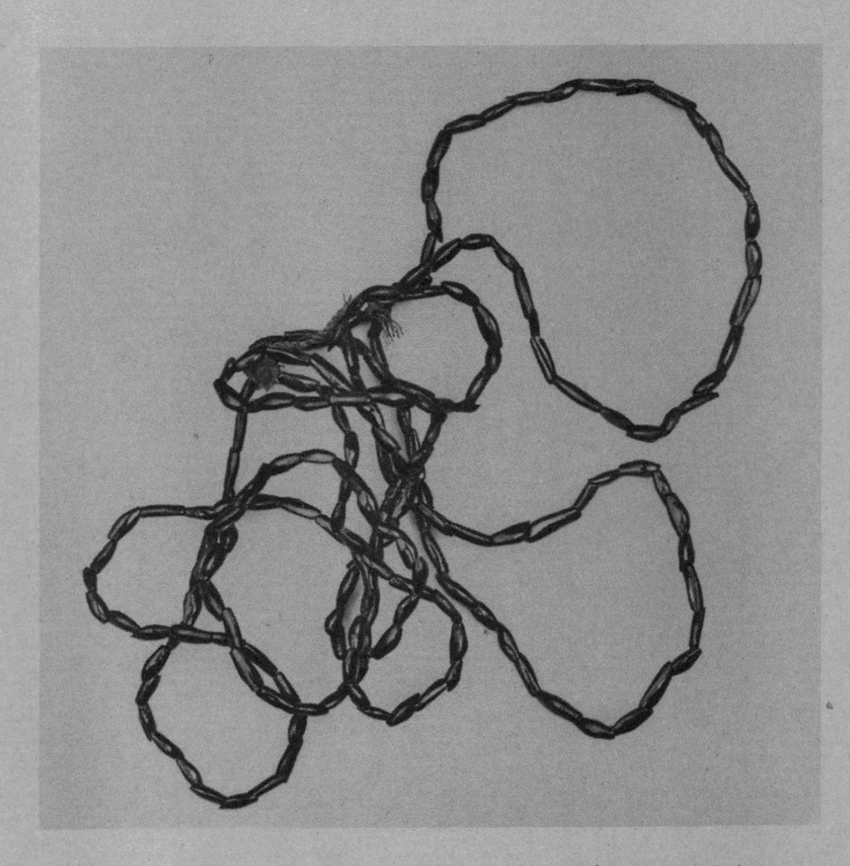

208 Neck ornament. A chain made of beetle femora from New Guinea.

The Brazilian Tortoise Leaf Beetle *Desmonota variolosa* (Chrysomelidae) gleams richly in brilliant emerald green. It is sometimes mounted like a jewel and worn in a necklace. The beauty of colouring and the hardness of the chitin of the Tortoise Beetle *Aspidomorpha miliaris* (Chrysomelidae) has also resulted in its use as an item of jewelry.

Beetles were also used for similar purposes in the ancient civilization of Japan. There is, for instance, the famous Buprestid Beetle Shrine Tamamushi-no-zushi, dating from the year 600, in which reliquaries were probably stored. It belonged to the Empress Suiko (593–628). The wing cases of the beetles are used to depict Buddhist motifs.

210 Lower border of an Indian breast ornament (detail) from Montana (South America) in which the elytra of Metallic Beetles *(Euchroma gigantea)* (Buprestidae) are used.

Interestingly enough, there are also Indian head ornaments in which beetles and parts of beetles occur as important decorative elements (Fig. 207). The elytra of the giant buprestid beetle *Euchroma gigantea* (Buprestidae) are used by the South American Indians to make into long chains (Fig. 210).

In the Middle Ages, the art of making casts from nature, which had already been known in ancient civilizations, began to be developed further. Animals and plants were coated with molten silver in particular, producing a durable copy of the original. These casts from nature were used as decorative elements in important products of the goldsmith's art. Particularly well known is a silver writing set, the work of the Viennese goldsmith Wenzel Jamnitzer (1508–1585), on the lid of which are casts of stag beetles (Lucanidae) and rhinoceros beetles (Scarabaeidae). Beetles of free design were also a feature of the goldsmith's craft. A famous example is a ceremonial bowl worked by the Viennese goldsmith Konrad Hedeneck (died 1616) on which, among other creatures, beetles are portrayed.

Painting on porcelain and porcelain statuary has frequently made use of the beetle motif. For example, a cockchafer (Scarabaeidae) features on plates of the Viennese National Manufactory (1744–1750). A chocolate beaker with inset cup, from the same factory, is decorated with painted ladybirds (Coccinellidae). A table centrepiece from the Meissen factory is ornamented with a moulded stag beetle.

Craftsmen working in precious stones quite frequently portray insects, and among them, beetles. A masterpiece of the Augsburg gemcutter Heinrich Gottlieb Lang uses the twelve stones known as the birth stones, to which magic powers were ascribed. Some of these stones have been formed to the shape of beetles.

Glass painting, which flourished particularly in the 18th and 19th centuries, produced many paintings in which insects are depicted with the greatest precision. Glass of the Biedermeier period is frequently decorated with ladybirds, together with flowers, fruit and butterflies.

Beetles on coins

Only a very few Greek and Roman coins carry pictures of beetles. The sole motif is the Scarabaeus (Scarabaeidae) with a ball of dung. Since that time, beetles have not featured on coins at all. It seems that it is only the coleopterists who are to be found on commemorative coins and medals, such as the famous naturalist Gustav Kraatz (1868–1924) on the Kraatz medal, which is conferred upon entomologists of international renown.

Beetles as motifs on gems

Representations of the *Scarabaeus* (Scarabaeidae) have been found on Greek gems dating from as early as the year 700 B.C. For several centuries, these beetles were the principal motif of the Greek art of gem carving. In the 4th century, the use of the beetle motif declined. The gems were worn by the Greeks both on the fingers and as pendants round the neck. In addition to the Sacred Scarab, the larva of the Great Water Beetle (*Dytiscus* spec.; Dytiscidae) can be found on gems.

Beetles in coats of arms

In heraldry, certain heraldic animals such as the lion, bear, stag and eagle play an important part. It is, on the whole, less widely known that insects, even beetles, also occur in this context. And of the beetles, it is primarily the stag beetle (Lucanidae) that is found on various armorial crests. The German popular name for the stag beetle in many areas is *Schröter*. For this reason, families by the name of Schröter have sometimes incorporated a stag beetle in their coat of arms. The following are a few examples. In 1699, a certain Johan Wilhelm Schröter and an Ernst Wilhelm Schröter were granted a coat of arms on which stag beetles are depicted both on the escutcheon and above the crown. On the coat of arms of Christoph Schroetter, which dates from 1777, several stag beetles appear. Or there are the armorial bearings of Johann Georg von Schroeder, which in addition to three golden ears of corn, also carries a brown stag beetle. Another coat of arms with stag beetles is that of the Schröttl family, and several more examples can be found. Apart from stag beetles there are only a few other motifs in heraldry, such as black beetles in the coat of arms of one branch of the von Rehlingen family and also in the coat of arms of the von Reutern family. It is also possible that the beetles in the latter coat of arms are to be interpreted as grain weevils (Curculionidae).

Beetles in ethnic cults

In addition to the cult of the sacred scarab in ancient Egypt, there exist many other beetle cults, of which a few examples are mentioned below.

In many ethnic groups, particularly among those at a less advanced stage of social development, there exists a belief known as totemism, in the existence of intimate unseen relations between men and animals or inanimate objects. Insect totems are relatively rare, and are known with any degree of certainty only among the aborigines of Central Australia. They include two beetle totems. These are the larva of a lamellicorn beetle (Scarabaeidae) (*uchalka*) and the larva of a longhorn beetle (Cerambycidae) (*idnimita*). As part of the ceremonies (*intichiuma*) involved in a fertility rite, the totem animal is eaten. If this is not done, there is a danger that the insect will not occur subsequently in sufficient numbers. Undoubtedly this totem cult is linked to the importance of these larvae to the Australian aborigines as a source of food.

Even before the cult of the sacred scarab began, there already existed in Egypt a strong beetle cult. This is indicated by archaeological finds in the form of grave furnishings consisting of beetles, usually enclosed in special containers. In the ancient Egyptian city of Thebes, embalmed buprestid beetles (Buprestidae) were found.

211 Coat of arms of Johan Wilhelm Schröter, 1699, with Stag Beetles (Lucanidae)

In earlier times, priests of the South African tribe of the Bechuana wore amulets made out of large weevils (Curculionidae). The amulets were worn on a string across the brow and round the neck. The significance of these amulets is uncertain.

Even in our latitudes there exist traces of a beetle cult. The ceremony of bringing in the first cockchafer (Scarabaeidae) from the forest persisted into the 17th century. The creature was regarded as a "sacred" harbinger of spring, like the swallow and the stork. A vestige of this cult can perhaps still be seen today in the occasional announcement in a local newspaper of the arrival of the first cockchafer of the season. Much more extensive and considerably more deeply rooted is the cult of the ladybird. Ladybirds (Coccinellidae) are reputed to have been the sacred animals of Freyja, the ancient Norse Goddess of Love. In Sanskrit, the name of the ladybird is Indragopa (Indra = herdsman). Later on, the beetle came to be associated with the veneration of the Virgin Mary. (One belief was that she would remain angry for nine days with anyone who killed one of these beetles.) The many popular names given to the beetle are still today an indication of the cult. Starting with the most common name of ladybird, they go on through the names of ladybug, ladycow, ladyclock, ladyfly, lady's beast, God's beetle and more. In other countries too, the ladybirds have many names of corresponding significance, for example, in German *Gotteskühlein*, *Herrgottstierchen*, *Marienvöglein*, *Marienküchle*; in French *vache à Dieu* and *bête de la Vierge*; in Russian божья коровка; in Italian *boarino dal Signor*. It may be that the cult of the ladybird arose in connection with the total of seven spots found on the most common European species (*Coccinella septempunctata*), since from the earliest times, the number seven has always been considered a mystical number. Even today, the cult of the ladybird has not completely died out and traces of it may still linger in the use of the motif in all kinds of toys, talismans, patterns, bracelets, souvenirs and amulets. In Provence, if a ladybird alight upon a young man, it signifies marriage. If a girl wants to know the year of her marriage, she must place a ladybird on the tip of her index finger and count off the years aloud. The year she has reached when the beetle flies away is the year of her wedding.

In the Middle Ages, the dor beetle (*Geotrupes* spec.; Scarabaeidae) was known as the "devil's steed." As the "devil's beetle," the dor beetle has a lot to do with treasure. If it is placed in a money chest, the supply of money will never be at an end (Carinthia). If someone sees money burning, and afterwards finds dor beetles, these beetles will turn back into money (Westphalia). If the first dor beetle of the year flies, it will be a joyful year, if it runs along the ground, grief will follow. Flying dor beetles seen in the morning portend bad weather, but in the evening, fine weather. Treading on a dor beetle will bring on a storm. Anyone finding a dor beetle lying on its back should turn it over lest lightning should strike the farm, and hail destroy the crops (Finland, Carinthia).

Stag beetles (Lucanidae) were supposed to have been sacred to Thor, the Germanic God of Thunder, and to be able to attract thunderbolts. This belief may have arisen because the beetles often inhabit isolated old oak trees which are likely to be struck by lightning. Many of the vernacular names in German refer to this feature: *Donnerkäfer* (thunder beetle), *Hausbrenner* (house burner), *Feueranzünder* (fire raiser), *Köhler* (charcoal burner), *Feuerschröter* (fire beetle). The name of *Feuerschröter* (fire beetle) is explained by the German naturalist Lorenz Oken (1779–1851) in the following way. "Because they will bite violently into a glowing ember or burning tinder that is held in front of them; but this does them considerable harm; they will certainly die of it, for they burn the jaws and lips badly. The stag beetle is also called the devil's horse, because lightning strikes the tree in which it lives." The word *Schröter* comes from the verb *schroten* meaning to crush, bruise, shred, break up, all of them activities in which the larva at least is constantly engaged, and which will certainly also have been ascribed to the beetle itself, on account of its large mandibles.

It was said that the stag beetle could take up fire from a charcoal pile in its pincer-like mandibles and carry the glowing coals to the house roofs. However, not everything that was ascribed to the stag beetle was of an unfavourable nature. It was widely believed that carrying the head of a stag beetle in one's pocket would bring riches and good fortune. Or worn on a hat or in the braids of someone's hair, it would ward off the evil eye. Sometimes the heads were worn as amulets. They were even used as oracles. If a herdsman did not know where to find a cow that had strayed, he would shake the beetle's mandibles within his closed hand, at the same time putting the question to them. When he opened his hand, the right-hand mandible would indicate the direction in which he was to seek.

Monuments to beetles

Occasionally the contributions made by beetles to the well-being of mankind have been so highly appreciated that monuments to them have even been set up. One of the most notorious pests affecting cotton is one of the Curculionidae, the Boll Weevil (*Anthonomus grandis*). After it entered North America from Mexico in 1915, this beetle several times devastated the harvest in the North American State of Alabama, with a 60 per cent loss in yield, as a result of which the farmers were driven to cultivate different crops (peanuts, maize, potatoes, sugar cane); unexpectedly these yielded a substantially higher profit. Indeed, the returns were obviously so high that they could not have been substantially diminished by the erection in the town of Enterprise of a monument to the Boll Weevil.

Classification of Coleoptera (Beetles)

1. Sub-order: Archostemata
   1. Super-family: Cupedoidea
      1. Family: Cupedidae

2. Sub-order: Adephaga
   2. Super-family: Caraboidea
      2. Family: Rhysodidae (Wrinkled Bark Beetles)
      3. ,, Paussidae (Paussid Beetles)
      4. ,, Cicindelidae (Tiger Beetles)
      5. ,, Carabidae (Ground Beetles)
      6. ,, Trachypachidae
      7. ,, Haliplidae (Crawling Water Beetles)
      8. ,, Amphizoidae
      9. ,, Hygrobiidae (Screech Beetles)
      10. ,, Noteridae (Burrowing Water Beetles)
      11. ,, Dytiscidae (Predacious Diving Beetles, Carnivorous Water Beetles)
      12. ,, Gyrinidae (Whirligig Beetles)

3. Sub-order: Myxophaga
   3. Super-family: Sphaerioidea
      13. Family: Lepiceridae
      14. ,, Sphaeriidae (Minute Bog Beetles)
      15. ,, Hydroscaphidae
      16. ,, Torridincolidae

4. Sub-order: Polyphaga
   1. Series: Staphyliniformia
   4. Super-family: Hydrophiloidea
      17. Family: Hydraenidae
      18. ,, Hydrochidae
      19. ,, Spercheidae
      20. ,, Georyssidae (Minute Mud-loving Beetles)
      21. ,, Hydrophilidae (Water Scavenger Beetles)

   5. Super-family: Histeroidea
      22. Family: Sphaeritidae
      23. ,, Synteliidae
      24. ,, Histeridae (Hister Beetles)

   6. Super-family: Staphylinoidea
      25. Family: Ptiliidae (Feather-winged Beetles, Fringed Ant Beetles)
      26. ,, Limulodidae
      27. ,, Dasyceridae
      28. ,, Leptinidae (Mammal-nest Beetles)
      29. ,, Colonidae
      30. ,, Liodidae (Round Carrion Beetles)
      31. ,, Catopidae
      32. ,, Scydmaenidae (Stone Beetles)
      33. ,, Silphidae (Carrion Beetles)
      34. ,, Scaphidiidae (Shining Fungus Beetles)
      35. ,, Staphylinidae (Rove Beetles)
      36. Family: Pselaphidae (Ant-loving Beetles)
      37. ,, Micromalthidae

   2. Series: Scarabaeiformia
   7. Super-family: Scarabaeoidea
      38. Family: Lucanidae (Stag Beetles)
      39. ,, Passalidae (Betsy Beetles, Patent-leather Beetles)
      40. ,, Trogidae
      41. ,, Acanthoceridae
      42. ,, Scarabaeidae (Lamellicorns, Chafers, Dung Beetles)

   3. Series: Dascilliformia
   8. Super-family: Dascilloidea
      43. Family: Calyptomeridae
      44. ,, Clambidae (Minute Beetles)
      45. ,, Eucinetidae (Plate-thigh Beetles)
      46. ,, Helodidae (Marsh Beetles)
      47. ,, Dascillidae (Soft-bodied Plant Beetles)

   9. Super-family: Byrrhoidea
      48. Family: Byrrhidae (Pill Beetles)

   10. Super-family: Dryopoidea
      49. Family: Psephenidae (Water Pennies)
      50. ,, Ptilodactylidae (Toed-winged Beetles)
      51. ,, Eurypogonidae

52. Family: Chelonariidae (Chelondrid Beetles)
53. ,, Heteroceridae (Variegated Mud-loving Beetles)
54. ,, Limnichidae (Minute Marsh-loving Beetles)
55. ,, Dryopidae (Long-toed Water Beetles)
56. ,, Elmidae (Drive or Riffel Beetles)

11. Super-family: Buprestoidea
57. Family: Buprestidae (Metallic or Jewel Beetles)
12. Super-family: Rhipiceroidea
58. Family: Callirhipidae
59. ,, Rhipiceridae (Cedar Beetles)

13. Super-family: Elateroidea
60. Family: Cebrionidae
61. ,, Elateridae (Click Beetles)
62. ,, Trixagidae
63. ,, Cerophytidae
64. ,, Eucnemidae (False Click Beetles)

14. Super-family: Cantharoidea
65. Family: Brachypsectridae
66. ,, Telegeusidae (Long-lipped Beetles)
67. ,, Homalisidae
68. ,, Karumiidae
69. ,, Drilidae
70. ,, Phengodidae
71. ,, Lampyridae (Fireflies, Glow-worms)
72. ,, Cantharidae (Soldier Beetles)
73. ,, Lycidae (Net-winged Beetles)

4. Series: Bostrychiformia
15. Super-family: Dermestoidea
74. Family: Derodontidae (Tooth-necked Fungus Beetles)
75. Family: Nosodendridae
76. ,, Dermestidae (Skin, Larder, Hide, Bacon Beetles)
77. ,, Thorictidae
78. ,, Sarothriidae

16. Super-family: Bostrychoidea
79. Family: Anobiidae (Furniture Beetles)
80. ,, Ptinidae (Spider Beetles)
81. ,, Bostrychidae (Wood-boring or False Powder Post Beetles)
82. ,, Lyctidae (Powder Post Beetles)

5. Series: Cucujiformia
17. Super-family: Cleroidea
83. Family: Trogositidae
84. ,, Chaetosomatidae
85. ,, Cleridae (Checkered Beetles)
86. ,, Melyridae (Soft-winged Flower Beetles)
87. ,, Phloeophilidae

18. Super-family: Lymexyloidea
88. Family: Lymexylidae (Ship Timber Beetles)

19. Super-family: Cucujoidea
89. Family: Nitidulidae (Sap-feeding Beetles)
90. ,, Smicripidae
91. ,, Rhizophagidae (Root-eating Beetles)
92. ,, Protocujidae (Dry Fungus Beetles)
93. ,, Sphindidae
94. ,, Hypocopridae
95. ,, Passandridae
96. ,, Cucujidae (Flat Bark Beetles)
97. ,, Silvanidae
98. ,, Helotidae
99. ,, Phycosecidae
100. Family: Propalticidae
101. ,, Cryptophagidae (Silken Fungus Beetles)
102. ,, Biphyllidae (False Skin Beetles)
103. ,, Byturidae (Fruit-worms)
104. ,, Languriidae (Lizard Beetles)
105. ,, Erotylidae (Pleasing Fungus Beetles)
106. ,, Phalacridae (Shining Flower Beetles)
107. ,, Cerylonidae
108. ,, Corylophidae
109. Coccinellidae (Ladybirds)
110. ,, Endomychidae (Handsome Fungus Beetles)
111. ,, Discolomidae
112. ,, Merophysiidae
113. ,, Lathridiidae (Plaster Beetles, Brown Scavenger Beetles)
114. ,, Cisidae (Minute Tree Fungus Beetles)
115. ,, Merycidae
116. ,, Mycetophagidae (Hairy Fungus Beetles)
117. ,, Colydiidae (Cylindrical Bark Beetles)
118. ,, Pterogeniidae
119. ,, Nilionidae
120. ,, Tenebrionidae (Nocturnal Ground Beetles, Darklings)
121. ,, Lagriidae (Lagriid Bark Beetles)
122. ,, Alleculidae (Comb-claw Beetles)
123. ,, Zopheridae
124. ,, Monommidae
125. ,, Tetratomidae
126. ,, Boridae
127. ,, Perimylopidae
128. ,, Elacatidae
129. ,, Inopeplidae

130. Family: Salpingidae (Narrow-waisted Bark Beetle)
131. ,, Cononotidae
132. ,, Mycteridae
133. ,, Hemipeplidae
134. ,, Trictenotomidae
135. ,, Pythidae
136. ,, Pyrochroidae (Cardinal Beetles, Fire Beetles)
137. ,, Melandryidae (False Darkling Beetles)
138. ,, Scraptiidae
139. ,, Mordellidae (Tumbling Flower Beetles)
140. ,, Rhipiphoridae
141. ,, Oedemeridae (False Blister Beetles)
142. Family: Cephaloidae (False Long-horn Beetles)
143. ,, Meloidae (Blister Beetles)
144. ,, Anthicidae (Ant-like Flower Beetles)
145. ,, Aderidae
146. ,, Thretothoracidae
147. ,, Petriidae
148. ,, Aculognathidae

20. Super-family: Chrysomeloidea
    149. Family: Cerambycidae (Longicorns, Longhorns)
    150. ,, Bruchidae (Seed Weevils, Pulse Beetles)
    151. ,, Chrysomelidae (Leaf Beetles)

21. Super-family: Curculionoidea
    152. Family: Nemonychidae
    153. ,, Anthribidae (Fungus Weevils)
    154. ,, Belidae
    155. ,, Oxycorynidae
    156. ,, Proterhinidae
    157. ,, Attelabidae (Leaf-rollers)
    158. ,, Brenthidae (Giraffe Beetles, Straight-snouted Weevils)
    159. ,, Apionidae (Clover Weevils)
    160. ,, Curculionidae (Weevils, Snout Beetles)
    161. ,, Platypodidae (Ambrosia Beetles)
    162. ,, Scolytidae (Bark Beetles, Bark Borers)

Index of Beetles (Species, Genera, Families)

Bibliography

Andrée, K.: *Der Bernstein*. Stuttgart, 1951

Bei-Bienko, G. J.: *Obstschaja Entomologija*. Moscow, 1966

Bodenheimer, F. S.: *Materialien zur Geschichte der Entomologie bis Linné*. Vols. 1 and 2, Berlin, 1928

Brandt, H.: *Insekten als Rohstofflieferanten*. Orion-Bücher, vol. 135, Munich, 1960

Buchner, P.: *Endosymbiose der Tiere mit pflanzlichen Mikroorganismen*. Basle and Stuttgart, 1953

Buhr, H.: *Bestimmungstabellen der Gallen (Zoo- und Phytocecidien) an Pflanzen Mittel- und Nordeuropas*. 2 vols. Jena, 1964 and 1965

Burmeister, F.: *Biologie, Ökologie, Verbreitung europäischer Käfer*. Krefeld, 1939

Crowson, R. A.: *The Natural Classification of the Families of Coleoptera*. Hampton, 1967

Dumpert, K.: *Das Sozialleben der Ameisen*. Berlin and Hamburg, 1978

Evans, G.: *The Life of Beetles*. London, 1975

Evans, H. E.: *Das Trillionen-Volk. Die unbekannte Welt der Insekten*. Bergisch Gladbach, 1969

Fabre, J. H.: *Souvenirs entomologiques*. 10 vols. Paris, 1879 ff.

Farb, P. (Editor): *The Insects. The Time Life International* (Nederland), 1964

Freude, H., Harde, K. W., and G. A. Lohse: *Die Käfer Mitteleuropas*. Krefeld, 1964 ff.

Frost, S. W.: *Insect Life and Insect Natural History*. New York, 1959

Ganglbauer, L.: *Die Käfer Mitteleuropas*. Vienna, 1892 ff.

Hennig, W.: *Stammesgeschichte der Insekten*. Frankfurt/Main, 1969

Hieke, F.: "Ordnung Coleoptera-Käfer," in: *Urania Tierreich*, Vol. 3, *Insekten*. Leipzig, Jena, Berlin, 1968

Horion, A.: *Faunistik Deutscher Käfer*. Krefeld, 1941 ff.

Horion, A.: *Käferkunde für Naturfreunde*. Frankfurt/Main, 1949

Horion, A.: *Verzeichnis der Käfer Mitteleuropas*. Stuttgart, 1951

Jacobs, W., and M. Renner: *Taschenlexikon zur Biologie der Insekten*. Jena, 1974

Kaestner, A.: *Lehrbuch der Speziellen Zoologie*. Vol. 1,3, Part A and B. Jena 1972 and 1973

Keilbach, R.: *Die tierischen Schädlinge Mitteleuropas*. Jena, 1966

Kéler, S. von: Entomologisches Wörterbuch. 3rd edition. Berlin, 1963

Klausnitzer, B.: *Bestimmungsbücher zur Bodenfauna Europas—Ordnung Coleoptera (Larven)*. Berlin, 1978

Kuhnt, P.: *Illustrierte Bestimmungs-Tabellen der Käfer Deutschlands*. Stuttgart, 1912

Lampel, G.: *Biologie der Insekten*. Munich, 1973

Lengerken, H. von: *Die Brutfürsorge und Brutpflegeeinstinkte der Käfer*. Leipzig, 1954

Lengerken, H. von: *Lebenserscheinungen der Käfer*. Leipzig, 1928

Linsenmaier, W.: *Knaurs Grosses Insektenbuch*. Munich, Zurich, 1972

Martini, E.: *Lehrbuch der medizinischen Entomologie*. 4th edition. Jena, 1952

Nachtigall, W.: *Gläserne Schwingen*. Munich, 1968

Reitter, E.: *Fauna Germanica*. Stuttgart, 1908 ff.

Reitter, E.: *Der Käfer. Ein Wunder der Schöpfung*. Stuttgart, 1960

Scheerpeltz, O., and A. Winkler: "Coleoptera," in: P. Brohmer, Ehrmann, P., and G. Ulmer: *Die Tierwelt Mitteleuropas*. Leipzig, no date

Schimitschek, E.: "Insekten in Brauchtum, Kult und Kultur," in: *Handbuch der Zoologie*, 4th vol. Berlin, 1968

Schimitschek, E.: *Insekten in der Bildenden Kunst*. Vienna, 1977

Schröder, C. (Editor): *Handbuch der Entomologie*. 3 vols. Jena, 1925–1929

Sedlag, U.: *Wunderbare Welt der Insekten*. Leipzig, Jena, Berlin, 1978

Stanek, V. J.: *The pictorial Encyclopedia of Insects*. Hamlyn-London, New York, Sydney, Toronto, 1972

Strassen, R. zur: "Käfer," in: *Grzimeks Tierleben*. Zurich, 1969

Tuxen, L.: *Insektenstimmen*. Berlin, Heidelberg, New York, 1967

Weber, H.: *Lehrbuch der Entomologie*. Jena, 1933

Weber, H.: *Grundriss der Insektenkunde*. Jena and Stuttgart. 5th edition, revised by H. Weidner, Stuttgart, 1974

Wigglesworth, V. B.: *The Life of Insects*. London, 1964

Winkler, R. J.: *Das Käferbuch*. Prague, 1964

Sources of Illustrations

Jacana, Paris 15, 16, 147, 148
O. Jarisch, Eberswalde 192
Helmut Orth / Bavaria, Munich 143, 145
Root / Okapia, Frankfort (Main) 52
Dr. F. Sauer / Bavaria, Munich 149
Shostal Associates Inc., New York 13, 14, 144, 146
ZEFA, Düsseldorf 12
Carl Zeiss, Jena 92

All other photographs were supplied by Manfred Förster, Leipzig

Sources of the line drawings

after Bodenheimer 1928 pp. 10, 11, 12, 13, 14
after Dumpert 1978 pp. 136, 137
after Erber 1971 p. 69
after Freude, Harde, Lohse 1965 pp. 23, 27, 138
after Harde 1970 p. 115
after Hennig 1969 p. 79
after Horion 1949 pp. 82, 121, 122, 144
after Jacobs, Renner 1974 pp. 20, 23, 24, 27, 62, 64, 113, 124, 125, 147, 175, 186, 193
after Kästner 1973 pp. 23, 25, 27, 67, 113, 120, 121
after Klausnitzer 1974 p. 114
after Klausnitzer 1978 pp. 62, 123, 138, 139, 180
after Klausnitzer 1979 p. 21
after von Lengerken 1928 pp. 83, 149
after von Lengerken 1954 pp. 145, 179, 181, 183, 184, 185, 186, 187, 189, 190, 191, 192, 193, 194
after Linsenmaier 1972 pp. 25, 69, 136, 179, 180, 185, 192, 194
after Reitter 1909 p. 176
after Schmitschek 1977 pp. 196, 201
after Sedlag 1978 p. 70
after Stresemann 1978 pp. 18, 24, 138
after Zwölfer 1978 p. 119